The Master Builders

The Aswan Dam in 1900

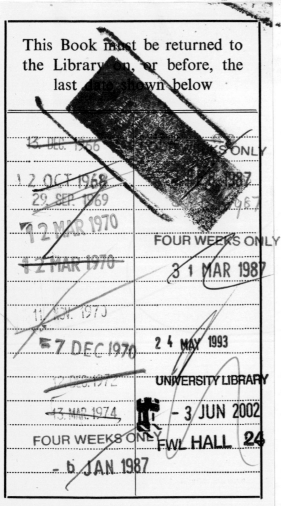

ROBERT KEITH MIDDLEMAS

The Master Builders

THOMAS BRASSEY;
SIR JOHN AIRD; LORD COWDRAY;
SIR JOHN NORTON-GRIFFITHS

FOREWORD BY ASA BRIGGS

HUTCHINSON OF LONDON

HUTCHINSON & CO. (*Publishers*) LTD
178–202 Great Portland Street, London W.1

London Melbourne Sydney
Auckland Bombay Toronto
Johannesburg New York

First published 1963

*This book has been set in Bembo type face, it has been
printed in Great Britain by William Clowes and Sons
Ltd, London and Beccles, and bound by them.*

To my Tutors
William McElwee and David Joslin

Exegi monumentum aere perennius
regalique situ altius pyramidum
quod non imber edax, non Aquila impotens
possit diruere, aut innumerabilis
annorum series

I have created works to outlast bronze
To stand more proudly than the pyramids;
Eroding rain and icy winds shall not
Destroy them, nor the illimitable waste of years.

HORACE; ODES, BOOK 3, 30

ACKNOWLEDGEMENTS

I MUST gratefully acknowledge the help given me by many people, in material, memories, and advice. I should like to thank in particular the following, for having given me access to their private records or the benefit of their excellent memories: Lord Brassey, Sir Charles Norton, Miss Ruth Peto, Colonel Sir John Aird, Mrs. Phyllis Cunliffe, Mr. Peter Aird, Lord Cowdray, the Hon. Clive Pearson, the Hon. Lady Burrell, Mr. C. H. Reid, Lady Norton-Griffiths, Sir Peter Norton-Griffiths, Mrs. J. H. Thorpe, Sir Bernard Docker, Mr. James Baxter, and Glyn Mills and Company.

I am deeply indebted to Professor Asa Briggs for his foreword. Professor Herbert Addison, lately Professor of Hydraulic Engineering at Cairo University, has very kindly given me the benefit of his many years' experience of the Nile; I should like to thank whole-heartedly Mr. David Joslin, Dr. T. C. Barker, and Mr. Robert Rhodes James, who have read the manuscript in whole or in part and made many helpful and constructive suggestions.

I owe a considerable debt to the Staff of the House of Commons Library who have met my requests for obscure books and periodicals with the utmost help; and I would like to acknowledge permission to quote from published works from the following:

George Allen and Unwin Ltd. F. Delaisi; *Oil; its influence in politics.*
W. Blackwood and Sons Ltd. Sir William Willcocks; *Sixty Years in the East.*
Beaverbrook Newspapers Ltd. *The War Memoirs of David Lloyd George.*
Jonathan Cape Ltd. L. H. Jenks; *the Migration of British Capital to 1875.*

7

Cassell and Co. Ltd. J. A. Spender; *Weetman Pearson, Lord Cowdray.*
Frederick Muller Ltd. A. Barrie; *War Underground.*
Hodder and Stoughton Ltd. Grey of Fallodon: *Twenty-five Years.*
Michael Joseph Ltd. Henry Clifford: *Letters from the Crimea.*
Longmans Green and Co. Ltd. T. S. Ashworth: *A History of the International Economy.*
Mrs Robert Napier. R. S. Baker: *Woodrow Wilson, Life and Letters.*
Odhams Press Ltd. W. S. Churchill: *The River War.*

The books from which I have quoted are given in the Notes at the end.

I am most grateful for permission to reproduce illustrations from the following:

Professor H. Addison—Frontispiece, and Plate 16(b).
The Trustees of the British Museum—Plates 2, 3(a), 3(b), 4(a), 4(b), 6(c), and 7; all are taken from the *Illustrated London News.*
Central Press Photos Ltd.—Plate 6(a).

CONTENTS

Foreword by Asa Briggs   13
Introduction   19

ONE

THOMAS BRASSEY

1   Black Friday   29
2   England and France   33
3   The Railway Mania   46
4   Half Way House   52
5   The Grand Trunk   61
6   Europe at Peace   70
7   India   82
8   The English Background   90
9   Before the Bombardment   94
10   The Year of the Locust   105
11   The Hapsburg Dream   111

TWO

Sir JOHN AIRD

1   A Samuel Smiles Story   121
2   Aird the Younger   128
3   Lucas and Aird   134
4   The Nile   141
5   Edwardian End   156

THREE

WEETMAN PEARSON, Lord COWDRAY

1	A Yorkshire Dynasty	165
2	Anatomy of a Contractor	171
3	First Flush	179
4	Flood Tide	188
5	A Place in the Country	203
6	Mexican Oil	209
7	War	231
8	The Changing World	239

FOUR

Sir JOHN NORTON-GRIFFITHS

1	A Pioneer from Africa	251
2	The 'House of Lords'	260
3	Empire Jack	269
4	Fortunate Soldier	274
5	Illusions	286
6	Realities	293
7	The Nile	300

Conclusion	307
Notes	313
Bibliography	319
Index	321

ILLUSTRATIONS

Frontispiece Building the Aswan Dam, 1900

	facing page
Thomas Brassey	32
Railway at Balaclava	33
Bilbao–Tudela Railway	48
Victoria Dock	48
Victoria Bridge over St. Lawrence	49
Panic in the City, 1866	49
Sir John Aird	128
Sir Ernest Cassel	129
Cartoon of Aird in Egypt	129
Millwall Docks	129
Metropolitan Railway, Westminster	144
Admiralty Pier—Dover Harbour	145
The Shield, East River Tunnel	145
Lord Cowdray	176
President Porfirio Diaz	177
Lord Cowdray, President and Madame Diaz on the Tehuantepec Railway	177
Cowdray House, Mexico City	177
Tampico Refinery	192
Dredger on Mexican Canal	192
Oil Rig	193
Potrero Gusher	193
Tanker *San Fraterno*	193
Sir John Norton-Griffiths	256
Benguella Railway	257

facing page

Norton-Griffiths and Portuguese officials	257
Oil wells, Ploesti	272
Burning oil wells	272
Work in Colombia	273
Heightening the Aswan Dam	273

MAPS

Page

Canada	67
Britain and Europe	75
India	85
The Nile Valley	148
Central Mexico	212
South America	261

FOREWORD

BY PROFESSOR ASA BRIGGS

Much economic history is concerned with quantities and with trends. Some of it also is concerned with *isms*. All these preoccupations are necessary, but none of them are sufficient. Behind the quantities there are qualities, behind the trends people. The *isms* provide clues to more general understanding, but they are capable also of imprisoning the historian. There is a further danger that a particular style of writing economic history may rob it of its interest for the general reader. There is, of course, a need for highly specialized articles and monographs, making use, where relevant, of the most sophisticated verbal apparatus; but there is also scope for books of wider appeal, books in which economic and social themes interweave and individual motives receive as much attention as economic variables.

Mr. Middlemas's study of four outstanding contractors, each representative of a different phase in the neglected history of one of the most colourful branches of economic enterprise, is as much of an adventure story as it is a monograph for economic historians. Contractors have always been among the most interesting of *entrepreneurs*. As long ago as 1868 a writer on English engineers claimed rightly that although a few novelists had attempted portraits of contractors, 'the imaginary contractor of the novelist is far from possessing the full flavour, the very pungency, of the representative contractors of actual life'.[1] He dwelt not only on their business achievements but on their 'loud and fearless self-assumption'. 'In sudden elevation of unprepared men to stations of consideration, or of power, the comic element is

[1] 'A Civil Engineer', *Personal Recollections of English Engineers* (1868), p. 192.

13

always mingled with a striking didactic moral.' Mr. Middlemas, without looking, in approved Victorian manner, for didactic morals, ignores neither the comic nor the tragic in his pictures of four very remarkable men. Nor does he overlook the private background of their business achievements. Money and marriage both form part of his plots. So too does politics. The artificial separation of economic and political history may make for analytical precision, but it robs each branch of history of much of its realism.

Behind the outstanding contractors who are described in this volume, the men who worked for high stakes and were necessarily caught up in the web of politics, there were scores of local contractors, many of them choosing, like builders and contractors today, to operate on a small and limited scale. The reasons why they chose to limit their scale are as interesting in their way as the reasons why others saw no bounds to their enterprise. Some, of course, did not choose. Their limits were set by finance or incapacity in handling a labour force of more than a certain size. For those who did so choose, however, it seems likely that both psychological and social elements determined choice. They were content with a certain level of success, and they were unwilling to sacrifice increased leisure and the social rewards that went with it. The men whom Mr. Middlemas describes were driven from within. They were individualists whose finished work was a collective achievement. Their lives might not reflect all the Smilesian virtues— they depended more than Smiles would have liked on both ruthlessness and luck—but they were heroes of self-help. They played a most important role in nineteenth-century economic growth, and through the provision of public services in what were then remote and undeveloped parts of the world prepared the way for industrial growth in the twentieth century.

Yet they have received far less attention from historians than industrialists. This is not simply because they left few records but because until recently we have had over-simplified notions of what constitutes an industrial revolution and what factors have to be taken into account in disentangling 'imperialism'. As we pass from the study of the British industrial revolution to the story of economic growth in other countries and from British social history to world social history, the contractors will have to be given their place. Even in relation to the British industrial revolution itself, it is remarkable how many stock accounts tend to leave out individuals once the great spate of early inventions had come to an end. Mr. Rolt's work is exceptional in this respect, and Mr. Middlemas's book follows naturally from it.

There was—and is—a close connection between engineers and contractors, although none of the four men described by Mr. Middlemas was qualified as an engineer. Sometimes civil engineers preferred the profit to be secured from a good contract to the smaller certainties of salary or of fee, and there was an actual transfer of occupation. More frequently there was association, not always harmonious. Engineers and contractors both depended on 'native ability and gusty energies'. Both were 'intensely individualistic even for an individualistic age'.[1] Yet while engineers could afford to be uncompromising in their social philosophies—they invented the term 'private enterprise'—contractors had to be willing to bargain and to compromise. While engineers complained of the 'difficulties thrown in the way of the rising generation of engineers by the governing classes of the country', contractors had to make their terms with governing classes in the cities, in Parliament, and in distant and difficult countries like Egypt and Mexico. A local contractor would have to learn how to handle the Mayor: an international contractor had to learn how to handle Prince Couza or Porfirio Diaz. The engineer's skills came to depend more and more on the possession of expert knowledge, even though there was often long and bitter disagreement between different experts about answers to particular problems: the contractor's skills were more varied, requiring a combination of judgement and imagination. They were also far more precarious. From being extended it was all too easy to become overextended: the greater the rise, the greater the fall. *Facilis descensus Averni.*

The skills could only be learnt through experience, and no single job, not even the building of a railway, was exactly like any other job. Four of the skills implied different kinds of judgement—first, financial manipulation; second, knowledge of bricks and mortar, iron and steel; third, ability to handle a heterogeneous and often foreign labour force; and fourth, political capacity, measured not only by the winning of contracts but by the orderly and profitable completion of them. A contractor could fail because he was deficient at the vital moment in only one of these skills. He could succeed only if he displayed them all. In his interesting conclusion Mr. Middlemas, comparing the four men with whom he is concerned—Brassey, Aird, Pearson, and Norton-

[1] S. E. Finer, *The Life and Times of Sir Edwin Chadwick* (1952), pp. 439-40.

Griffiths—states that there was no common denominator in their qualities of success. They had none the less to combine each of these skills with immense drive to achieve what they did, and when Norton-Griffiths proved deficient in two of the skills his career ended in tragedy.

What complicated matters further was that each skill might itself involve separate components. Financial manipulation itself, for example, included not only the ability to finance the pay-table but to raise huge initial sums of capital. It meant being willing to take great risks and yet at the same time to calculate costs with enough care to allow for a wide range of contingencies. Political manipulation included not only the ability to deal effectively with politicians but with bankers and bureaucrats. It is not surprising that the great contractors did not usually found family businesses. They could not reasonably have expected their sons to combine all the skills which they themselves had learnt not from other people or from other people's books but from life itself.

If there was a kind of tradition in British contracting, it was not a family tradition but a tradition of powerful individual achievement, represented in the work of the four men with whom Mr. Middlemas is concerned. 'Because British contracting abroad, begun in 1840 by Brassey, had by 1920 become legendary, Norton-Griffiths found it easier to capture his Brazilian market.'[1] Mr. Middlemas shows how the conditions within which the British contractors worked—both economic and political—changed during the course of eighty years and hints at some of the reasons why the tradition was largely lost after 1920. The very success of the contractor's work unleashed new forces in foreign societies: it also opened up the world not only to new techniques but to new ideas. The contractors did not foresee the general outcome of what they were doing, but each new generation of contractors was confronted with a different set of social and political circumstances. Changes in the world of finance itself also influenced their capacity to act. 'International aid', with or without strings attached, has recently provided a quite different *milieu* from that known to Brassey, Aird, Pearson, and Norton-Griffiths. And British competitive costs in international contracting are determined by a number of technical and economic factors outside the individual contractor's control. It would be interesting to have further studies of the develop-

[1] See below, p. 310.

16

ment of the contracting business in other countries which now compete keenly with Britain. Only such studies would show how far there has been a qualitative change in the nature of British 'enterprise' and 'adaptability'.

To look for morals of this kind would be the favourite twentieth-century version of Victorian didacticism. Mr. Middlemas is not didactic. He tells the adventure story for its own sake, recognizing that it does not have a happy ending. He catches the flavour of Victorian achievement and the complexity of perpetuating it. He ranges as widely over world history as the contractors themselves ranged over the world of space. He reminds us also of the curious way in which we in Britain have converted economic power into social status. Behind Cowdray Park is Bradford. This looks like a long-term contrast, yet it has been achieved in a remarkably short period of time. The process of conversion is illustrated over an even shorter period of time by Lord Brassey's comment on his father. 'He never failed in consideration for the feelings of others, recognizing the superior social position which they enjoy who possess long lineage and large landed estate, yet knowing that in his own busy and remarkable career there was something honourable which it was a distinction to have achieved.'[1] There certainly seems to be a moral in such moralizing, a very different moral from that which the son intended.

For economic historians Mr. Middlemas's book should suggest many themes for further detailed study. Some of them will lead back to statistics and trends, and some will provide further material for the examination of two of the *isms* which are most frequently expressed in slogan form—nationalism and imperialism. His book begins, however, with the transport revolution which made both *isms* meaningful. It also provided Britain with what is still its greatest achievement in forceful economic enterprise—the building of the railways. Of one of the most remarkable engineering and contracting works of that period, the bridge over the Menai Straits, a contemporary pamphleteer wrote that 'it is pre-eminently a work of our era; it is one of those vast and complicated efforts of skill which no previous period of the world's history could command. No one appears to have dreamed of such a thing before. It is a work which Egypt and the ancients might have been proud of, but could never have executed. . . . We may justly consider it the triumph of science—the masterpiece of human skill, and wonder

[1] See below, p. 58.

of the nineteenth century.'[1] Many of the achievements of the contractors whom Mr. Middlemas describes were of this order, well deserving not only contemporary rhetoric but historical re-appraisal.

ASA BRIGGS

University of Sussex

[1] *The Triumph of Science: An Account of the Grand Flotation of One of the Monster Tubes over the Menai Straits, Britannia Bridge* (1849), p. 3.

INTRODUCTION

A SMALL group of men dominate the crucial industrial years of the nineteenth century and to a lesser extent the half-century afterwards, up to the First World War. Among the most important of these 'men of enterprise', were the contractors who, by the railways, roads, and harbours which they built and often financed, spread over the world a transport revolution and affected profoundly the development of modern industrial society. Yet the contractors are the hidden men of history, hard enough to discover, and almost impossible to describe, but whose world-wide activities are explicable only in terms of their lives and personalities. Just over a century ago the Victorian writer Samuel Smiles, published his *Lives of the Engineers*—a view of the growth of Britain through the men who were then accepted as the leaders of the Industrial Revolution. Since then, the biographical approach to industrial change has been less in fashion.

Only the inventors or innovators, men like Boulton, Watt, Crompton, George Stephenson, McCormick, Daimler, or Sir Frank Whittle fit easily as individuals into economic history, because they can easily be shown as the originators of change. The activity and sheer number of phenomena in any large-scale society or industry make it much more difficult to approach the individual afterwards, though they may ultimately depend on a single man. Instead of *Lives of the Engineers* comes the study of classes of men, defined by their activities or their motives as a group; merchants, mineowners, middlemen, trade unionists.

But inventors or even engineers are not enough and do not by any means lead directly to change or development. The first iron ship was launched by John Wilkinson in the 1750s, but it sank; and wooden

19

ships did not give way to iron for more than a century after. The first wagons ran on rails in the seventeenth century, but were drawn by horses; and the railways waited 150 years for money and men of vision.

Change needs the combination of many circumstances. Eighteenth-century Britain could hardly have become an industrial nation without, not only its inventors, but a vast rise in population which gave mobility of labour, an agricultural revolution which transformed the traditional use of land, a developed banking structure, available capital, and the number and quality of its entrepreneurs. Without any of them, but especially without the entrepreneur, industrial change would have been different, slower, and incalculably altered in its effect; for the process which grew in the thirty years after 1760, and reached its peak in the nineteenth century, made Britain not only the 'workshop of the world' but changed the whole world economy.

The man of enterprise is the first capitalist—organizing the output of the society in which he lives, in a directed, profit-making way. His is the restless urge which surrounds the original invention with the means to grow; which determines whether or not it shall live, by giving it money, research, labour, skill in production, organization, and marketing. This function is the foundation of industrial society, even when directed by the ideological pressure of the State. But, during the Industrial Revolution, development depended quite haphazardly on the motives which attracted him and at the end of the eighteenth century, because Britain with her medieval roads totally lacked a transport system, the entrepreneur helped to provide the canals and turnpike roads. Aristocrats like the Duke of Bridgwater or engineers like Rennie or Telford took on all the various skills of organization and management.

In the process they brought into being a new class of professionals: the contractors. The old-fashioned master-builder who for centuries had led a small gang of skilled men from work to work slowly rose to the ranks of the entrepreneurs as he employed more men and equipment and acquired specialized constructing knowledge, The extent of their works, the great size of the canals compared with anything done before, and the drifting mass of labourers whom they employed: landless Irish peasants, Scots from the depopulated Highlands, English driven out by enclosures or attracted by the higher wages paid on the 'navigations', combined to make a hierarchy at whose peak were the great independent contractors like William Joliffe, Sir Edward Banks, or Thomas Cubitt, who of their own knowledge and courage were able to give estimates for a complete work and finish it within a stated time.

Although some of the canals were masterpieces of civil engineering, they could be built with only the services of engineers. But the complexities of railway building demanded new skills which engineers were not able completely to supply. Even though the railways of the 1830's were built by the great pioneers like the Stephensons, I. K. Brunel, Joseph Locke, or Braithwaite, they showed the lack of organization and contracting skill. By the early 1840s industrial growth could not be contained within the framework of canals, nor the few railways which had then been built. In a still predominantly agricultural Britain, railways had been slow to develop because they had neither enough capital nor enterprise behind them. They waited for the agreement of circumstances—until the interest shown in the work of the engineers in the 1830s by country bankers and provincial towns and industrialists had spread, on the clear evidence of profit, to London; and until new, more advanced, contractors came who could take over from the engineers what they were fundamentally unfitted for, and blend into an organized whole the disparate elements; the vast labour force needed for the railway demands of the late 1840s—the Railway Mania—and the high cost of capitalization; the arts of promotion; the needs for accurate estimates and time schedules; all on a scale hitherto not only unknown but inconceivable. Then and then only, within ten years, having completed the first stage by spreading main lines all over Britain, contractors carried them to Europe and the Americas, until the marvellous phenomenon became a necessity and countries blessed with the gift were moulded by its own response —either to breed their own self-sufficient industry or be shaped to the needs of the power which supplied it.

The Transport Revolution, the basic premise of modern society, was the work of combinations of financiers and entrepreneurs—who were, in large number, contractors. Their works were limited only by the consideration of profit. It is possible that without them the ports, railways, dams, roads, and factories would have been built, but in the hands of others less able, they might all have been one decade later and the difference to modern history beyond speculation.

The mere existence of such men stimulated expansion; and throughout the nineteenth century their activities widened, until they were not only employed by promoters, but were also the originators, partners in the enterprise and in the later management and profits. They created the world railway system; when steel ships superseded wooden, they enlarged and rebuilt every harbour in the world; laid the gas mains; brought fresh pure water to cities; dammed rivers for reservoirs and electricity; cut canals; laid down roads; drained old towns and re-built new. No facet of the modern world is untouched by their activity.

But, following in the tradition of Samuel Smiles, the engineers collected much of the glory, the financiers the credit. When the bankers were ennobled, the contractors were lucky to be knighted. Once the railway is built, the contractor's job ends, and his triumph of organi-zation is less noticeable than the splendid design of a bridge, or a loan projected into the next century. The most important men have been neglected. The reasons are the same as those which have delayed the equally important history of banking and bankers—lack of records and information, and the wrong approach.

Only a handful of remarkable contractors in the economic century 1830–1930 had the abilities which raised them to such significance; they left few records, and, absorbed in their undertakings, rarely looked for publicity. They cannot be studied, any more than bankers or financiers, in the same way as the 'classes of men'. Their importance depended on personal decisions, private skills and abilities, and the in-finitely diverse activities of individuals; and their whole complex organizations were tied to the life of their founders. (In no other economic activity did the firm almost always disappear at the death of its principal.) Their business was a personal affair, not an offshoot of managerial science, and was almost wholly unhampered by tradition. The activity of contractors was, in fact, a phenomenon which can only be explained by an inquiry into their attitudes, successes, ambitions and works, to discover a rule of action or an indication of the human motives which determined them.

When Thomas Brassey died in 1870 he had built one mile of railway out of every twenty in the world. He had shaped the world more effectively than the conquests of Alexander the Great; and his successors were inhibited from such grandeur only because there was less left to do. He had employed a labour force which rose to nearly 100,000 men (comparable to the very largest industrial combines of today) at home and abroad—so great a number then that if at any time he had been bankrupted, the unemployment rate of Britain would have risen by

I per cent. John Aird gave gas and clean water to half the capitals of Europe and consolidated the thirty years' long British direction of the waters of the Nile Valley. Weetman Pearson, Lord Cowdray, built harbours and railways all over the world, electrified Chile, and dominated Mexico as a giant of the early oil industry. Sir John Norton-Griffiths flung rails and roads across mountains and deserts and his spectacular career marked the end of the classic age of the individual contractor.

These four are representative of the varying changes of enterprise in the century 1830–1930. There should, all the same, be an explanation for choosing solely British names, though of the greatest stature. The most significant part of their work was done as pioneers abroad. Others, such as the Americans, Wheelwright and Meiggs in Latin America, the Germans, Baron Hirsch or von Siemens in the Middle East, or Frenchmen like de Lesseps, worked on a broadly similar basis, and on as great a scale. But in this period, British work was, in quantity, far the greatest; and the British export of technology and capital which is closely related to, and often part of the contractors' work, was more important before 1870, than that of any other country, and still preponderant until 1914. And the characteristics of this export help to differentiate British contracting, because, after the financial crisis of 1866, British finance houses shrank from participating in the public works they had initiated; but in Germany, France, and the U.S.A., partly to offset increased competition, banks and financiers took an increasingly active part.

The contractors have left very few records. Only Brassey and Pearson, Siemens and Meiggs have found a biographer. There are many disadvantages for the historian: nineteenth- and twentieth-century enterprise is extremely difficult to unravel, and all business history is cursed with the loss or destruction of vital records. Financiers and contractors are not noted for their autobiographical urge. Few men have left more lasting memorials; yet a railway tells nothing of its builders. Occasionally in engineering records, in a crisis or a triumph, there is a glimpse of the contractor himself; but there is virtually no personal material. Of their nature, they confided little to paper, either from inability to express themselves, or sheer unwillingness. With the exception of Cowdray, they left no family tradition or firm—otherwise, like Rothschilds, or Barings, they would not only have been famous but possessed archives.

I have used a number of sources which have not previously been touched: private letters, diaries, family deeds, wills and trusts, and the memories of families and friends.

Of the two biographies, Sir Arthur Helps's *Life of Brassey* is a Victorian eulogy of the good employer. Despite the gloss, it contains some shrewd assessments and much contemporary information. J. A. Spender's *Life of Cowdray* is a model of compendious facts, mainly authoritative, and somewhat dull. Both have been very useful; but show up the twin difficulties of an industrial biography—the 'story of dull tycoons'. Between the mass of things built, and the laudatory build-up, the man, plain and unvarnished, has to be found.

What they tried to do and what they believed they were doing— their individual ambitions—are the key. Later summaries, particularly Marxist, forcing the entrepreneurs into categories and systems, inevitably distort. The contractors, less than any other men of enterprise, had no grand design. From the very first, contracting abroad was no different from contracting at home; a great adventure for Brassey, a daring innovation, but conducted on the same lines; and this is true of the others. They did what they were already doing, in the plain path of business, for clearly defined reasons, either because of lack of opportunity at home, or more enticing chances abroad. The contractor, who had to keep his army of men, his mass of equipment and his skilled managers together, had to follow wherever advantage led him.

They believed in themselves and their work, and only secondly in the benefits they conferred. The ideal world for them was one free for contractors, for their kind of cosmopolitan enterprise. In the nineteenth century Brassey was a free trader who advocated the nationalization of British Railways to save the colossal waste of private promotion. Aird, though nominally a Conservative, did his greatest work in the wake of Liberal policies for defence in Africa. Cowdray was also a Liberal; and when world free trade was a lost hope, Norton-Griffiths championed Empire Free Trade. None of them pretended to be impartial; they were against anything which upset the balance, whether war, tariff walls, or aggressive imperial expansion. And none of them betrayed any consciousness of the ultimate effects of his work beyond a well-meaning gesture to the benefits of civilizing progress.

This explains why the results were as much random as planned: there was no more a great conspiracy to subject countries to 'economic imperialism' than there was to its territorial equivalent. It might have been more profitable for Britain if there had been, if Government, instead of keeping its traditional distance from business had co-ordinated their activities.

For the contractors' work in this period has an affinity with the territorial British Empire. The old colonies were acquired haphazardly and were regarded as poor investments unless they paid their way. Later, particularly in Africa, the problem of defence intruded; in spite of the high-minded excuses, it was Middle East strategy, based on India, which led to the acquisition of East Africa and the occupation of Egypt. In the same way British trading, financial, and industrial influence was built up pragmatically and at different times, throughout South and Central America, Africa and Asia, but was largely destroyed after the First World War.

The contractors could have built a lasting economic empire. In 1880 Britain controlled unparalleled overseas resources, many of them based on contractors' railways and public works. There was no tiresome need for annexation, only for intelligent planning and management which made allowances for national feelings, to have achieved a later relationship more satisfactory than conflicts for 'independence'. Instead, just as Britain was overtaken industrially by the U.S.A. and Germany in the twentieth century, the influence held through loans and the ownership or control of public works was lost to nationalisms which arose as much from the export of industrial knowledge and hatred of its external control as from any internal need. In this way also, the 1920s mark the end of an era—there follow the 'guided' offers, loans with political strings, public works designed and financed for the prestige of the giver, which we know today.

But in that century, after 1830, the contractors largely controlled the development of the world's transport. By laying down communications in the way and at the time they did they bound countries to certain types of development; by bankrupting some, as Henry Meiggs did Peru, by making others, as Cowdray in Mexico, rich; by raising great financial cosmopolitan combinations, and, by speculation, setting off economic panics like 1866; sometimes purposefully and sometimes blindly, they initiated events, which they could not, nor wished to control, and whose end was lost in a future about which they had only the narrowest ideas.

Others would not have done the vital work in the same way. It is no more than speculation to consider how different would have been the history of Europe if France had not had a railway system until after 1848, or of America if the Panama Canal had been cut when de Lesseps planned it in 1879; but it indicates the importance of the contractors. Economic development is seldom inevitable and in this hundred years it waited upon them.

ONE

Thomas Brassey

1

BLACK FRIDAY
May 11th, 1866

LOMBARD STREET was impassable: thousands poured along the Strand, past Temple Bar and St. Paul's, where it became hard to walk at all. At Mansion House the crowd was so thick that a carriage could not pass and all approaches to the Bank of England were blocked. The mass was a curious mixture of reputable citizens and stockbrokers clutching boxes and papers, cheques and bonds, of their staid clerks and runners, sightseers, shareholders and the tousled inmates of City taverns; all silent and grimfaced, prey to anxious rumours, quiet and waiting yet wild with scarcely disguised desperation. One word echoed even within the pillars of the Bank itself—Panic.

From early morning leading figures in the City had been forcing their way through into the comparative freedom inside, all of them asking for money, for credit, anything to tide them over the crisis. The whole of England saw a colossal run on banks. For the day before, Henry Gurney, principal of Overend and Gurney, billbrokers, had made that journey to ask the Court of Directors of the Bank for a loan of £400,000, the least sum which could save his famous financial house, the largest in England. They had listened to him gravely and refused, judging the securities he offered to be worthless. And at half-past two on May 10th, Overend and Gurney closed the doors of their Corner House in Lombard Lane and stopped payment. On Black Friday morning it was known that they had liabilities of £18,727,917.

'Before the Chancellor of the Exchequer was out of his bed, we had advanced the half of our resources,' said the Governor of the Bank; 'we refused no legitimate application for assistance'; but by lunchtime the reserve was dropping at frightening speed.(a) Then came the crushing news that the great railway contracting firm of Peto and Betts had failed for £4 million; Shrimptons, smaller contractors, went down in their wake. Other bankruptcies poured in before hectic midday. Already Sir Stafford Northcote, the Conservative M.P., feared 'a run upon England'. Consols slumped to a disastrous 84 and railway shares, around which the boom had been built, dropped by two-thirds of their value in a day. Bank Rate rose, in the almost unprecedented crisis, to 10 per cent.

About eleven o'clock a coach was seen to drive up Cheapside stopping where the crowd became too thick. Two men got out: one tall and aristocratic, the Irish financier Edward Blount; the other a broad, dignified old man, strongly built and prosperous, with a fine sensitive face—Thomas Brassey, railway builder and the greatest contractor of his generation. They pushed their way through the press beside Mansion House, holding on to their top hats, and struggled up Lombard Street to Glyns Bank, where a frightened doorkeeper at once showed them to the office of George Carr Glyn himself.

The partners were in conference. Blount asked them, as Brassey's banker, 'to advance a certain sum. After much consultation they gave him £30,000, but old Mr. Glyn said he must have "some stuff" in exchange, meaning securities. We returned to Mr. Brassey's office in Great George Street and filled a large box with securities, which we took back to Mr. Glyn. He would not even open it, but gave it to a clerk—"Put that in the safe." He wanted Mr. Brassey to promise that he would not give all his money away to his friends. To this he demurred, and on leaving the office asked me if I wanted any money. I told him I did not, but on the steps of the bank he met a gentleman whom he knew well was in a less happy condition, and in spite of my protest Mr. Brassey presented him with £10,000.'(b)

Brassey, who of all men in London could get only £30,000, yet gave a third of it away, was himself in the most grievous crisis of his life, and his wealth and the unparalleled organization he controlled were in danger of the same total ruin as Sir Morton Peto, his friend, partner and rival. The panic of May 1866 was the result of speculation in railways; and before evening a host of bankers and promoters had been swept away into bankruptcy and the civil if not the criminal courts. At the height of this classical age of *laissez-faire* the Foreign Office felt compelled to issue a circular to all Embassies which betrayed the extent of the disaster.

'Her Majesty's Government have no reason to apprehend that there is any general want of soundness in the ordinary trade of this country which can give reasonable ground for anxiety or alarm.'(c)

Yet in spite of this reassurance, England reeled. Henry Drummond Wolff, the banker and diplomat, saw that 'no single bankruptcy, perhaps, as Overend and Gurney, had ever caused so wide a shock to credit. The day produced the wildest agitation ever known in the City.'(d) Credit was not to be had at any price and the directors of the soundest concerns trembled at every rumour which flurried the Stock Exchange floor.

When the House of Commons met in the afternoon, Disraeli asked Gladstone, the Chancellor of the Exchequer, if he had yet authorized the Bank of England to break Peel's Act and exceed its note issue (which had calmed the panics of 1847 and 1857). Gladstone replied that he had not yet done it, but that a delegation of bankers was to wait on him during the day: 'They conceive the state of panic and disaster which prevails in the City to be without parallel in the recollection of the oldest men of business.'(e) Members thought of their fortunes, wide open to the cold winds of panic, and shifted uneasily in their seats.

By four o'clock the Bank's reserves had fallen from £7 million to £3 million. The distinguished joint-stock bankers who met the Chancellor were almost desperate and when the Directors begged the Chancellor for his authority to break the law the letter of indemnity was duly sent.

It had its effect; some degree of credit returned and the worst of the panic, the freezing of business and frightened despair was over. But disaster lasted long: Bank Rate stayed at 10 per cent for another two months and long before then the railway and Indian bankers Agra Masterman & Co. had gone down; followed by a dozen others. The Liverpool and Manchester cotton kings and the East India merchants were hard hit, but this last great panic of the nineteenth century cut deepest at its most astounding symbol of development, and the railway interest staggered.

Thomas Brassey survived. More susceptible than most to loss of credit, with undertakings in five continents, employing then 75,000 men, paying in wages alone £100,000 a week, he passed the crisis, and emerged weakened, poorer, but fundamentally unhurt.

The age he lived through was stormy; one of development, speculation, fraud, and ingenuity on an immense scale. Government left it severely and wisely alone even when nine years of violent energy and the mania of finance companies and limited liability collapsed in ruins. It was an age 'of extraordinary financial invention and enterprise, partly legitimate, partly the reverse. It was like these monumental epochs we read of, such as the South Sea Bubble or John Law's schemes in France. The public was eager for speculation and easily found purveyors of financial sensation.'(f)

It was an era when promoters were prophets and money spilled out into sound and wild schemes together, a time of restless enterprise and profit seeking; and it was based on the essential service without which the nineteenth-century capitalist economy could hardly have come to maturity—the railways. And the king of the railway age was not George Hudson nor Robert Stephenson, Jay Gould nor Cornelius Vanderbilt, but Thomas Brassey.

Thomas Brassey

The Railway at Balaclava

2

ENGLAND AND FRANCE

HE WAS born sixty-one years earlier at Baerton near Chester on November 7th, 1805. The Brasseys were of yeoman stock and respectable antiquity and had owned the half-timbered Bulkeley Old Hall with 300 acres for generations. Careful farming and the profits of agriculture during the Napoleonic Wars left John Brassey well enough off to pay the large sum of £850 a year for a farm on the Marquis of Westminster's estate, and he was able to send his son to a grammar school in Chester at the age of twelve.

Nothing else survives of Thomas Brassey's youth; and the education he got was significant only in a certain ability for mathematics. His father apprenticed him to Mr. Lawton, a local land agent and surveyor who found him apt for the work with an extremely active and imaginative mind. One of his first qualified jobs was to work as assistant to Telford, on the early Cheshire turnpike roads.

Birkenhead, which at the turn of the century had been only a scattered hamlet beside the dreary bank of the Mersey, was beginning to spread as railways opened out in the first lines of Lancashire and Cheshire. Lawton judged it time to open an office there and he offered Brassey a partnership at the age of twenty-one. The young man rapidly matched his master's foresight; with money borrowed from his father he bought a brickyard and limekiln and with something of a corner in building materials set about inspiring further development. When Lawton died he took over the business and with it the management of the Price estates including almost all the land on which Birkenhead was built. For eight years he was content to watch it grow, building up in Dixon's Bank of Chester a balance which any estate agent might have envied.

Meanwhile railways continued to astonish the countryside. Long before London woke to it, provincial banks and farseeing landowners entered the business. Almost by chance Brassey was caught up in the movement: he owned the Stourton quarry, mining a hard and resilient stone which was needed for the Sankey viaduct of the Manchester and Liverpool Railway. During the negotiations he met the engineer Joseph Locke, then working under George Stephenson, who liked him, finding something infectious in his dry humour and adventurous mind. Clearly the young man was more than a provincial land speculator and Locke persuaded Brassey to try building railways as well as supplying material for the lines.

Because the engineers, the Stephensons, Vignoles, and Locke were still in a position of monopoly, a company formed to build a railway was in its engineer's hands; yet, with the dozens of railways projected, their skills were greatly overtaxed; and they had every interest in the rise of new men, the contractors, whose ability was organization and command, who could fix their price for a length of line, find their workmen, plant, and materials, build to the engineers' specifications, and deliver the finished work on time at an agreed date. Such men were rare and it was as important to the engineers not to waste potential as it was to have contractors with whom they could work amicably.

So Brassey tendered for the Dutton Viaduct on the Grand Junction Railway, working the figures out himself. They were too high, but in 1835, after some local experience, he put in another for the Penkridge Viaduct and 10 miles of the Stafford and Wolverhampton line which was accepted. Stonework and masonry gave him no trouble, because he could use his own workmen, but earthworks and the laying of the track were entirely new and he learnt as the line progressed. The tender had only been possible on credit from Dixons Bank, who respected his judgement, and the need to economize developed his knowledge of costs, wages, and materials. Then Joseph Locke succeeded Stephenson as engineer and found Brassey congenial as well as able because he showed an apparently inherent command of men which was priceless to the Company; one of the hardest tasks being the creation of an organized labour force out of roving navvies (lately the 'navigators' or cutters of canals) and the chaotic mass of labourers who until the depression after Waterloo had been working on the land. To keep them together month after month, so that work never slackened, even in harvest time, was extremely difficult. Hundreds had to be fed, housed and looked after, camps set up and kept in some sort of law and order, problems which might have tested an army commissariat.

Brassey succeeded, using then as he did for the rest of his life a system of subcontracting; parcelling the work among four or five he trusted, who in their turn employed gangers to find and oversee the men. It was simple, cut his losses if part of the work was held up, and delegated his responsibility without depriving him of control.

This first job went well and, before it was finished, Brassey was called south by Locke who had been appointed engineer[1] of the London and Southampton Railway. It was an important line, from Nine Elms westwards, a pet project with the War Office who wanted a direct line to the southern port, and its directors looked ahead to capturing the French trade of Rouen and Le Havre and the Seine route to Paris. Varied interests were grouped in the Board—William Moss the Liverpool banker, William Chaplin[2] once head of the largest coaching business in Britain, whose mails had covered every town in the south, and the merchant bankers, J. L. Masterman and Matthew Uzielli.

Locke was now becoming the prototype of the great engineer, soon to be gilded and flattered as the Stephensons never were. His powers were considerable and he offered Brassey the 36-mile line from Basingstoke to Winchester. This was probably his most severe test, for it not only demanded vastly greater powers of organization and understanding of large-scale construction (since Brassey knew nothing of the South or southern workmen, and could provide none of the materials from his own quarries) but it also made it imperative that he would have to set up business in London. The transition which this demanded, the faculty of sudden growth it implied, was enormous. No less was the transformation of provincial into Londoner, the proverbially narrow to the patently wise.

He abandoned Cheshire, and between 1837 and 1840 became a full contractor in the modern sense. The work went so well that the next

[1] In place of Francis Giles who planned the terminus at Bristol. This did not suit the Liverpool interests on the Board and he was forced to resign.

[2] Chaplin sold up his entire concern in 1836, judging the days of the horse drawn coach over. He took a fortnight's holiday in Switzerland to clear his mind, returned and put most of his capital in the London and Southampton undertaking. He became Chairman of the Company and in due course Member of Parliament.

year he was able to take on another 40 miles: the Chester and Crewe, the Glasgow, and part of the Sheffield and Manchester Railway. This latter included part of the cutting of the Woodhead tunnel, one of the most difficult works projected at the time, which cost £700,000 and was not finished till 1845;[1] but long before then he was known in London as well as he had been ten years earlier in Birkenhead. Brassey got things done on time, he made no trouble over terms he had once agreed, his works did not peter out because his men moved on to better wages and conditions; and when the London and Southampton Company decided to beat the London and South Eastern in the race for the French carrying trade by establishing their railway in France itself, they turned to him.

In his thirty-fifth year the contractor had achieved remarkable success; he seemed to personify the virtues of progress and scientific civilization. He was of middle height, broad and well-proportioned, firm yet graceful in his movements, with a lazy assurance more in keeping with one of aristocratic birth. A wide forehead, the eyes set deep and apart, a straight and challenging nose redeemed by the amused turn of full, almost sensuous lips; something quixotic and inquiring, with a hint of melancholy behind the quick teasing sense of humour. He seemed already to have what was recognized later as 'a certain completeness of character'. Though there was nothing formidable in his appearance, firmness tempered with courtesy, made him a bad man to argue with; there was a core of ruthlessness, even, at times, of cruelty; he would give way with grace where he could, but if not, say so with complete finality.

He married in 1831, Maria, daughter of Joseph Harrison, forwarding agent of Birkenhead who, with the same shrewd foresight as his son-in-law, marked the rise of the village and made himself its first merchant. The match brought wealth and affection; later, since both were sympathetic and full-blooded, love. Maria Brassey even in middle-class provincial Cheshire was strong-minded enough to hold her own views and express them. She wanted greater worlds and urged her husband on to move south. Seeing how few contractors were yet in the railway business she was determined he should reach the top, and proved herself capable of the equally vast change which the London and Southampton contract brought. Setting up house in

---

[1] Passengers found that the air in its three-mile gloom smelt of cheap port.

London, the country look of them, the provincial speech, fell away. Three sons had been born and now, without letting it corrode her personality, she nursed immense ambitions. It was as well she spoke French fluently, for Brassey could not and would not learn; when he was thrown almost unprepared into the first foreign contract she had to travel with him and interpret.

Although he owed his success at least in part to the favour of Locke, there was much to bring him to France after setting up in London. English railways suffered, after the early 1830s, from the collapse of the U.S. cotton boom as well as other purely internal handicaps.

Apart from Glyns and Mastermans, railway promotion had not attracted the interest of London banks. Lack of general direction, the high cost of rivalry and of promoting the necessary Private Bills in Parliament, led some to talk of State control; many companies invested extravagantly and overcapitalized their lines, large numbers of which were unproductive from the start. Until 1844 railway promotion languished in the country where it had first seemed so profitable.

Railway promotion was not wholly unknown in France. Marc Séguin had built 11 miles from St. Etienne to Andrézieux in 1830; Rothschild interest produced a line from Paris to Versailles; but no provincial manufacturing class existed as in England to invest in this kind of enterprise; French speculators preferred to play the funds, and investors preferred their Government *rentes*; and no class of entrepreneurs or contractors possessed the ability to undertake the works. Government initiative was needed to provide the stimulus.

Ninety-nine-year concessions were therefore sanctioned, on routes determined by the Ministry, and the contracts opened to tender. Though a planned system had many advantages over the often duplicated English routes, French capital was not expected to support the venture. Since the only interests capable of raising the money or industrial strength were British, the first concession offered was to connect Paris with the Channel ports.

The directors of the London and Southampton had been steadily campaigning for this. In their long rivalry with the London and South-Eastern, the Channel crossing and the route to Paris was decisive; Southampton–Rouen was longer than Folkestone–Boulogne but whoever had a railway direct to Paris would have a monopoly of passenger traffic. The actual initiative was won in France by Edward Blount: an

Irish Catholic, political agent for the Duke of Norfolk's wide interests, a friend of O'Connell, Brougham, and the supporters of Reform as well as the international money powers of Rothschild and Montefiore, he was in a position to tap immense capital resources by friendly persuasion.

He offered these services to Dufaure, Minister of Public Works. Blount would find a third of the £2 million capital in England, and a third in France, if the French Government found the rest. Dufaure was hard pressed to raise anything and thankfully agreed. Blount returned to England and in an almost casual three-day journey between London, Liverpool, and Manchester, gained his support: Moss, and Chaplin, Sir John Eastbrook, the Whig M.P. and newspaper owner, and Lawrence, banker to the London and Birmingham Railway. In France he co-opted Charles Lafitte, son of the almost legendary Jacques who had financed the Bourbon Government until the Revolution of 1830, and confronted the new Minister, Count Joubert, with his two-thirds share. Technical difficulties followed or were manufactured because so much British control was unpopular with the new Government, and there was still pressure from the interests favouring the L. & S. E. Easthope and Chaplin visited Guizot, then Ambassador in London, and brought pressure to bear; worried about support for France in the Mehemet Ali crisis, he was easily persuaded to force Joubert to agree. The path smoothed, the Chamber of Deputies voted the concession with the necessary loan, and the Corporation of Southampton showed their appreciation at a banquet for the Ambassador in a splendid marquee by the sea.

The British directors being in a large majority nominated their favourite Joseph Locke as engineer. Tenders were invited for the first 10 miles of track. Locke strongly advised Brassey to enter: he wanted the young man he trusted so well on this quite novel venture. In the end both he and William Mackenzie put in tenders; the similarity of their judgement, and probable collusion, resulted in two estimates of £157,000, so far below the nearest French figure that they were asked to make their calculations again. They decided to collaborate openly without altering the sum and the Ministry joyfully accepted it.

Brassey soon dominated the seven-year partnership. Mackenzie was an old, experienced, contractor who had built bridges for Telford, but was tired and complaisant and content to let the younger man develop his own methods. The key relationship lay between Brassey and

Blount. During the years of the Paris–Rouen they became more than banker and client; friends complementing in each other the sense of adventure and shrewdness in promoting railways. They had a sense of infinite possibilities; being sure of themselves and the virtues of their work, it was their enthusiasm which carried the peculiarly British side of the transport revolution to France, and in doing so, helped to turn her into an industrial nation.

There were Englishmen in business abroad already, some in very large undertakings: John Cockerill at Seraing, Aaron Manby, with his engineering works at Le Creusot, Ainsworth with a textile factory at Twente, but none of these had tried to set up an undertaking on the Continent with English machinery and materials, English direction and almost exclusively English labour.(a) Yet it had to be done: the large-scale engineering facilities did not exist in France in 1840 and the French labourer was not yet accustomed to the navvy's work.

Brassey visited the route, travelling slowly by coach along the atrocious roads of the Seine valley between the quiet Norman villages, marking the minute care and almost pedantic labour of the peasants, their evident thrift and sobriety. Somehow his rough English and Irish navvies must be lodged and kept from the cheap brandy of the district. At least the level bed of the valley did not worry him, and in Paris he had been promised a corps of gendarmes to keep order if necessary. As the horses drew into Rouen and the coach clattered on cobbled streets down to the port, he made his estimates. All tools, rails and ironwork must come through this port and be stored or shipped in barges up the Seine. He would pay £10 a ton for rails in England as against £15 in France if he could get them at all; but there was an import duty of 70 per cent.

He amassed workmen in Southampton with Mackenzie's help and in the spring of 1841 5,000 were shipped across and billeted in the small villages he had marked down. He soon realized that if he was to finish on time he must have more. Unable to commit his own entire labour force abroad, and aware that completion meant the entrée to the host of other projects planned by the Ministry, he decided to hire Frenchmen. Neither then nor later could he speak French; his agents had to learn and his wife helped. They got 5,000 more, a polyglot crew of a dozen nationalities, and out of the babel grew a lingua franca which the wandering navvies, like medieval scholars, were to carry all over the world. The new men learnt by watching, and as their muscles

grew used to the labour they were put to work side by side with
the English.

Importing all his materials became far too expensive. He was compelled to learn that if French engineering did not exist, it must be
created; and with Mackenzie he not only persuaded William
Buddicom, the locomotive builder, to set up a factory in Rouen,
but bore a large share of the cost. Soon this factory was turning out
the same 'Buddicom' and 'Crewe' locomotives which ran on the
Grand Junction.

The work itself presented no great difficulty. In addition to the track,
the contractors had to build fifteen stations, the Rouen terminus, a
goods yard, four tunnels, and five bridges including one over the Seine.
Buddicom provided all locomotives and carriages. With the trained
staff the resemblance to an army increased; during his three years in the
south he had come to know those who were now his agents: Edward
Mackenzie, Jones, Day, and Goodfellow. They in turn knew the subcontractors and gangers well and the enterprise moved smoothly.
Labour relations were not, however, entirely easy. By 1842 the number
had swelled to 20,000, some still billeted, but most in the sprawling
camps to which the English countryside had grown accustomed.

There were all the expected troubles: drunkenness, quarrelling, and
fighting, though surprisingly little between the different nations. In the
generally poor communities it proved difficult to provide the navvy
with his usual quantity of meat. The French labourer quickly mastered
the technique of the work but remained quite different in outlook 'a
more independent person than the British and a more respectable one'.
The English earned higher wages by piece work since they could do
more in a day but the French navvy took home far more than his
peasant neighbour; and he preferred to be paid fortnightly and actually
saved money—an aberration which the navvy after his weekly carousal
could barely understand. Brassey, continually afraid to lose good men,
was provident; subscribing to hospitals to ensure the good care of his
men, sending clergymen and, when a horde of families followed the
men, doctors and schoolmasters to look after them and educate their
children.

But the most serious problem was the curse of the age: the fluctuating
demand for labour, which always passed the hardship of uneven industrial advance on to the undefended. Brassey could rarely budget for
more than two months ahead, but had to parcel out the work so

that all his men should be fully employed. In bad weather this was impossible; some works had to be shut down, but masons, for example, could sometimes continue when the earthworks were a flooded morass. In the severe winter of 1842 many were unemployed, without money and nearly starving, hanging about the windy corners of streets in the snow. French workmen could return to their houses; Brassey had to organize relief for the others. The loss involved in keeping large numbers of men idle even for short periods was considerable and came entirely out of his own pocket. Brassey learnt by experience that elemental disaster could bring ruin to a contractor as easily as his own errors.

Such prodigious labour amazed those with leisure to come and watch. Parisian dandies made a pleasant sport by riding out to observe the works near Argenteuil: they remarked on the silence in which the navvies worked: 'Mon Dieu, les Anglais, comme ils travaillent!' Brassey's son wrote, years later when the world had seen far greater works, 'perhaps so remarkable an exodus of English labour never before occurred and it is improbable that it will ever be repeated'.(b) Brassey himself had no intention of trying: his experiment with French labourers proved their undoubted ability and he would use them as far as possible for his succeeding work. Apart from the winter, his navvies vastly enjoyed it: their morale had never been so high as when showing off to foreigners, whether drinking in the bistros of Rouen or prize-fighting in the market places of St. Pierre du Vouvray. Tolerable discipline was kept without the aid of the gendarmes and the line was opened on May 3rd, 1843.

Overnight he became famous. Unparalleled speed and efficiency made him the darling of the Paris Bourse. The railway was an immediate success, carrying more than its promoters had dared hope for; it initiated twenty years of Anglo-French co-operation, set the seal on Blount and Lafitte's partnership and made Brassey indispensable to their ambitions. For he had proved that in spite of higher raw material costs railways were no more expensive to build than in England; the low costs of promotion outweighed the risks, and if the Norman peasants could be trained as navvies, so in the future, could those of the Midi or the Rhine. The Directors' personal profit was £2 million and at no time had they needed more than £300,000 or £400,000 working capital. This was the secret: 'once an enterprise is set going, the means are derived from the source of operations, money being raised from local capitalists on loan and shares disposed of to foreigners at enhanced prices',(c) and the foundation of this lay in the closest understanding between Brassey who knew the progress of the line and Blount who found the money as it was needed.

When the Paris–Rouen paid its excellent first dividend of 10 per cent Brassey undertook to carry the line up to Le Havre. He was already at work on the massive 294-mile Orleans–Tours–Bordeaux Railway. By 1843 he had five French-speaking agents he trusted completely and an organization which was the admiration of Europe. Locke and Robert Stephenson and the French engineers Neuman and Pepin Lehalleur were his friends and equals. Buddicom had moved to Sotteville near Rouen and now had the largest locomotive and rolling stock works in the country. France lay quietly under this English domination.

Brassey had climbed from employing 700 men in 1837 to 35,000 six years later. Edward Blount wrote, 'I never met a more excellent man,' and their close friendship was the heart of the flexible, brilliant, and far-sighted groups which they collected round them. As an employer he showed a genuine interest in his men and among them grew a feeling of corporate loyalty—of belonging to the firm and of direct trust in the dynamic ability of their chief. Brassey's 'integrity no less than his ability accounts for the esteem in which he was held in Europe'.(d)

The continuation from Rouen to Le Havre was a logical but much more difficult task. The line rises steeply out of the sheltered Seine and drops again at Barentin where a large viaduct of twenty-seven arches carries it across the narrow valley. It strikes across the exposed windy plateau past Yvetot and drops again after crossing many smaller bridges to Honfleur and Le Havre. Though it was only 58 miles Brassey asked for two years; a new bridge had to be made over the Seine in Rouen itself, and the works included ten tunnels and an immense quantity of brickwork. The Ministry again found a third of the capital and again Blount and Lafitte found the rest. The men moved straight on from the Seine but Brassey had to import more specialized labour, this time bricklayers whom he found a bad class of workmen, troublesome and unruly. Their main grievance was that their skill entitled them to wages about a quarter higher than the ordinary navvy, but in this depressed year they had fallen to the guinea a week which even navvies had been earning in 1840.

Work went on night and day in shifts but the whole timetable was nearly broken when in a violent storm the great Barentin Viaduct collapsed. Brassey was at Rouen and left at once when the news came in. It had been built too quickly, in wet weather, and according to terms in the specification which he had opposed, of local and inferior lime.

In the grey morning, with rain still driving down, Brassey watched the muddy swollen river sucking round the broken stumps of the parapets and heaps of shattered masonry, and decided to rebuild at his own expense. He could easily have begun a prolonged battle in the courts but instead reported to the Board: 'I have contracted to make and maintain the road and nothing shall prevent Thomas Brassey from being as good as his word.' He showed, not for the last time, a flair for making a reputation out of disaster. The cost was £40,000—hydraulic lime had to be brought in and millions of new bricks bought, but by employing almost every mason on the line the viaduct was finished in six months. Boldness repaid him; he gained a sizeable bonus for finishing three months ahead of schedule and the Company paid him the cost of the repair; and without other advertisement, Europe knew that Brassey's word was his bond.

Meanwhile another of Blount's groups of British bankers, Barneds, Masterman, Thomson Bonar & Co. among them, had promoted the Orleans–Bordeaux, a simpler though far larger undertaking, and part of Brassey's firm was steadily employed for nine years on it under Mackenzie's supervision. When Mackenzie died Sir Morton Peto took his place, and began an association with Brassey which lasted more than thirty years. Peto, who helped build the Houses of Parliament, had just entered the railway contracting business on his own with a fortune of half a million pounds; Brassey, who had begun with nothing, had now the same working capital. And the network of English enterprise spread wider when Buddicom established another factory at La Bastide and supplied all the rolling stock for the line, which was, until the Paris–Lyons–Marseilles, the premier route of France.

Meanwhile other promoters were busy. The London and South-Eastern had their route to Paris, and when they built the Boulogne–Amiens section found it convenient to employ Brassey, whose services were never too committed not to take on a good proposition. After his Rouen–Dieppe line in 1847 it could be seen that the earlier show of competition was fading fast in a lucrative British monopoly of the system of the Nord. With Masterman and Uzielli, Peto and Brassey built a connexion from Orleans to Vierzon to connect the Ouest with the beginnings of the P.L.M., a footing in what was expected to be the most profitable concession of all.

This flood tide, which established a large measure of English control in French railways, did not pass unchallenged: heavy criticism was launched at the number of English directors—at their disregard for French shareholders, at their ignorance of French and at their supposed inefficiency. Brassey as a contractor was not under fire, since no one doubted that the railways were well built and only the most zenophobic believed that Frenchmen could at that date have done his work. But he and his partners by 1848 had built three-quarters of all the railways in France, and control lay very largely with the companies woven by and around Blount. There were more logical objections, which incensed those who had not been able to acquire the shares which now sold at such a premium. One of the chief sources of waste lay in the manner in which the lines were promoted, for when several companies flourished for each concession, most had no purpose but to profit from speculation in their own shares and the proceeds of having their interest bought out. There was even in England a faint rumbling of displeasure, and *Punch* disapproved of helping the oldest enemy; but the last to be worried by the nationalist press were the closely knit Anglo-French banks. Minor opposition in France was easily settled also; Guizot's Ministry was far from incorruptible, and the Duc d'Orleans himself was a silent partner in Lafitte, Blount & Co.

£27 million was poured into French railways by English investors before 1848, a rush explained by the dividends which they paid, 8 to 10 per cent against 3 or 4 per cent at home. But this satisfactory arrangement depended on a stable exchange rate, peace, and convertibility of securities. Nothing was more fatal to railway promotion than war or civil disturbance. Potato famine in Ireland, repeal of the Corn Laws, the collapse of Hudson, and the Railway Mania heralded the disastrous revolutions which shook Europe in 1848.

The monarchy of Louis-Philippe collapsed in February like the Barentin Viaduct, leaving Brassey in an extremely unpleasant position. He was unpopular, as an English agent, and in that August he still had £36 million worth of contracts on hand in Britain and France. He was paying a fortune every week in wages to 75,000 men and had just taken the Barcelona railway contract in Spain, which was proving more awkward than its size justified, when the Revolution broke out.

Blount, who took an enthusiastic and active part in the trouble in Paris, drove a locomotive to Amiens with the message which called General Cavaignac to bring his army to crush the armed workers of the capital, and then organized the necessary troop trains; and was ruined. In the political desert which followed, Brassey saw there would be no more contracts for a while. Those he was engaged on in England would tide him over at home and he could hope for eighteen months' more work in France on the Dieppe, the Vierzon, and the Bordeaux lines. Fortunately he was employing largely French labour and the problem of unemployment was not so serious as among the huge numbers thrown out of work on the other side of the Channel. What was most dangerous was that the new contracts, on the hope of which he was now dependent to keep his organization in being, would not be forthcoming, or if they were, that the confidence on which promotion was possible would not be enough to call up cash.

The first step was to re-create the promoters. He and Buddicom pooled nearly all their private fortunes and set up Blount again in business as Blount et Cie, Paris. His charm, flair, and connexions were essential to prise contracts out of unsettled and recalcitrant Governments. The other two remained as sleeping, though not slumbrous, partners. Brassey believed profoundly in the future of French railways and relied on his reputation and the enormous advantage his pioneer work had given him over competitors to bring him work when the country had settled down. But the course of French politics and the desperate need to prevent his organization from running down gave him no peace and for three years after the Revolution there was no inducement for him to return.

3

THE RAILWAY MANIA

LOOKING back in 1850 at the last six years' work he had done in England Brassey rightly considered it as the Golden Age; for it gave him a position in the contracting world beyond anything which had previously been dreamt of. The French enterprises, though full of excitement and importance for the future, were small compared to the undertakings of the great bubble, the Railway Mania, when for five astonishing years Britain went mad with the fever of speculation which is associated with the name of George Hudson, sometime M.P.; and of all that great endeavour Brassey himself constructed 1,000 miles of railway out of the three thousand which were built.

There was no doubt of his position: when he appeared in 1846 before the Select Committee on Railway Acts Enactments(a), James Morrison, the railway millionaire, asked him, 'Are you not the largest contractors?' Brassey replied, 'I think we are at present.' He was modest: no man in England had ever before disposed so widely of such an industrial empire.

He had built nothing in England after the London to Southampton because France kept him busy and the early forties were years of great inertia, culminating in 1843 in probably the worst year of the century for investment when £60 million lay idle in the City. Hostile tariffs and the formation of the Zollverein, the German customs union, cut trade with Europe. Yet in the general stagnation the railways built in the thirties paid high dividends, and the value of the land through which they passed and the importance of the towns they touched had grown out of all measure. Even at the nadir these signs foretold the coming boom and Brassey was ready at the beginning: a man to whom many came, who seemed to have infinite capacity.

His power of delegation developed with the extent of his work and he rapidly reached an eminence where he visited the line only when it was not going well and 'became, as it were, the great consulting physician on railway matters, only making his appearance on critical occasions.'(b) The story of the Railway Mania, of King Hudson and his crash, of the chaos of competing lines and uneconomic branches, of dividends paid out of capital, needs no retelling. There were hundreds of promoters, thousands of schemes and perhaps a million investors, but few actually to lay down the track. Brassey escaped disaster in the end because he was able to choose the contracts he wanted and the work they gave lasted him through the lean years after the crash. He was not, like Hudson, sidetracked into Parliamentary ambition; he did not attempt to become a rich landowner, not having the 'special education to be idle' which he felt a gentleman's life required. He preferred to state his ambition 'to be the great contractor and to furnish large and continuous employment to his countrymen and the world'.(c) And he had friends where Hudson made enemies. Among the most useful was Joseph Locke, in the forties the idol of railway England, engineer to many lines but chiefly those which were to become the London and North-Western, most powerful of the early combines.

He made Brassey one of his closest friends, and brought him as much work as he could take until, in the making of the London and North-Western between London and the Highlands, Brassey's lines covered more than half its extent.

Speculative fever develops quickly. The forty-eight Acts, authorizing companies with capital of £18 million in 1844 became 190 and £40 million in 1847. By 1848 the mileage in Britain had risen from 2,148 to 5,127, and it was estimated that half a million men had been employed in constructing them.(d) How much this high tide of employment helped to prevent revolution in 1848 is debatable; certainly the Mania saw the complete decline of the Chartist troubles.

Among the thirty contracts showered on him Brassey kept strict economy of effort, concentrating in three areas: the lines of Locke and the future London and North Western; East Anglia; and the Midlands. His labour force moved from one camp to another, starting work on a new contract as soon as the old was done, because workmen were scarce and a skilled navvy lost difficult to replace. Once the Mania began, the old days of plentiful excellent labour and cheap provisions vanished.

In 1844 Brassey began the Lancaster to Carlisle Railway and part of the scattered Eastern Union network from Colchester to Ipswich, but the first major contract was the Trent Valley Railway of 1845, one of the crucial lines laid down, because it shortened the west coast route to the North by 50 miles, and was a stage in the formation of the London and North Western. Shortly after, the banker, George Carr Glyn, one of the key figures in railway history, joined the Board as Chairman: a man with whom Brassey was shortly to do much business. In the same year, his Chester and Holyhead Railway, which included Robert Stephenson's masterpiece, the tubular Britannia Bridge across the Menai Straits, brought Ireland hours nearer London.

The Caledonian Railway reaching 125 miles north from Carlisle was also a major undertaking, the first link between England and Scotland,[1] and included the difficult Beattock Summit; it was an unprofitable affair whose Parliamentary expenses were enormous, and helped to put the Company hopelessly in debt. Brassey offered to run it himself but the board was incompetent to decide and the shareholders scared; nothing came of it, and the steep gradient remained to curse the London and North Western which shortly took over the line. However, it brought him three other contracts in the Lowlands, and the Scottish Central, while he added the Kendal and Windermere to the total of this astonishing year and with a line from Ipswich to Bury St. Edmunds kept his men in the Eastern Union area at work.

With so much on hand he took on less in 1846. Rumours were beginning to disturb the bubbling enthusiasm. His important Lancashire and Yorkshire line (93 miles) linked Hull to the Liverpool area where he added Ormskirk to the Lancashire system: while in the West he added the Shrewsbury and Chester to the widening sphere of London and North Western interest; and the Shrewsbury and Wolverhampton to that of the Great Western, giving him a broad gauge foothold in the West and sowing the seeds of a future railway war.

His agent, Mackay, saw this year as 'the height of the mania; demand for labour excessive, very much above supply. Beer given to the men as well as wages. Lookouts on the road to intercept men tramping . . . work night and day. Provisions dear, excessively high wages, excessive work, excessive drinking, indifferent lodgings caused great demoralisa-

---

[1] Carlisle to Glasgow, branching later to connect with Edinburgh: carried on to Perth by the Scottish Central.

Bilbao-Tudela Railway

The Victoria Dock

The Victoria Bridge over the Saint Lawrence

The Panic in the City, 1866

tion.'(e) Wages[1] were half as much again as in 1843 (and higher than they were to be for thirty years ahead) though, to economize, contractors let them live in camps so appalling that a Select Committee was moved to issue a sane and revealing report which was disregarded.

Brassey's main work, in 1847 was the Great Northern. This was one of the last great trunk lines left, held up for years by the opposition of G. C. Glyn, of the London and North Western interest on one side, and of Hudson, on the other, who was trying desperately to link his Midland Railway with his holding in the Eastern Counties. After a Parliamentary battle unparalleled in railway history,[2] Edmund Denison, M.P. for the West Riding, won an independent route for his Great Northern from London direct to York. Though through traffic was the aim, the first section was expected to tap the rich agricultural trade of the Fens as well as Cambridge, and, in spite of the objections of his friend Glyn, Brassey contracted for the first 75 miles to Peterborough.

He was soon in difficulties, having to complete the first 60 miles by July 1849 on a penalty of £5,000 a month, the rest sixteen months later on the same terms. It caused him embarrassment and he lost a great deal of money. The results of the financial crisis of October 1847 and the Revolution abroad stopped work and though it was partially resumed the crisis destroyed public confidence as other scares had not and it made all companies, speculative or not, unpopular. The Great Northern had spent a large part of its capital in getting its Bill through Parliament and was chronically short of ready money. To stop labour and abandon works was exceedingly dangerous, since repair and renovation added heavy extra costs, and to avoid it, Brassey was reduced to taking payments in mortgage bonds on the dubious promise that the Company would make it up after the crisis. Apart from this, there were some notable engineering difficulties.

The route to Peterborough lay across Whittlesea Mere, a fen or 'quaking bog—you can stand on it and shake an acre of it together' as Brassey put it. Clearly the railway could not float. Stephen Ballard, the

[1] Masons and Navvies—per week in shillings:

1843	1846	1849	1851	1855	1857	1860	1863	1866	1869
21	33	24	21	25/6	24	22/6	24	27	27
16/6	24	18	15	19	18	17	19	20	18

[2] The Bill lasted three months in Committee in the House of Commons and the Parliamentary expenses were £400,000.

agent, who had learnt engineering in Fen drainage, urged the same method George Stephenson had used to cross the shallower Chat Moss, in Lancashire. Logs were cut and made into large rafts on which were piled peat and earth; as the structure sank, more weight was added until finally a solid mass made a causeway through the morass. When bridges had to be made, the rafts were built up with bricks on the same principle, and served as piers resting on the bottom. Time had to be allowed for all this to settle down; the Mere was passed only just before the terminal date and the first train made the run from London on August 5th. Brassey provided an elegant lunch for 400, with suitable speeches; on the return run the party narrowly missed collision with a stationary locomotive on the track.

For years the Great Northern ran at high speeds on the easy gradient; it was well worth Denison's while to pay Brassey the loss on his bonds and the Company added a suitably large silver-gilt shield, emblazoned with the names of all concerned.

If the Great Northern proved a hard bargain for Brassey, its completion meant a death warrant for Hudson's ambitions. Thinking to do a deal for his Midland Railway he signed an agreement giving the Great Northern running powers on his line and entry to York. It was probably his only choice, for Denison had no scruples about building the parallel road for which he had Parliamentary power, but the shareholders screamed for Hudson's blood. Investigations showed up the great pompous vainglorious sham; a shoddy façade of words, based on the payment of dividends out of capital. He resigned his seat in Parliament and the boom days were over.

And in spring 1851 Mackay wrote: 'The contracts are all completed. Great depression on the labour market, but little work going on: political affairs on the Continent unsettled.'(f)

Only small lines had been taken on in 1848; and were all now finished. Abroad there was nothing. The railways of the forties had been too expensive and their promotion had swallowed enormous sums which profited no one but the landowners who were bought out and the lawyers who practised at the Parliamentary Bar. Indeed both Brassey and Locke were avowed supporters of State regulation: of regional control under a general Government concession. At an average of £40,000 a mile the cost of building was out of proportion to the possible return. Much of this huge capitalization was lost in competing and useless lines. As far as the contractors went, the hilly nature of

Britain and the wide margins of safety allowed by the engineers kept costs high. So England sat back to digest and in 1849 only thirty-four Railway Bills were promoted with capital authorized of a mere £3 million. There was no work for contractors in 1850 and unemployment repaid the railway labourer for the nation's progress.

Brassey could not save his navvies; he was able to retain the skilled men but the majority spent months unemployed, barely above starvation level, before jobs opened up again. There were certain things which he himself could hold on to in order to rebuild the firm. The groups of bankers and friends, Glyn and Masterman, and promoters like Chaplin and Eastbrook were not dissolved by the crash. Having begun, their future interests lay in further development. Even more important, perhaps, the railway companies themselves were rapidly consolidating into large undertakings under the influence of such men as Mark Huish, Edward Watkin, and Denison; Huish's ruthless manner of adding lines to the London and North-Western might have served as a model for the most cut-throat American railway kings but it created an immense power, the largest company in Britain, and Brassey could be sure of most of its work. He and Peto having built nearly all the East Anglian lines were securely entrenched in the sphere of Denison and the Great Northern/Eastern Counties bloc. No matter how reputations had suffered, Brassey, with one mile in three of all the work achieved during the Mania, was unassailable.

Nevertheless, Hudson's fate worried him, and in the unstable circumstances, he put aside £153,000 in trust for his children; shares in the railways he had built, shrewdly chosen to retain their value if any would. His personal fortune, after fourteen years as a contractor, was one million pounds; but such a sum could be lost in a single contract.

4

HALF WAY HOUSE

IT WAS time to take stock, to decide whether to go on or retire in considerable comfort. Once the mirage of the Mania cleared away, a contractor's life appeared uncommonly hazardous. At the age of forty-four Brassey was at the turning-point of his life.

The temptations of wealth were not attractive to him: to enter politics, acquire estates, and live the life of a gentleman at ease; to lay out money in good works and the hope of a title, or to enter the fashionable world and by the dazzle of his money try to hide his lowly origins. The pull of his family and the children, to be more at home and settled instead of endlessly travelling, sleeping in huts, worrying about progress of the line, was stronger, but there was something in him, like the organization he had created, which had to go on or run down. Years before, he had discovered the lure of his profession; time only deepened his perception of his task. It satisfied him to be the greatest contractor of all, but at heart it mattered simply to build.

Brassey was not a silhouette cut in all the industrial virtues by Samuel Smiles. Strength and honesty he had in large measure but he was neither the good industrious example nor the opposite, the rough drunken place-seeker Sir Roger Scatcherd, whom Trollope sketched as the archetype of an early Victorian contractor. There was too much wit about him to take seriously professions of officious respectability; though he was, genuinely, humble. He did not wish by the attentions of his tailor to appear anything but what he was, but as he grew older, he matured. At sixty he was an 'elderly gentleman of very dignified appearance and of singularly graceful manner, suggesting at once the idea of a gentleman of the old school'(a) but not a socialite, though

Edward Blount observed that he cut a fine figure in society with his gentle wit and humorous eyes that women found attractive.

He was a great conversationalist, devouring the spoken rather than the written word. Ill-educated at Chester, he had taught himself by listening to be a connoisseur of public speaking and adept at assimilating information and ideas from others. He read little, thinking literature a waste of time for such a man. But the virtues which mattered to him as a contractor were born rather than acquired: command of men and a genius for organization.

The navvy was not an easy man to control or win respect. When Edwin Chadwick investigated the conditions of their life in 1846 he found appalling squalor.(b) The Mania spawned a hundred contractors of the Scatcherd brand, large and small, concerned only to make their profit. Work came in so fast that they simply could not care, and the system of subcontracting helped to move misery to a suitable distance from the contractor's responsibility. Gangers forced the pace—none of the factory legislation applied to them—and men paid on piecework would, often of their own accord, work so many hours a day, seven days a week that the physique of the best was broken down. Chadwick found that most died in their forties.

Their food was usually good, their housing bad. Quantities of beef were given them for the ordinary day of a navvy was to move 20 tons of earth, shovelling it six feet up into a railway truck. Wages were better than they had been either on the land or the canals, but they had no security. When the contract was finished they moved out, wandering in gangs till they found work. So long as the Mania continued there was plenty, but in 1851 men remembered the grim unemployment following Waterloo, or the year of '42 when they had swelled the Chartist ranks.

Living conditions, however, were Chadwick's main attack. The turf hut camps in which they lived, thousands at a time, were utterly insanitary, overcrowded, and often verminous. Perhaps they were no worse than the slums of nearby industrial cities but the camp was the only home most of them knew; wives, campfollowers, and children lived hugger-mugger, twenty to a hut. The good Chadwick was shocked at their morals, at the sharing or trading of women for a jug of beer. Drunkenness reigned, syphilis was rife, 'no man cares for them, they labour like degraded brutes; they feed and lodge like savages; they are enveloped in vice as earth with an atmosphere'.(c)

Their masters plundered them, with 'truck' in their own shops, and by paying them monthly in their own beerhouses. Fatal accidents were commonplace and the contractors made no safety arrangements. Funerals were cheaper than precautions, and subcontractors scraped the barrel of economy. And for all Chadwick's dreaming of employers' liability and workmen's compensation, the Select Committee's Report was totally disregarded.

There was another side to the navvy, and it was Brassey's genius to bring this out. Their life was corporate, bound by fierce loyalties; they were independent, unhampered by the traditions of the peasant or the apathy of the slumdweller. If their pleasures, drinking and prizefighting, were rough, they enjoyed them; while work lasted their morale was high and they were aware of being an élite among the labourers of the day, marked out by their strength and freedom. Unworried by death they thought little of killing, and regarded the rest of society with the free contempt of the warrior.

Brassey appeared quiet-spoken and mild-mannered, yet these men followed him, instinctively recognizing the ruthless side of his character. Good wages, genuine interest, care for their dependants,[1] schools, churches, and chapels were part of it; so was his treatment of them as individuals, his talks with gangers on the line; and there was something more. Half his navvies had been soldiers, many were Irish, all claimed an intuitive right to follow a leader. Peto and Brassey were the two largest contractors of the age but it was this which marked them out; for this Peto's men nearly sacked the town of Norwich to get the peaceable Baptist elected to Parliament, and Brassey's navvies laboured in the harsh cold of the St. Lawrence, or ran the armed blockade in the Austro-Prussian War.

As employers they were responsible for many of the improvements of the fifties, setting themselves, in their own interest, against the great evil of unemployment. It was bad to lay off, and have to find again, experienced loyal men. But their concern went far beyond self-interest. Peto, friend of Spurgeon, and benefactor of chapels, laboured in Parliament against truck and spoke up for employer's liability and against the liquor trade. Ministers and doctors looked after his men and they proved less drunken than was usual.

Brassey cared less about liquor. He made what for his generation was

[1] He gave away almost a quarter of a million in his life; but not to public charity.

54

an astonishing discovery that the *cost* of labour in any country was practically the same whether the workmen were English navvies or Chinese coolies living on rice. If he paid better wages, men did more in less time. The side benefits of improved physique, health, and leisure served to prove the worth of his rule. 'At the start of the North Devon railway wages were 2/- a day. During the progress of the work, wages were raised to 2/6 and 3/- yet it was found that the work was executed more cheaply at the higher rate than the lower'.(*d*) In the age of *laissez-faire* and Cobden this was bold economic theory, but it worked. The fact that he was competing for labour anyway in a difficult market would have meant paying wages substantially higher than those of agricultural labourers; but by making a virtue out of it, Brassey made himself not only the ablest competitor but the one with the greatest reputation.

He would never be party to cutting wages: quite apart from loss of confidence, it did not pay. In one case when competing tenders cut the price to the bone 'the calculations were based on reduction of wages. He desisted from all further examination of the estimate, saying if business could only be obtained by screwing down wages, he would rather be without it.'(*e*) If he gave a subcontractor a hard bargain with his section, he would make it up as the line progressed.

As a result, his works were rarely troubled by strikes. He disliked unions and their activities, preferring the men to come to him direct; and he never failed to discuss their grievances on the spot. He gave piecework, old-fashioned but effective, which, before the unions organized against it, brought him the best and fastest men.

A benevolent but practical autocrat, he rarely exposed the harsh side of his nature, and by this alone stood out from almost all his contemporaries. Still, he was not a humanitarian—allowing his agent in Rio de Janeiro to use chained slaves on the drainage works until their extreme debility made it necessary to employ their Portuguese masters instead.

Loyalty of his men, loyalty and admiration of his deputies. Over the years he built up a corps selected with immense care. Brassey never forgot good work and was prepared to pay highly for it. The men he chose, proving their ability in small works first, were with him for thirty years. He gave them more responsibility, better work, and a higher position than they could have hoped for elsewhere; they dealt with governments and princes, often across half the world: Willcox ran the railway in Australia at three months' remove from London. In return they gave unquestioning respect to the patriarchal figure at their head. He never looked over their shoulders; when Stephen Ballard reported on the Dutch Rhenish line in 1852, Brassey had to sign the preliminary contract on this alone and examined his estimate closely. 'He went into the matter in a quarter of an hour, turned it over and stopped at the difficult points. In the case of one of the bridges he went over my figures minutely to see whether I had included all the details of the foundations. At the end he said, "That will do!" Never again did he look into my estimates in such detail.'(f)

Often in desperate competition, he had to have work to keep the business alive, yet to select with the greatest care, for once committed there was no way out but to finish the line, cost what it might. If the estimates were wrong, or the work more expensive, if the exchange shifted or the Government went to war, there was no remedy. 'In the difficult vocation of a railway contractor the fluctuations and anxieties of business are felt with peculiar severity.' Even when he had chosen, he was sometimes outdone and his unsuccessful tenders totalled £150 million in forty years; yet they were not wasted, because he enjoyed calculation, and though he had no vast mathematical skill, experience taught him to estimate broadly and accurately in all the departments of railway work. He relied greatly on his agents but could with justice revise their figures. He had a keen eye for faults in a contract, and the different estimates on the length of line required, often based on inaccurate maps, or over-optimistic descriptions of terrain which cursed early contracting.

Possessing a prodigious memory, he rarely made notes, loathed secretaries and wrote nearly all his own letters with great clarity of expression and in a firm, fine script. In common with many self-educated men, he worked incessantly. When shooting in Scotland, a guest noticed that a bag of writing materials went out with the lunch, and that the host shortly afterwards retired behind a wall to carry on business as if in his London office; and Blount remembered a night in a sleazy Italian station when he left Brassey writing late at night and found thirty letters neatly piled in the morning.

He hated lawsuits; a contractor could become known as 'troublesome' and they always wasted money and time. Out of disasters like the Barentin viaduct he preferred to gain in other ways. Only twice was he forced to sue: on the Great Eastern and the Barcelona, and in the latter case got nothing for it. Simplicity was part of his character; he would not argue and was ready to admit himself wrong. To the chagrin of an engineer he would ask a navvy's opinion of a disputed point. Prejudice infuriated him, and his integrity was remarkable considering the men he worked with and the examples of the day: the Vanderbilts, Strousbergs, or Meiggs. The most corrupt undertaking he was implicated in was the Grand Trunk of Canada, and most of the blame for that may be put fairly on the shoulders of self-seeking local politicians. He cut out, on his own works, the skimping of work, and bribing of inspectors or engineers, which were commonplace; and like Peto[1] he lost contracts because he would not pay officials their cut nor manipulate the shares of his own companies.

For a man of his origins, his vision was remarkable, greater in all ways than that of Hudson; in the forties the French venture, in the fifties the Canadian; then the development of eastern Europe and India; the dreams of the Euphrates Railway, the Channel Tunnel, and the Panama Canal. After 1850 he added financing to the already wide duties of a contractor and in the sixties he and Peto were building railways for governments of undeveloped countries with the sketchiest of assets. Idle, speculative, wild schemes were launched about him. The only failing was over enthusiasm: he could not turn down an attractive proposition or a challenge, and though his own judgement was good he was uncritical of the ability of his friends; leading him, with Peto and Peto's brother-in-law, Edward Betts, into a number of brilliant but shaky undertakings.

So much of his life was taken up that there was little real warmth left for his children. He gave his elder son a classical education which was incomprehensible to him after his own upbringing, and he let him go his way, giving advice without using his prerogative to interfere. Maria Brassey instead underpinned their life. Her greatest fortune was that her husband grew in stature and wealth to match her ambitions without ever growing away from her possessive affection. So greatly did he succeed that there was no occasion for her to waste her ambitions in a frustrated feminism which might otherwise have obsessed her

---

[1] Peto negotiated in 1856 with the Portuguese Government for the £3½ million Northern line. Baron Erlanger, the King, and some Ministers were in his favour. French competitors bought the opinion of the Board of Works and Peto lost the contract by refusing to pay the £5,000 which his agent said would tip the balance.

highly individual mind. It was she who gave her three sons the stability from which they walked armoured at all points into the upper-class life of London.

Without being estranged, contact with their father in later life was limited to the courtesies of respect. He had been too long away; he was not indulgent to his children; what he admired in others he would find fault with in them, fearing the ostentation and spoilt nature he imagined would follow money too rapidly acquired. But he did them well, considering that he knew they had not the talent to follow him, with great estates and mansions for their married life. Samuel Smiles spoke enviously of them as the 'Brassey Grandees' and Morton Peto described the elder son's wedding:

'I am just returned 5 o'clock from the Wedding-Breakfast . . . a *very* well arranged affair. 14 Bridesmaids, 14 Groomsmen!! There were 100 to breakfast which went off very well indeed. Excellently managed. . . . The House and grounds are *well* worth seeing, the Pictures are *very* beautiful—all in the best taste.'

Yet Brassey was not a snob, keeping, but one face to the world, courteous to all but pungent: suffering fools but despising servility.

Thomas the elder son, when an M.P., liked to theorize on his father's life: 'He never failed in consideration for the feelings of others, recognizing the superior social position which they enjoy who possess long lineage and large landed estate, yet knowing that in his own busy and remarkable career there was something honourable which it was a distinction to have achieved(*g*).' The compliment smacks of late Victorian attitudes: 'Intelligent in observation, with an excellent command of language, only in some slight provincialisms betraying in how small a degree he had in early life enjoyed the educational advantages of those with whom his high commercial position brought him in constant communication.'(*h*)

Brassey was much more than this; of the same calibre as bankers like Thomas Baring or George Carr Glyn rather than prosperous tradesmen with their 'slight provincialisms'. Edward Blount, whose own ancestry was impeccable, called him his greatest friend and introduced him to Gladstone who was amazed at his conversation and breadth of understanding. Not all contractors were squalid place-seekers like Scatcherd; and his contemporaries, who saw Brassey as the giant of his age, had a truer judgement than the next generation. 'Natural selection' the engineer Hawkshaw called it. There had been a few great contractors before, and many would follow, but the state of mid-Victorian England was peculiarly suited both socially and philosophically to receive such a man. His own navvies had perhaps the best appreciation: 'If Brassey had been a parson he would have been a bishop, and if he had been a prizefighter he would have won the belt.'

His interests were wide and he could drop a curtain over the business world leaving him free to enjoy his hobbies: he loved engineering, all manner of projects like the ocean telegraph and the Mont Cenis tunnel. He was enthusiastic for Hawkshaw's Channel tunnel and at his own expense surveyed the Isthmus of Darien for the first, abortive, canal. Mountains and landscape, architecture of all kinds, moved him. Baedeker in hand, he trudged the cities of Europe drawing inspiration from their monuments. He loved sculpture and fine porcelain, patronizing the masters of his generation, but he had no real appreciation of painting, though in his late years he spent quiet hours at Christie's, buying haphazardly to please his wife.

Honours were disregarded. It was pleasant to dine with Louis Napoleon and delightful that the Empress should talk to him in English; rewarding that the King of Italy and the Emperor of Austria should be beholden and ask his advice; but he never wore his Legion of Honour and thought only that, 'Mrs. Brassey will be pleased to possess all these crosses.'(i) The jubilant Italians who hailed him as 'il re degli intraprenditori' left him as indifferent as the abuse of Canadian newspapers. He possessed priceless resilience; the ultimate early-morning courage which gave confidence to his subordinates and a legend to posterity.

There was in fact no choice for him but to go on. Horses, wagons, miles of rails, sleepers, locomotives, tools, millions of bricks, and thousands of men waited to be put to use. As master of an entity 'whose energy could not be restrained by political accidents and which was loath to cease activity when domestic opportunities became restricted',(j) the contractor had become an industrialist. During the next seven years 'railway building became a service which Great Britain could dump abroad when her financial and constructing plant could not be employed at home'.(k) So, in the search for work, Brassey and Peto became financiers among their peers; their prestige came to control the loans of governments and the public subscription for them. They were unhampered by the traditions of banking and their enterprise ran parallel to the growth of a more elastic organ of credit: the finance company. By a logical process they began to build railways on their own initiative and then organize companies to buy them; with no guide but their own integrity among colossal risks. But the profits matched the risks, and in the next fifteen years the contractors and financiers permanently affected the destinies of many countries in Europe and the world.

5

THE GRAND TRUNK

IN THEIR search for more work in 1852, Sir Morton Peto, his brother-in-law, Edward Betts, and Brassey, drifted into an association for mutual advantage. In the uncertain flux of business it seemed important to preserve as much monopoly as they could and this grouping was intended to cut their overhead costs. It was limited only by their friendship and resources. Almost by chance they became interested in one of the most magnificent of the old schemes proliferated in the forties for joining the desirable parts of the earth: a 650-mile trunk line in Canada to connect the Great Lakes to the Atlantic and capture for the whole year, rather than the six summer months, and for Canada rather than the U.S.A., the grain trade of Chicago and the Middle West; and they took up this at the very moment when Canadian efforts to get the line built reached their peak. Though the transatlantic railways in the United States were still on paper, they argued that such a line could surely be built by England in a colony. So also reasoned the glib promoter, Sir William Jackson, M.P. (a friend of Brassey's from Birkenhead days) who joined them. All the groundwork, the political manœuvres and negotiations were done; what they hoped to take over was a plum which had taken twenty years to ripen.

Railways had been slow in development in Canada, set aside by the Revolution and the Durham Report which focused local energies on politics rather than transport. Only in the late forties, when there was a danger that U.S. railways running north would take the Canadian trade, did the provincial legislatures clamour for them, and one of the first in the game was A. T. Galt, the contractor. Local politics were tied up with it from the beginning, each town or province striving to get the lines which suited it best; and none of them had the money or credit to build the main routes which alone could be as profitable as the manifestly rich American. Mixed up with the fierce debate on whether the lines should link one town with another, or be chiefly for through traffic, was the assumption that it was the clear duty of the home Government to provide the cash.

Over some fifteen years various Canadian politicians crossed the Atlantic to try and wheedle at least a guarantee on the interest of the loans which the provinces would have to raise. Galt wanted local lines; leading politicians like Sir Allan Macnab, of Hamilton, and Francis Hincks, of Montreal, were for the through route; and it became clear that the Colonial Office was interested in nothing but this, partly as a military line and partly because it hoped that the unity which it would bring might effectively wipe out the separatist feelings still latent in Quebec.

Galt and his associates and Hincks fought it out in local elections. Finally in 1850 when the trunk route supporters had won in Canada, Sir William Jackson intervened.

The railways might still have been built piecemeal and tacked on to the U.S.A., but the contractors turned the flank of the Colonial Office with their siren proposals. Their entry had been carefully prepared. Brassey himself was greatly impressed by Hincks's forecast of the profits of railways in the building of the West. Throughout 1851, their agent, Archibald, tried to persuade Canadians to accept a package deal for their railway and had gone so far as to fight openly against Macnab in local elections in the Maritime Provinces. Finally, to solve the Colonial Office embarrassment, they proposed to build the whole trunk line and find the capital as a private company. Glyns and Barings were their bankers, and since these were also the agents for Upper and Lower Canada, could hardly be objected to. Such names were their own credentials.

The only distrust felt was from those, Galt among them, who thought that the line should be built by Canadians. Hincks had been talked over and taken in hand, lavishly entertained and promised wealth by Jackson, who talked airily of millions to what he regarded as open-mouthed colonials. Galt, a partner in the contractors Gzowski & Co., which had already begun work on part of the line, still demanded that the main work should be opened to tender; with some justification he asked: 'Is the instrumentality of Sir W. J. and his associates so essential for procuring loans of English capital that they should be paid from 30 to 50 per cent over the cash value of their work merely for the facilities they are supposed to possess as money brokers, or is it pretended that a little knot of railway jobbers hold the key to the great money markets of the world?'(a) But it was so, and he was silenced, shrewdly, however, taking refuge in control of a key link in the works, from which he was only dislodged at great cost to the new Grand Trunk Railway of Canada Company.

Of course, if Canada wanted such a railway quickly, there was no choice but this. What was never even considered was the real value of the trunk route at this stage. All that counted was the glittering prospectus of the Company, its illustrious roll of bankers, contractors, and politicians of the highest reputation. It stirred the imagination. Before a rail of the Union Pacific was laid, this was the first Trans-continental. In England as much as in Canada it seemed the triumph of an age of mechanical and civilizing progress.

Such expectation discounted expense, made light of the fact that Galt's price had been the building of a bridge across the St. Lawrence at Montreal to connect with his own lines, and that at the western terminal, since the existing company refused to sell out, yet another of his concessions had to be taken over. Before a rail was in place the Grand Trunk had paid out £2¼ million and Gzowski & Co. retained the contract for building the line for whose concession Galt had just been paid.

However on a total capital of £9½ million this did not worry the three promoters unduly. Such sums were on a scale greater than anything they had before dealt with and this betrayed them into a much more serious mistake. They kept back half the issue of bonds which were left after paying out compensation; whereas those which were sold, part in debentures, part in ordinary shares with a promised yield of 11½ per cent were, not surprisingly, oversubscribed and sold at a premium. The presence of G. C. Glyn and Thomas Baring on the board may have influenced public confidence, though in fact they were no more than sleeping directors, but it was the project itself which fired the investors. Unfortunately Brassey and Peto had not then learnt that no issue is ever so good as when it first appears. Shares were never so high again—a year later the Bank Rate stood at 8 per cent for the Crimean War and, as the price fell and continued to fall, the syndicate suffered heavily on their unsold stock.

The early promise clouded rapidly. Brassey organized the work as he had done in France; Betts was to go to Canada as agent and Jackson remained there for a while as a figurehead. This would serve to close the 3,000-mile gap in control between the Board and its railway. Since work could hardly proceed in the Canadian winter, the greatest effort had to be made in seven months of the year. No Canadian foundries existed on the scale needed to supply rails, ironwork and rolling stock so Brassey decided to make it all at home. The Canada works at Birkenhead, one of the largest plants in England, grew up under his direction, equipped with the latest machine tools from Whitworth's and new inventions from the U.S.A. The work turned out was impeccable, but in spite of cheap sea transport charges it became exceedingly expensive.

However, already a certain disregard for economy had been observed. The style in which Jackson lived in Canada surpassed that of the Governor-General, and the scarcity of labour, despite the hunt of agents for strong labourers through French Canada, forced the contractors to send out 3,000 men; all of whom earned the higher wages prevalent in Canada—7/6 a day.

Conditions were quite new to them: national feeling being what it was, there was no chance of profiting by American experience in laying lines across earth which was frozen 10 feet deep in winter. The contractors only learnt with time and money that special bogies and wheels were needed to contend with the irregularities and results of the climate. And money began to run short. 650 miles looked different on the terrain than it had from London. Great forests, outcrops of rock, hills, winter snow and spring flood, all on a grander scale than those of Europe opposed the work. Some Canadian papers noticed at the start of 1855 that Brassey was making payment in depreciated bonds and that his line was costing more per mile than that of Gzowski. Rumours soon came out openly that the line could no longer pay interest out of capital because the capital was exhausted. The shares were low and almost unsaleable. Finally the Shareholders Committee, with the Governor of the Bank of England in the chair, suggested that Canada should be asked to reprieve the contractors from approaching disaster by giving a 5 per cent guarantee of interest on the total share capital for ninety-nine years.

To put this bitter and highhanded solution to the Canadians, Brassey and Betts embarked in March 1855. They were clearly in very deep water, but could, with a show of legitimacy, complain that since the

Canadian Government had invited them in, it should tide them over their difficulties. And Francis Hincks, who owed a great deal in cash as well as power to them, was now Prime Minister.

They sailed by Cunard to New York, Brassey hoping first to learn something of American railroad methods. His reception was spectacular; special cars ran for him on every line and, ushered by managers and directors, he moved like royalty through New England. His shrewd eye missed little; and he was most interested in the lines reaching out towards the West, none of which yet reached as far as his. The railway, he was told, does not link place to place: 'like a river it is the natural channel of civilization; it precedes population and is laid down even before common roads are thought of'. This, in his notes, he put in more practical terms: 'As the expectation of traffic is small, the cost must be kept low . . . timber instead of iron used in this country, trestle bridges for viaducts, and instead of a solid embankment, a light structure.'(b) He noticed also the American custom of paying the contractor in part with a mile-wide grant of land which he could develop to his own profit.

The four weeks Brassey spent in America had an enormous effect on his ideas—were perhaps the decisive influence in the later works. But Canada remained to be sold into bondage.

Matters had gone too far to be solved by economy of materials or labour. Aided by the good offices of Lord Elgin, the Governor-General, Brassey persuaded the Legislatures to give the guarantee and issue, as well, a loan of £900,000 which was at once swallowed up in the works. Even this failed to push the stock up enough to off-load the promoter's share. One thing Brassey would not do was to follow American practice and 'water the stock' by issuing more shares, and before he left, it was painfully clear that another loan was necessary. Now that the weight of responsibility had been accepted, however unwillingly, by them, the Canadians' dilemma was thrown into sharp relief. If they refused the new loan, they would be faced with finishing the railway themselves. One form of persuasion used to coerce them was the publication by Ross, President of the Grand Trunk, of Brassey's letters to him, stating that the contractors could not continue their undertaking without assistance. In horror, the Governor of the Bank of Upper Canada was moved to write, 'Do Glyns think the Bank can safely continue negotiations with the agents of Peto and Brassey?'(c) With the reproachful air of a father paying his son's debts they agreed to lend

£2 million in July 1856. Interest on this loan was to be paid before all other commitments. So, as a consoling gesture, Brassey reduced the contract price of the Victoria bridge by £150,000, to his own serious loss.

But even such a loan could not clear the Grand Trunk's liabilities. The contractors again pressed for relief and, faced with taking the railway over under the mortgage, the Government consented to forgo all interest on the debt for five years. The contractors were still not happy. Jackson had only a small financial stake in it, but Brassey was reduced to helping the other two, and Peto also became heavily indebted to Glyns and, when they grew increasingly wary, to Overend and Gurney. Brassey was able to keep his share up from the profits of European contracts, but Peto was forced to accept other, wilder undertakings to offset his losses on the Grand Trunk.

Meanwhile, in spite of near bankruptcy and the slow awakening of Canadian opinion to the cost of their railway, the Grand Trunk neared completion. Nearly £4 million in more loans were needed but distance and the wilderness were at last spanned. Perhaps the soundest comment came again in 1856 from the Bank of Upper Canada— 'Messrs. Peto and Brassey are driving on their works with astonishing vigour and everything seems to prosper with them just now ... (but) railway people ought never to have attempted it. I should recommend the Provinces to finish it if such a thing could be done.'(d)

Four years too late the London Board decided to investigate what mistakes had crept into the great scheme. Traffic had not developed properly because the line was not fully connected up. Kingston, Coburg, and Port Hope stations were so far from the waterfront that they needed branch lines to load goods; there were two stations in Toronto because the Corporation would not allow a line into the city; the Sarnia terminus was 'on the bare shore of the Lake without any means of intercepting any of the western traffic down Lake St. Clair to which all the original ideas of the promoters must have had reference'.(e) However by the time the Board had digested this, the line was finished.

It was easy to criticize; yet the Grank Trunk was without parallel in the world in 1859.

What was astonishing was that it was finished at all. From the Great Lakes it stretched across the open lands and virgin forest of Ontario through difficult rocky hills by Guelph, Toronto, and Kingston to

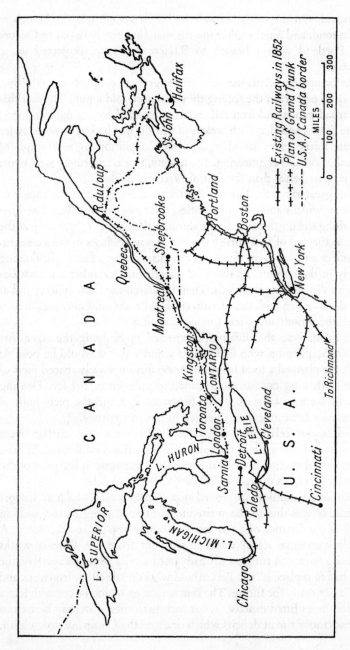

Montreal. On the other side of the St. Lawrence was the branch to Richmond, and Sherbrooke, and the main line reaching out to Quebec and Portland with a branch to Rivière du Loup, projected on to Halifax.

Unfortunately, Canadian resentment grew in proportion to the line, at least in part from the feeling they had been sold a pup. The fact that the broad gauge and iron rails were superseded by standard and steel in the sixties, and that with wear and tear the line had to be relaid twice within thirty years stood against its recognition as a triumph of organization and engineering. For its date, it was extremely well built; and no part better than the famous Victoria Bridge.

The great river St. Lawrence after pouring through the rapids of Lachine, widens and calms its restless flow past Mount Royal and the city along the north bank. In the summer the river is 15 feet deep at the most at the end of La Prairie basin but as winter closes in the ice begins to collect and build up into heavy packs, 20 or 30 feet high, floating slowly in the current. As the frost deepens in December the mass becomes solid and the level falls. Then in March the thaw splits it and at first slowly, then with thunderous crashes, breaks up. Enormous stresses smash the mountainous ice, forcing it against the banks.

So great were the difficulties expected in bridging the river that Robert Stephenson who designed it wondered if it would be possible at all. He planned a total length of 8,660 feet on widely spaced piers of stone with long cutwaters to resist the pressure of the ice. Floating caissons were to be sunk in the limestone bed and the piers built of perennially hard limestone quarried in Indian territory.

Bad labour relations dogged the bridge's progress. Strikes were frequent and the work in the caissons was hard and unpleasant. Worse, epidemics of cholera dogged the navvies' camps and at the peak of the summer of 1854 a quarter of Brassey's men were sick.

Working conditions improved after Brassey's visit. Much of this sort of trouble was due to the wastefulness of attempting to run such an army at the distance of 3,000 miles; the same applied to machinery. A highly expensive steam traveller sent out from the Canada works proved a failure. A rough-and-ready one built by Brassey's agent on the spot had to replace it. The Birkenhead works made all the ironwork and sent it out ready for fitting. The centre tube of 10,309 pieces with half a million holes fitted exactly. What such perfection cost may be seen in the enormous rise in deficits which dragged the Company down until, in June 1860, most of the line was taken over in working condition. Yet the glory of the iron network striding across the St. Lawrence was undeniable. Robert Stephenson remarked: 'The contractors left even the engineers themselves little more than the poetry of engineering.' But Brassey's own agent with a truer sense of proportion, as he might have, responsible for the men employed, 'looking back at all the various difficulties . . . in the hands of other less energetic contractors, it would not have reached the successful issue to which it has been brought.'(f)

The Grand Trunk taught Brassey a great deal; not only of organization, but of the difficulties to be met in undeveloped countries, and of the problems of large-scale finance; and he was exceedingly fortunate in his position that, between the Colonial Office and the Colony, his company could not be allowed to go bankrupt, cost what it might. It greatly strengthened his links with Glyns, who became his bankers in 1858, and it helped by bitter experience to set him on the path he consciously adopted, of freeing himself as far as possible from dependence on the credit of the London market. His friends came worse out of it, and in 1860 Peto wrote: 'How keenly I feel this mistake I have made no one can tell. Mr. B. said that in 5 or 6 years if we had our health and strength we ought to gain more than we have lost. If we wind up in five years and get nothing we shall still be worth £200,000 so I suppose we must be grateful.'(g)

Canada could scarcely afford gratitude. The accounts of the Grand Trunk in 1860 showed a current deficit of one million dollars and a total debt of 13 million dollars. There was nothing to pay the interest after the five-year moratorium and complete reorganization was necessary if the Company were not to collapse into utter chaos. Charges of corruption were flung widely about with strident complaints against what today would be called economic imperialism, even when Edward Watkins, lately of the L. & N.W. took it over; because though he ran it well, the Grand Trunk could never cope with the load of debt, capitalized at par. Brassey lost nearly a million himself. Galt and Gzowski made their fortunes and Francis Hincks wrote his memoirs in self-defence.

6

EUROPE AT PEACE

Although the Grand Trunk was the most spectacular effort
by which Brassey sought in the fifties to diversify his undertakings and escape rapidly narrowing competition at home, he
was at work in nearly every European country after 1852, using his
good name and his connexions formed before the 1848 Revolutions. In
Italy, however, he became more than a railway power: he became an
associate of Government, his work a stage in the Risorgimento.

His connexion with Cavour, Prime Minister of the State of Piedmont, was not purely a business one. Their characters were in some
ways similar, though Brassey never aspired to the lengthy diplomatic
subtlety of the Italian. Cavour saw in the Englishman one of the powers
to whom he could appeal; a force which, loosed in Italy, would help to
bring progress, prosperity, and the extension of the Piedmontese
Monarchy and the eventual unification of Italy under that monarchy.
Brassey trusted a man liberal in the same sense as himself, a progressive to
whom civilization meant national benefits as well as intellectual freedom;
not so common perhaps in Europe as in England. No one who listened to
Gladstone could be ignorant of the misgovernment of the countries in
the Italian peninsula, and though Brassey professed himself a Tory,
party labels meant little to him. Above all, he and Cavour liked each
other; and an enterprise which promised to the one, the flow of English
capital which had done so much for France, and to the other, a clear
field uncomplicated by political difficulties, also appealed keenly to
Blount and Charles Lafitte.

Though railways had become a force in politics, most Italian States
failed to use the opportunity. Placid Tuscany under a complaisant ruler
was made a cockpit of avid speculation. But Cavour, slowly turning

the straightforward aggrandisement of his country into a larger dream of a united Italy by removing the Austrian Hapsburgs and the Bourbons from the peninsula, negotiated with Brassey, the best contractor he knew, and well aware of his views on the cost and irritation involved in railway promotion in England offered him a simple favourable agreement. His Government would find a quarter of the capital, the Provinces another, the public and Brassey the rest. Two important lines were planned, Prato–Pistoia and Turin–Novara, but Cavour had over-estimated his support. The Provinces declined to assist and the public was apathetic. He was forced to ask Giles, Brassey's agent, that Government and contractor should bear the cost together. As soon as the capital was paid up, the Italians clamoured for the shares, giving the Government a handsome profit. Brassey returned his own extra allotment unsold; an act of integrity which did not pass unnoticed.

The 60-mile Turin–Novara line, completed in 1855, was immediately successful. Its strategic implications were obvious; as Cavour began to draw in the threads of his fine strategy to bring Louis Napoleon to war with Austria on his behalf. If war broke out it offered a rapid route for mobilization. The initiative of the Government, the public support in Piedmont, and the fame of Brassey 'considered the first in all Europe', had an effect on opinion in the Italian peninsula out of all proportion to the undertaking. The visible sign of Piedmontese progress lay across the land and the status of the monarchy of Victor Emmanuel rose.

It was highly profitable: soon yielding dividends of 14 per cent and, comparing it with English railways, Brassey noted that the entire cost was less than the money spent in the Parliamentary fight for the Great Northern. More works were created, with a scarcely disguised military objective. Austria also was building; from Buffalora on the Ticino frontier across Lombardo-Venetia, past the fortresses of the Quadrilateral to the frontier of Austria proper.[1] In a speech to Parliament in 1854 Cavour spoke of 'public works; the most necessary objective and one which will have most care'. The same year Brassey signed a contract to link Turin with Susa and Novara with the Ticino; there would soon be through traffic from the Alps to the enemy border. Henfrey, his agent, who knew Italian politics, wrote, 'the facility for the movement

---

[1] This line, financed by Anselm de Rothschild, had reached Rome when war broke out between France and Austria. Its military efficiency, however, was much impaired by the fact it was largely operated by Frenchmen.

of troops and supplies from Paris to the Austrian frontier was perhaps not the weakest argument in soliciting Napoleon's aid'; and before these lines were finished Cavour had made his spectacular bid for notice among the Powers of Europe by sending a Piedmontese contingent to the Crimean War, demanding on its return a place at the Congress of Paris. While Cavour tormented himself in Paris at his inability to move the cautious Napoleon, Brassey signed the contract for the railway from the French frontier (as it then was) through Savoy to the Alps. There the military road built over the mountains by the first Napoleon completed the link.

For rapid transport in the plains Brassey built a short but important line between Chiasso and Ivrea, uniting two prosperous provinces and providing access to the defensive works along the Po which la Marmora, Minister of War, had ready in case the Ticino front gave way.

Brassey did not achieve complete monopoly, because Cavour dealt with whoever he could. British trading interests pressed him to construct the Lukmanier line from Locarno to connect up with the Rhine system and rehabilitate the port of Genoa and the Levant trade, free of French or Austrian customs, but Cavour became extremely shifty as it affected his French interests. He refused to share the expense on the usual basis, 'the Swiss are so extremely tricky about any interference of a foreign Government . . . but I should be glad if Mr. Brassey could see his way . . . without any assistance from us'.(a) They were to meet at Coire in July 1858. But Brassey was summoned to the opening of the Cherbourg railway by Louis Napoleon himself. Cavour regretted that he had not had 'his lesson from the most experienced contractor in Europe', but the project died. It was rumoured that the Rothschilds were against it; and it was far too near the crux of his policy for Cavour to risk a break with France. The same shadow fell on the Victor-Emmanuel railway, as Brassey's route across Savoy was called. Louis Napoleon was busily seeking a hold in Savoy, his hidden price for going to war, and Cavour allowed a French promoting group to override the British contract. Agreement was reached: the French took the concession and the honour, Brassey built the works and kept the substance; a sop which satisfied the pride of one and the pocket of the other.

War came at last. Napoleon failed to live up to his great name, fought two disastrous victories and retired; yet one thing consoled Cavour for his rage that the Emperor had backed out: railways whether British or

Austrian were patently uniting Italy. Brassey too had his consolations; to Italians he was 'il re degli intraprenditori', the king of the entre- preneurs; and under the new, wider monarchy of Victor Emmanuel he began to build again.

Friend of Cavour, friend of Napoleon, Brassey's eminence in France had suffered only a short decline after the 1848 Revolution. The Emperor's first gift was the long awaited, bitterly fought concession for the P.L.M.—Paris–Lyons–Marseilles Railway. This enormously profit- able concern was divided among many; chiefly Rothschilds and Barings; however Masterman, Devaux, and Uzielli were among them, and Brassey, Peto, and Betts held an 8 per cent share. They built the P.L.M. from Lyons to Avignon and, as before, Brassey worked with Edward Blount: now as partner in Blount et Cie, Rue de la Paix, from which he drew a quarter of the profits. (The bank prospered greatly until it became absorbed in the Société General de Paris at the 1870 Revolution.) But Blount's main concern was with the Ouest, the West of France Railway Company which he founded in 1852 to cash in on the boom which the P.L.M. concession had begun. Competition had increased, and promoters like J. L. Masterman and John Sadleir were now backing such new contractors as Wythes, Sir Charles Fox, or Henderson and Company.

Blount et Cie owned virtually all the shares of the Ouest and nominated a board of directors, none of whom even spoke French, G. C. Glyn and W. Chaplin among them. Brassey and Sir Charles Fox split the work. Brassey himself built the Nantes–Caen (113 miles), Le Mans–Mézidon (84), and the Caen–Cherbourg (94) lines by 1857. Such total monopoly, however, could now only be achieved by merger and negotiating and even so was highly unpopular in France itself; he built no more except the 4,000-metre Bellegarde Tunnel between Lyons and Geneva, which was cut with machinery from Buddicom's Sotteville factory. British influence in French industry perceptibly declined after 1855 as Louis Napoleon matched one interest against another in the allotment of concessions.

Brassey of course moved on; his holdings prospered behind him, but his men had to be employed. By the mid-fifties they again numbered nearly 100,000 in England and abroad. In Belgium he built the Sambre- et-Meuse line, revived the Dutch-Rhenish Railway (a concession from Amsterdam to the German frontier which he had taken before the

1848 Revolution), and in Denmark began work with Sir Morton Peto.

So closely associated in Canada, their ambitions interlocked in this decade. After the success of a joint railway in Norway,[1] they decided to build, lease, and exploit the Royal Danish Railways. Having already built and leased the London Tilbury and Southend Railway, and created a fleet of merchant ships, the North European Steamship Navigation Company, sailing from Peto's own port of Lowestoft, they hoped quite simply to corner the entire Danish agricultural trade and bring it to London in record time; thus creating a type of traffic which before refrigeration hardly even existed. This railway was planned as a 500-mile network from Tonning in Schleswig to Åalborg, chief town of the northern province.

As far as the Danish Government went, the motives were mainly political and dynastic. The King hoped to bind the Duchies of Schleswig and Holstein to the Crown and solve the intricate question of their inheritance which had baffled the diplomatic brains of Europe. Brassey had hesitated; beside the obvious political dangers, the Government demanded the heavy deposit of £100,000 for the twenty-five-year lease and the contractors had to provide and maintain all the rolling-stock. However the payment offered for the work was satisfactory and the two contractors, as yet undeterred by the vagaries of the Grand Trunk, were keen to experiment with the new type of enterprise.

Work was begun in 1856 and the last, Schleswig, section reached seven years later; a length of time determined by the good but slow labour of Danish navvies. There were some very large earthworks and Brassey had to go out to supervise part of the work, but, for the rest, his agents were now skilled in handling labour of all nationalities. High wages brought dividends, continually proving Brassey's rule that they did not increase the cost of the undertaking; but at a higher level the agents ran into trouble: Danish military engineers supervised the works; with the highest technical training in the Polytechnic School of Copenhagen, they lacked experience and power of decision and proved such a nuisance that this irritating control influenced Brassey against the Indian Railway project, supervised by Government engineers, which he was considering at the time.

Until 1857 France, Italy, and Denmark occupied him fully. The Grand Trunk was losing heavily, but Brassey did not regard the money as completely wasted and in England the firm continued its

[1] Bergen to Oslo.

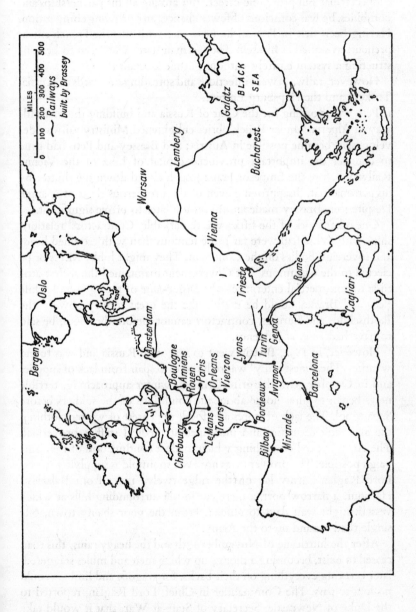

MILES

0   100   200   300   400   500

Railways
built by Brassey

BLACK
SEA

Galatz

Lemberg

Bucharest

Warsaw

Vienna

Rome

Trieste

Cagliari

Oslo

Amsterdam

Lyons

Turin

Genoa

Bergen

Boulogne
Amiens
Rouen
Paris
Orleans
Vierzon

Barcelona

Cherbourg

Le Mans
Tours

Bordeaux
Avignon

Bilbao

Mirande

unspectacular but profitable career. But among all his partnerships and combines, he was conscious of fewer chances and growing competition. Having been first in France, he now met with surprise French entrepreneurs as skilled as himself. The German states were seen to be constructing a system entirely without outside assistance.

However, railways were infectious and spreading outwards to Russia, Turkey, and the Hapsburg Empire.

Peto was working for the Czar of Russia and building the first railway in Algeria. Under Brück's brief enlightened Ministry railway development became possible in Austria; and Brassey and Peto had time to connect the important provincial capital of Linz to the Vienna Railway before the Emperor Franz Joseph closed down the shutter by his personal fiat, disapproving even of the prosperous signs of change. Despite this, Brassey made an impression later to prove significant.

One other work of the fifties was remarkable. Contractors' relationships with Whitehall were far more tenuous than with crowned heads and sovereign bodies on the Continent. They might lobby M.P.s or be elected to the Commons, but Government maintained the stiffest attitude to commercial enterprise—the *laissez-faire* of the age—and while Peto and Brassey could be useful, like the great money powers, the Rothschilds and Barings, contractors cannot, before the 1890s, be said to have had *political* influence.

However, in 1854, Britain went to war with Russia and was found wanting. The 'finest army' was reduced to despair from lack of supplies and in October with the grim Crimean winter approaching, terrible news began to filter home about the conditions of the soldiers before Sebastopol. The lack of stores and food, the barest of winter clothing, the appalling casualties and incompetent medical staff is proverbial. The Army lacked everything which made a continuation of the campaign possible. The problem was not even so simple as supplying stores: Lord Raglan's army lay on the ridge twelve miles from Balaclava Harbour, a narrow port, a mere cut in the surrounding hills at which vessels might wait days to unload. From the poor shanty town, one single road wound up to the Army.

After the hurricane of November 13th and the heavy rains, this road ceased to exist, becoming a morass up which men and mules staggered, later carrying everything on their backs, for wagons and limbers could no longer pass. The Commander-in-Chief, Lord Raglan, reported to the Duke of Newcastle, Secretary of State at War, that it would take

1,000 men two months to rebuild it; an impossibility for his over-worked and half-starved men.

The idea was Morton Peto's—to build a railway and pull the wagons up it, by mules or fixed steam engines, transporting the stores, guns, ammunition, and food for want of which the army was wasting away. Newcastle accepted with alacrity when Brassey and Peto offered to ship all their men and materials to the Crimea, build the line, and run it for no more than their net expenses. In the state of the War Office commissariat and its relations with other civilian contractors the proposal was miraculous.

Edward Betts organized the transport, and his detail is a measure of what these three were capable at a stage when the Government was on its knees to provide for an army of 30,000 men, less than half Brassey's normal number of employees.

Speed was essential, and Betts pointed his orders with extreme urgency. On November 30th he wrote to Newcastle:

'Suggestions for a civil engineer Corps for the Crimea for laying a double line of rails from Balaclava to the Heights round Sebastopol.

'200/250 plate layers, navvies and miners, 10 gangers or foremen, 20 rough masons or bricklayers, 80 carpenters with 3 foremen, 20 black-smiths and foreman, 10 enginemen and fitters, 4 timekeepers, 1 chief clerk, 1 draftsman, 2 practical assistant engineers, 1 chief engineer, tools etc. . . . .

'To prevent any difficulty in civilians working with military engineers this force must act entirely with the direct superintendence of the (company's) engineer.'(b)

On January 12th 50 horses, 40 drivers and smiths, and six months' forage were added, and by the end of the month Betts was writing: 'From the great difficulty of obtaining ships we have been obliged to pay higher rates for chartering and have been compelled to buy three screw steamers and a sailing ship instead of hiring.'(c) Peto had been forced to strip his North European Steam Navigation Co. and take their ships on charter—a blow to the continuity of the trade he was building up, to put them in jeopardy of war.

Newcastle approved the excess expenditure. Perhaps he compared the careful arrangements with those of his own department; for with the little force sailed four trained nurses and two doctors; and the men were liberally supplied with tarpaulins for shelters until their wooden huts should be ready. Brassey offered to get more of these for the

77

troops, but the Ordnance Department found this 'most irregular', while Sir Charles Trevelyan at the Treasury warned that no more excess expenditure would be sanctioned.

Meanwhile, Beattie, the Chief Engineer, had secured a wharf in tiny Balaclava harbour. Good relations were established with Lord Raglan: 'the business of the road was one of life or death to many of our soldiers if not indeed to the army',(d) he admitted, since all loads were now being carried on mule-back.

But the steamers were held up by fierce westerly gales in the Bay of Biscay. The martial ardour of the navvies who had left London in January armed with Colts and vowing great things against the Russians was damped, though not enough to prevent them 'storming the Rock' and repeating the riot in Malta, where they demonstrated prize-fighting to the inhabitants of Valletta and got hugely drunk on the money which poured in. 'The eyes of Europe', as they had been told in London, were indeed upon them. Mercifully they were refused permission to land at Constantinople, 'as it didn't belong to the Queen'.

Most of the small fleet reached Balaclava in the first week in February; after commendable speed. Yet though in the first fortnight the navvies laid seven miles of track and set up their camp, the venture was so new and remarkable that many doubted. Captain Henry Clifford had little faith in the proposed railway: 'For my part I wish they would make us a good road'.(e) But Raglan's men were now so worn down by illness and privation that he could not even lend the navvies the help he had promised. The navvies' efforts were prodigious. Beside men who had been four months in the Crimea they were figures from another world. Soon Clifford 'was astonished to see the progress of the railway in Balaclava. The navvies, in spite of the absence of beefsteaks, work famously and do more in a day than a regiment of English soldiers do in a week. To be sure, they have in them the stamina of English living which has long since been worked out of our poor fellows.'

They fought and worked and drank, protected from martial law in their voluntary capacity, and the railway crept out of the main street of Balaclava up the long hill towards the front. It was an astonishing sight: the well fed and carefully tended horses; the men with their huts, waterproofs, and thigh boots among the cholera-infested soldiery; and the steam engines puffing busily, drawing up long ammunition trains, the wonder and delight of the Turkish infantry. *The Times* war correspondent noticed 'it is inexpressibly strange to hear the rumbling sound

78

of waggons . . . it recalls home more strongly than anything we have yet heard in the Crimea'.(*f*) A double track was laid, from the beginning; planked over the mud so that horses could use it as a road as well; direct from the wharfs where heavy guns could be loaded straight from the ships' sides. Brassey had sensibly instructed Beattie: 'You will, in laying your road, be not over-particular about levels; repair and make it more perfect after, for the promptitude with which you can supply the army with this road will be its chief recommendation.'(*g*)

In spite of difficulties the line reached Kadikoi on February 19th. By the 31st of March Raglan reported it in use to the top of the escarpment and the worst was over. As Clifford remarked: 'I hope this time we will not be at a loss for ammunition.' Twenty miles of double track were in operation with seventeen locomotives; and were handed over as a going concern to Colonel McMurdo with a full military wagon train. The Engineer Commander, General Burgoyne, wrote effusively to Peto; and in the great debate in the House of Commons when Lord Aberdeen's administration was attacked for its mishandling of the war, Gladstone called on this achievement in their defence. As a complete military operation carried out exclusively by a civilian organization, the Crimean railway has few parallels; such aid of captains of industry to the State was not equalled until the Rothschilds lent Disraeli the money to buy the Suez Canal.

The financial crisis which came in 1857 was not of British making and affected London only slightly. To Brassey, however, it was important, though its significance only later became apparent. An era of quiet, almost monopolistic, activity ended. Every year competitors obtruded themselves, working on narrower margins, forcing him to cut costs and revise his estimates. Afterwards he never again possessed the priceless balance of the fifties—as many sound contracts as he could possibly take up. As enterprise moved outwards from the industrial centre of Western Europe which he had helped to create, it became more speculative, and more subject to political and economic fluctuations. 'Cosmopolitan enterprise flourished on national pride'(*h*) and there was often little else to flourish on. Governments outside the traditional circle had to make heavy concessions, giving shares at a discount, a guarantee of interest or grants of land, pledging their future for the public works of the day. So great was felt to be the benefit which the contractors bestowed, 'that rarely was there demur to the principle that private enterprise should be rewarded with the profits and rarely was that enterprise suffered to sustain the loss'.(i)

Nevertheless contractors could and did lose heavily and the significance of the transition which began in 1857 was to put the initiative in the contractors hands. In underdeveloped countries enormous tracts of land or controlling blocks of shares were to be part of the price paid, and the contractor's return could not, in the nature of their agrarian economies, be in cash, but in increased land values, in the profits of colonization, in the growth of ports and of trade which increased the value of their holdings; in the improvement of cities and the profits of running the railways themselves. So Brassey's agents, scouring the earth, now projected railways and offered to build for others, stipulating their terms; in Peru, in the Argentine and Chile, in India, and in Central Europe. Brassey became a determining figure in the economy of whole states; enticing them by the initial and enormous capital outlay to acquire a huge national debt and in the end to the necessity of creating national industries—forcing them to specialize in order to trade with the West and to make the railways pay: an economic determinant of far greater importance than he himself saw, quite different from the promoter of civilized progress he took himself to be; almost a random consequence, beyond anything he could have imagined.

The 1857 crisis shifted the pattern of British investment to countries which of their own could not pay for public works. Brassey, Peto, the American Wheelwright, and others, skimmed the profits of this change without being its agencies. The origin lay in the changing institutions of finance. The only railways outside England which took up British capital in the early 1850s were in America, where money continued to flow until McHenry's railway brought disaster ten years later. But after 1857, investment, freed from the heavy drain of railway building at home, restlessly seeking an outlet, was poured into countries like Egypt, Turkey, the Argentine, Peru, or Mexico, as wholesale loans to governments to create new markets to replace those threatened by the competition of industrial Europe. It became tied up on a far more long-term basis than before, dependent on states whose credit was untried; and the dual agencies, the export of contractor's works, and of capital, interchange and are interdependent in the decade before 1866.

The 1857 panic began in the U.S.A. and ruined Hamburg whose loans had underwritten ten years of American railway building. In England the shock was peculiarly sudden and short. There had been a predictable drain of gold to India to help deal with the Mutiny and Bank Rate shot up even before it became necessary to suspend the Act of 1844. Thirty-one firms failed and Peto confessed to G. C. Glyn that his current liabilities were £11 million. But the crisis passed almost immediately after the Bank was authorized to exceed its note issue and this masked the real significance. The fact that the firms which had failed had unsecured liabilities of twenty times their authorized capital, largely escaped the City's notice. The warning was no check to this wildness developing on the fringe of cosmopolitan finance, and, in spite of it, a decade began which Henry Drummond Wolff, the banker and diplomat, called 'one of extraordinary financial invention and enterprise, partly legitimate, partly the reverse. It was like those monumental epochs one reads of, such as the South Sea Bubble, or John Law's schemes in France.'(j)

Brassey and Peto, with their eyes open, took on a novel and greater responsibility. In Canada and Europe they had been financiers and had already administered or been implicated in certain of their works, but now they had to base their choice of contract, not on the traffic for which the railway was designed, but on what was expected to develop in the future; they had to be colonizers and gamble on the future needs of a world market; and they had to base this judgement on the bonds of governments whose credit was old in the repudiation of loans. Having grown out of their traditional sphere, they had no guide but their own sound sense, and the whole fabric of the 'economic imperialism' of the nineteenth century came to depend upon them.

One of the first results of 1857 was a revival of interest in India.

7

INDIA

IN THE golden days of the early railways, promoters dreamed of
laying railways across the Balkans, Turkey, and Persia, to India.
Behind the façade of inspired hopes and fantasies, powerful forces
moved in the 1840s to secure the building of a sub-continental network
of Indian railways. While the Railway Mania still raged in England the
Great Indian Peninsular (G.I.P.) and the East Indian Railways were
founded, though no line was actually begun until 1853.

The financing of these railways, which no one doubted were necessary, depended almost entirely on commercial advantage. Apart from
the Lancashire cotton manufacturers who wanted to develop the
Nagpur cotton fields from Bombay, this was lacking in the forties;
the revenues of India came to England in the shape of profits from
estates and until Lord Dalhousie became Governor-General there had
been no overt Government action to attract any other form of investment. However, in the fifties the long shadow of Negro emancipation
grew in the southern U.S.A., where 80 per cent of British cotton imports were grown, and Manchester began to look more seriously to
Bombay. Not alone; other manufacturing interests, encountering
greater competition in Europe turned to India for the first time as a
possible market.

The East India Company could not and would not finance railways
on its own. Some sort of Imperial guarantee of payment of interest
would have to be given to entice English investors. The Company was
not impressed by Dalhousie's dream of railways re-creating a nation
out of the infinitely scattered communities and villages of India, a
vision which looked back to the imperial unity of the Moguls as well
as to a recognition of what railways had done for Europe. They set out

82

their objections in some detail: floods, violent winds, and the overhead sun, insects and vermin would delay and destroy the works, undergrowth would sap them, the vast jungle would close in on either side; and, paramount, 'the difficulty and expense of securing the services of competent and trustworthy engineers'.(*a*) They had neglected public works for a generation and their department of engineering, except for irrigation, scarcely existed.

Dalhousie could override this; from his central position he planned nothing less than a coherent trunk system, serving the social, commercial, and military needs of both Indians and Government. With the benevolently despotic attitude of his age he hoped for the improvement of backward peoples. (As Lord Salisbury said, 'they will enable us to propagate our civilization in the most peaceful and harmless way'(*b*)) The caste system would die and 'the barbarous customs of the Hindoos' in the light of moral progress running on steel rails.

Lesser aims were also provided for. The routes 'should be chosen according to the extent of political and commercial advantages which they are calculated to afford'.(*c*) So the G.I.P. lay from Bombay towards Nagpor and Madras, Calcutta was to be linked to Delhi and the North-West frontier, Bombay to Delhi. The administrative convenience would simplify the British rule and facilitate Dalhousie's policy of expansion and annexation while it reduced military commitments, delays, and the overweening cost of the Army itself. The line to the N.W. Frontier would provide against the vague but permanent menace of Russia across Afghanistan.

All this was summed up in his famous minute of April 1853. As for construction, the home Government would leave it to private enterprise and this was the rub. Private enterprise would not touch the scheme without security.

The G.I.P. and East Indian Railways had been given a 5 per cent guarantee on their first lines and this was demanded by all promoters who followed. Lack of knowledge of the conditions and the poverty of India could be balanced in shareholders' minds by the promise of 5 per cent on the capital invested regardless of profit or loss. The Government of India would pay the deficit and take the surplus if there was one. This system laid the whole burden on the Indian taxpayer in return for an agreement which operated in favour of the private companies in every possible way: giving them a ninety-nine-year lease with Government resuming control, which permitted the Company in the ninety-eighth year to demand the full cost price for the railway and its rolling-stock: which permitted Government engineers to harass the works without any real control over expenditure, and killed all effort for economy. It was, at the least, unsatisfactory for India and was abolished in 1870, but even with it, railways were hard enough to build; without it there would have been nothing.

Dalhousie noticed as early as 1850 the difficulty of getting good engineers. He wrote to G. C. Glyn: 'I have groaned over your railway troubles, excepting only Mr. Hudson's detection. We are bringing into this world here a railway *something*—no child of mine—which if it prove better than an absolute abortion will only have one leg or be otherwise incapable of sustaining itself. However I will do my best for it and be glad if in my time I hear the first *whistle*!'(*d*) Yet, though the very bones of a contracting organization were lacking, the investors expected 'something of the alchemy which British contractors had wrought in France'. Naturally they were disappointed when those contractors prudently refused to attempt the same in India.

Brassey began negotiations with the East Indian Railway in the summer of 1853. The company was keen to have him. Their engineer reported: 'It would be to the advantage of all parties concerned in the making of Railways to contract with someone of proved and extensive connexions. . . . From this it would follow that if we can get such men as Mr. Brassey or Mr. Peto to undertake our work at 10 per cent more than the actual cost of labour and materials, they being bound to relieve the Company from all contingencies incident to works of this nature... the guarantee we shall have obtained will be a full equivalent for the comparatively small additional sum paid.'(*e*) Large contractors, he implied, could stand up to trouble: small ones cost less but left no remedy when they failed. Brassey was ready to send out an agent to go over the line, 'but he and Mr. Peto would not be subject to any authority other than of the Railway Company's engineers'(*e*), and when his agent, Stephen Ballard, showed him how strict the supervision of the Government engineers would be, how foreign the work to his experience, and how worrying in the second year of the Grand Trunk, he put India out of his mind.

Railways were built, slowly, and with the bankruptcy of many small contractors. Still, when in 1857 the Mutiny shattered the old complacency for ever, the lines which existed and, even more, the telegraph, played a large part in its suppression. And the Mutiny proved

to be the lever; within eighteen months of the abolition of the East
India Company's rule, Dalhousie's full programme had been increased
and approved; and under eight companies 5,000 miles of track was projected, all under the guarantee. Lines stretched on paper to quarter the
sub-continent: to bring into mathematical cohesion the vast untidy

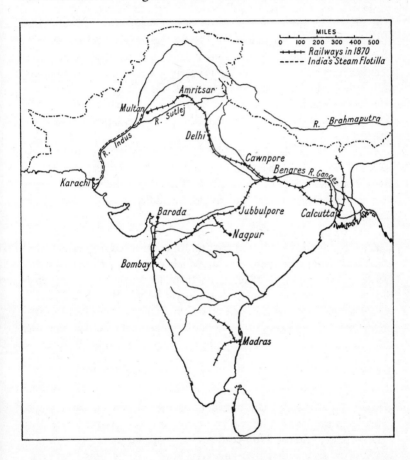

kingdoms, cities, and a million villages. The Mutiny did not merely
prove the need; it removed all grounds for argument, and because the
existing contracting system could physically not produce results on the
scale required, a Select Committee was appointed in 1858 to find out
why.

Their report was regretful (*f*): it would have been preferable for the Government to have built the railways themselves, but their engineers were 'necessarily men of less experience than can be obtained in Europe'. Too rigid control was blamed and, above all, the lack of resources of the small firms to which the work had been entrusted. The guarantee was found to be indispensable and the Government of India was advised to apply to recognized and reputable British firms when the circumstances warranted. With the Select Committee and the shareholders on the heels of the Indian Government, Brassey could expect less interference. In 1858 he was feeling a certain constriction after the panic of the preceding year; business was falling off in France and Italy. The Grand Trunk was at its worst. India offered immense work with no political risks. Yet with all these advantages his luck was uneven.

With Sir James Paxton, builder of the Crystal Palace, and George Wythes, until recently a competitor in France, he contracted for the East Bengal Railway, a 112-mile line from Calcutta to the main Ganges to intercept the river traffic and avoid the difficult navigation of the Sonderbunds. The railway ran across rich and heavily populated areas and was to be continued into the heart of northern Bengal. It was not a successful affair. Conducted by remote control from London, there were troubles in the management which compelled Brassey to send Henfrey out in March 1859. Even then no work was done before November as the Government had not yet bought the land. The contract price had been worked out on statistics taken before the Mutiny—since when the vast programme of public works had made labour scarce and dear, especially in Bengal, and sent the price of building materials up by 30 per cent. With too few men the line was not finished till 1862 and Brassey lost heavily.

A start had however been made, enought to convince him that his greatest opportunities lay outside Europe. Moreover, he believed strongly in the benefits he was conferring on India, moved by a plain sense of duty almost Non-conformist in its fervour, yet curiously modern, to realize that these material benefits were more important than the administrative justice of Empire; and naively, but no more so than the rulers of India, he dreamt of a progressive country which should reject its history and its 'barbarous' customs.

His entry had also coincided with a boom of extraordinary intensity centred on Bombay. Even before the American Civil War Lancashire's imports of Indian cotton were rising; when U.S. supplies were completely cut off, their total reliance on Bombay, and the money which poured in, sent land values in the city rocketing and the price of G.I.P. shares to heights undreamt of. An atmosphere of euphoria spread over India, softening Henfrey's account of the set-backs in East Bengal. When the traffic on that line in 1863 was seen to be beyond all expectations, Brassey took the Punjab contract, to connect the East Indian Railway at Delhi to the new port of Karachi in the west; leading 304 miles on from Delhi to Amritsar and Multan where it met the steamship flotilla on the Indus, running down to the sea; crossing rivers as difficult as the St. Lawrence had been, the Sutlej, Beas, Jumna, Gaggur, Markunde, all flood waters from the Himalayan snows, dry in summer and torrential in the monsoon. Six years were allowed; for though the track was simple, labour being more plentiful than in Bengal, all the ironwork for the bridges and all machinery and rolling-stock had to be shipped from England round the Cape.

Meanwhile Brassey warily declined to pursue the lure of the cotton boom. In July 1864 he wrote: 'The prospect of the cotton trade is very encouraging . . . but if successful I might be tempted to go on to a large extent and should in fact become another speculator for which I have no desire. If, on the other hand, I was to make a loss, I should feel annoyed that I had departed from my legitimate business as a contractor.'(g) Within months the boom broke, scattering ruin and disillusion over the west coast, but unfortunately the business methods of the speculators survived; and, of the railways, costing £30 million, built between 1858 and 1869, hardly one was completed within the estimate.

Henfrey began work in the Punjab in 1865. Workmen flocked to the firm now and the line pushed steadily and uneventfully on, moving inwards from both ends. No ripples of the crisis Brassey passed in London in 1866 disturbed it, and later in the same year he began on the Chord Line; a 147-mile short cut, taking off a wide bend of the East Indian Railway and making the line double-track from Delhi to Calcutta. Despite a year of drought and severe floods, followed by a general depression, the Punjab Line was half finished, a year ahead of schedule in 1868.

But great floods had in many cases altered the courses of rivers and the engineers, lacking experience of them, who tried to contain the flow rather than allow for the colossal impact of their high tide, were frequently disproved. The rivers were only slowly spanned; eventually and Viceroy, Lord Lawrence, was able to travel almost the whole length of India by train in 1868, and a year later only the six miles on either side of the Sutlej river remained. Meandering in a wide valley the river, which for eighty years had kept to the northern side, began to change course, and Henfrey had to increase the three-quarter-mile bridge by another thousand yards. Only the opening of the Suez Canal and the straight shipment to Karachi which followed made completion in October 1870 possible.

Meanwhile the guarantee system was becoming odious to the Government, appalled at overspending, particularly on the G.I.P. and Bombay–Delhi railways. Lines were now averaging £18,000 a mile instead of the £8,000 figure accepted after the Mutiny. Many works were built for which there was no real need.[1] All through the boom days the India Office had resisted the temptation to sell the colony out to speculators and no guarantee was, in fact, given between 1861 and 1866. At last the Government felt that, with the experience of ten years, it could build its own railways with its own engineers. Sir Juland Danvers, general railway administrator for India, noticed in Brassey's Chord railway, 'a disposition to increase works, and a continuing excess of expenditure over estimates'. There were often excellent reasons for it, and Brassey took a pride in his exactitude, but economy was not seriously enforced and India paid the extra cost.

Lord Lawrence remarked that, 'if the work were done over again, it could be done for two-thirds the price'(h) Yet it was undeniable that the pioneer lines, built without experience of conditions, and with untrained labour were built well. Too much had been expected of the contractor; and working from England at two months' remove hardly helped. That Brassey, after his crisis in 1866, could finish the Punjab Railway was a remarkable achievement. The significance of his work, however, does not lie in the debt with which India was saddled. Although the railways might have been cheaper if built on the departmental system which came back after 1870, they would have been built immeasurably slower. By that date India possessed an effective service. Without the guarantee and the prestige of contractors like Brassey, this could not have been possible.

[1] The Madras Canal and Irrigation Company took thirteen years and a million and a half sterling to build a canal for which there was no assured traffic or water supply.

The long-term effects differed from those planned by Dalhousie. The lines lost money; indeed they were never expected to make a profit. They did not exceed the 5 per cent till the 1900s, and the Indian taxpayer made up the deficit without deriving any immediate advantage. Whatever the political and commercial advantages to England, the railways did not bring direct prosperity to the peasant. Instead, by making it possible for officials to take holidays in England and bring out English wives, by furthering the uncomprehending civilization which destroyed local tradition and historic continuity, by breaking up a 'customary' economy, they helped in the divorce of British rule from the native population. They did not provide the very cheap transport which alone could make it a universal service. They did not reduce the establishment of troops but helped to make India into a colossal training ground for British troops for nearly a hundred years. By economizing on old forms of transport, they destroyed jobs, particularly since many of the new railway employees were British. They helped to set up a highly precarious balance of prosperity, increasing rather than diminishing the risks of famine, for the surplus was no longer stored in the village against bad years but exported, leaving no reserve. During the terrible Madras famine of 1877, Sir Anthony Cotton wrote: 'Besides the total failure of the railways to carry cheaply, they are at this moment found to be unequal to the conveyance even of the smallest quantities required for mere food. The whole length of the beach is covered with piles of rice and the railway is unable to carry it into the interior as fast as it is wanted.'(i)

The railways affected India also in other ways. Sir Charles Dilke had the foresight to see a vast and untidy thing taking shape, 'a country is being created under that name where none has yet existed'.(k) A restless nationalism was born even in the years before the new 'Imperialism' began. Brassey built, and the railways he left behind carried the stigma of their early years far into the twentieth century.

8

THE ENGLISH BACKGROUND

THOUGH all his hopes and ambitions were centred abroad, Brassey never made the mistake of closing down his business at home. After the end of the Mania, he had not expected again to have so great a monopoly in England. Though more miles were laid down in the fifties than in the decade earlier, Brassey built less; but he kept steadily at work a force of 15,000 to 20,000 men on contracts impartially divided between the railways who were then harshly fighting an internecine war of amalgamation. While Mark Huish of the L. and N.W., Denison of the Great Northern, and the directors of the Great Western and the Midland ran cut-throat competition, while Euston rivalled King's Cross, and the London, Chatham, and Dover ran suicidally beside the London and Brighton, he continued for fifteen years to tender for every major contract in the country. In the end he had made, in the West, seventeen railways, covering 350 miles, centred on Hereford, Shrewsbury, Evesham, and the Welsh border up to Dolgelly; and, in East Anglia, four lines, with 185 miles, to complete the Eastern Counties network.

His larger works were the North Devon, a spectacular scenic railway from Minehead to Barnstaple; the great Canada works at Birkenhead in 1853; several sections of the Highland Railway and the Direct Portsmouth line in 1855.[1]

The ambitions of the Midland (lately Hudson's pet) to reach London provided Brassey with the 62-mile Leicester–Hitchin line and in 1865 the

[1] This was the first of his 'contractors' lines, built to provide a direct route and be sold to a company as a going concern. It caused great rivalry between the London Brighton and South Coast and the London and South Western who eventually acquired it, and for an uneasy year, Brassey was left with an unused line on his hands.

important London to Bedford connexion, which had St. Pancras as its terminus: the symbol of competition running wild in its intransigence.

A line to Portpatrick giving the London and North Western an interest in the Stranraer–Larne ferry took him to Ireland where he dallied in land speculation and bought estates along Lough Swilly. In 1864 he constructed the Eniskilling and Bundoran and the Denny Railways, but his Irish work remained unprofitable perhaps because none of his railways crossed the land he had bought. In England he had a reputation for always making money by acquiring land whose value could be expected to rise with development.[1] In the sixties he rounded off the provincial lines at home; Leatherhead–Epsom; Salisbury–Yeovil, carrying the London and South Western at last into Exeter; Ringwood to Christchurch and Bournemouth; the Moreton Hampstead railway; and as an experiment, he bought the lease of Barrow Docks which he then built.

This was all secondary work, and Brassey gave it only brief periods of interest. No longer, as in the days of the Mania, would he rush home from France, to leap on a train for Rugby after a day's work in London, and then walk 16 miles along the track to Nuneaton, drive to Tamworth, walk over the works to Stafford and drive on to Lancaster.

His attitude is clear from Mackay's comment in 1855: 'Work still very slack in this period. Best men gone to France, Spain, Belgium, and Italy to Mr. Brassey's works.'(a)

There were many reasons: he disliked too vicious competition and as an ardent monopolist and advocate of State control (which were not incompatible), he loathed the struggling mob of railway promoters and directors. There were too many other small contractors (like John Aird at this time) who were content with profits on a scale too narrow to satisfy him or the enormous overheads of his organization. Retrenchment had followed the panic of 1857 and only turned towards new investment with the gold flowing in from the discoveries in California and Australia; in the expansion which followed, there were too many others to give Brassey a share large enough to keep so many men employed. In moving outwards to Europe and the world at large, he was still riding the first wave of the Industrial Revolution, where he himself felt most at home.

The English work remained a background; a counterweight to the

[1] Notably the Clifftown Estates in Southend at the terminus of his London, Tilbury, and Southend Railway.

risks of foreign business, and its secure profits an insurance against another Mania. Brassey now lived in an intense business isolation; his empire so large that he could look to no one for help. Living before the safeguards of limited liability and the contractual arrangements which have since covered contractors against rise in prices or falls in exchange rates, his policy after 1857 was to spread his work and obligations, losing perhaps on some but gaining in the end, subject to war and disease in one country and fine weather and good labour in another. He invested in an immense variety of undertakings, railways, telegraphs, steamships, insurance, coal, and steel so that, as near as possible in any decade, he would not be subject to the rise and fall of the market because more and more it seemed vital to keep himself above the tides and common flux of the Stock Exchange.

His partnership with Peto and Edward Betts showed how desperately this mattered. In a partnership which had developed from the groups with Blount and Buddicom, these three hoped to cut costs and deal on an altogether larger scale, shown in the attempt to corner the Danish agricultural trade, the Crimean railway, and the massive assault upon Canada, the Grand Trunk. But their undertakings were cursed with all the disadvantages of pioneering and few gave them any profit.

In 1852 they built the London, Tilbury, and Southend Railway. East Anglia at last had a serviceable network and Brassey hoped to spread the City of London eastwards towards Bow and along the Thames. The Tilbury line tapped a dense passenger traffic and reached Southend in 1856. For twenty-one years the contractors leased the line and ran it themselves. They were somewhat before their time; in spite of the passengers it did not bring the expected profits.[1] They bought large areas on the outskirts of Southend and developed them into the Clifftown Estates, but until the late sixties they were continually setting more money aside in order to improve the traffic.

The great Victoria Dock, begun in 1856, proved scarcely better financially, though its building initiated a half-century of dock work which left London indisputably the largest port in the world. *Magnum opus* of the engineer, Bidder, the 100-acre dock cost £870,000, with a 26-foot depth at high water, with vaults, warehouses, the latest hydraulic machinery, and a railway to Fenchurch Street station. It was a great engineering success and gave confidence to his successors, but during the sixties it ran at a heavy loss.

[1] Tilbury Dock was not completed until 1886.

Meanwhile Brassey constructed the Northern Level Sewer for the Metropolitan Board of Works; a 12-mile difficult tunnel under half London, from Kensal Green to the River Lea. He experimented with a gas undertaking, the Victoria Gas Company, supplying industrial firms near the Docks, but had no particular success, and sold out three years later. His lines to Epping and Woodford were part of the spread of London which he was actively encouraging, as was the seven-mile Kensington railway. He added the Minories Warehouses to his work in the London Docks and in 1865 the firm built the short but highly important East London Railway. Using the tunnel under the Thames built twenty years earlier by I. K. Brunel's father, this connected the London and Brighton at New Cross with the Great Eastern at Bishopsgate. Another important connexion running into the centre was the Crystal Palace and West End Railway; but although the East London Railway now forms part of it, Brassey did not live long enough to take part in the main development of the London Underground.

9

BEFORE THE BOMBARDMENT

I N T H E first days of the gold rush in Australia Peto and Brassey had
built some short lines in the State of Victoria. Having come into
wealth with the gold rush, other State Governments handed out
concessions with careful optimism. Brassey never held a monopoly, and
since there was no speculative boom, and no wild rivalry, in return
Australia got the railways she needed; though bedevilled in future
years by the variety of gauges which were laid down to suit the
different conditions and differing wealth of the states.

Between New South Wales and London lay a three-month sea
voyage and so Brassey sent Stephen Ballard with full powers to
negotiate terms of the 58-mile Western line from Sydney and make all
the arrangements; except for a final sanction, a contractor in his own
right. Rails, rolling-stock and locomotives had to be shipped from
England round the Cape of Good Hope and Brassey sent out 2,000
Scots and English navvies and paid their passage himself. Nominally
they were free to choose their jobs but since the contractors held nearly
all the work, it paid him handsomely in the end. Believing strongly in
the virtues of emigration here, as in the Argentine later, he saw railways
as the means of colonization. But the Australian contracts included no
grant of land which he could sell off to them; and though he did not
pay their return passage the navvies made poor emigrants. Still, they
were employed for several years; in 1863 he began the Queensland
system; a 278-mile network in the South and West of light 3½-foot-
gauge track, suited to the vast spaces and hilly terrain of a state which
could not afford the luxuries of the South.

In the same year he completed a 64-mile Northern and Midland
system quartering the island of Mauritius—a project which showed

94

how far the Colonial Office had changed its conception of its duty since their refusal to help with the Grand Trunk only ten years before.

In Europe the troubles of an industry which had outgrown its strength gave him numerous setbacks. The Bilbao–Miranda line in Spain, an important connexion from the great northern part up the long hilly route of the Cantabrian mountains to the central plateau, proved particularly troublesome. Local officials were universally corrupt and Government engineers interfering and incompetent; while guerilla fighting between Carlists and the Government of Queen Isabella interrupted the work. Paying the men was a monthly crisis for Brassey's agents—the rudimentary banking system did not extend beyond Bilbao and was not accustomed to the large cheques on which English work was based. Merchants were used to keeping bullion in their offices and his agent was forced to hoard more than a ton of silver, often in debased coinage, before each pay day, then 'send out a carriage with two civil guards with one of the clerks from the office, a man to drive and another to help if the mules gave trouble up the hilly country'.(a) Payday was not simplified by the need to teach the Basque workmen the use of the paper money issued by the Bank of Bilbao. 10,000 men were employed and Brassey lost heavily, through the flux of politics and the weather.

He had acted on Spanish information and bargained for half soil, half rock; but the steep ascents turned out to be almost entirely rock; no allowance had been made for feast days which among the Basques reduced the working year to 200 days; and the winters were much more severe and wet than he had anticipated or been led to believe. One disastrous autumn storm washed many works and bridges away and messages poured into Bilbao where Brassey was living. He refused to be disturbed 'wait till this rain has stopped, as when I go I may see what is left, and estimate all the disasters at once and save two journeys'.(b)

As soon as the France-Austrian war was over, work went ahead smoothly in Italy in spite of the political upheaval which followed Garibaldi's assault upon Sicily. Brassey extended the coastal route from Leghorn through Tuscany and the Maremma 140 miles to the border of the Papal States near Civitavecchia in the year of the Neapolitan defeat, and, when the South was at last united to the Piedmontese monarchy, he laid down the 160-mile Meridionale stretching south from Naples into the Mezzogiorno. The promoters of this were Blount, Talabot and the Spaniard Don José de Salamanca, whom Brassey was later to fight over the Rumanian railways. These were large undertakings and occupied the Italian branch fully during the sixties.

The passage of the Alps fascinated him. The American promoter, Wheelwright, had talked grandly of throwing a line across the Andes; Brassey had been itching to do the same in Europe since building the Victor-Emmanuel Line across Savoy. There, one of his engineers had invented a rock-boring machine; a hammer driven by compressed air and capable of giving 300 blows a minute. Brassey paid him £5,000 for it, intending to use the invention to cut through the Mont Cenis, but the idea was either stolen by or sold to the Italian engineers who, largely for reasons of prestige, eventually obtained the contract. In spite of this, Brassey seized on another invention and originated the hazardous scheme of a railway to run from the Savoy terminus in a bewildering series of hairpin bends beside the first Napoleon's military road, over the summit, and down to Susa. He used the Fell system, a triple track with an extra horizontal driving wheel clipping the centre rail, an idea widely condemned as impossibly dangerous and unprofitable; but Blount advised that in the four or five years before the Mont Cenis tunnel could be completed a great profit could be made. Until 1875 the line carried 40,000 passengers a year without a single accident.

French work was finished. Denmark proved extremely unprofitable, for the Jutland line had scarcely got under way when the old question of the Duchies broke out in war: in November 1863 King Frederick VII of Denmark died and the new King Christian IX signed a constitution incorporating Schleswig into the monarchy. The Great Powers were caught off balance: Bismarck wanted to recognize the Duke of Augustenberg as King and force both Schleswig and Holstein into the German orbit. An Austro-Prussian alliance was formed in January 1864 and within a month Schleswig had been occupied after fierce fighting. The war moved steadily into Denmark, in spite of a brief armistice engineered by Palmerston and it seemed that Denmark might be extinguished completely. However the principles of 'legitimacy' triumphed and peace came in August, leaving the two Duchies under the joint ownership of Prussia and Austria.

Most of the damages that contractors could suffer was heaped on Brassey and Peto's undertaking. Traffic ceased completely on the lines which they had built and leased. The Danish Government comman-deered the entire rolling-stock and used it for troop movements, in the course of which locomotives and carriages were shelled and badly maintained; subcontractors and their men were impounded for military earthworks, and railway embankments were used and bombarded as fortifications. Rowan, the agent, said: 'Both sides had no compunction about seizing our materials and making our people work for them.' Yet the contractors, having paid their vast deposit, had to keep the lease, repair the line, pay workmen, and replace the rolling-stock.

War was the worst of many enemies; and war was to be the danger in Brassey's work in the Austro-Hungarian Empire. Highly regarded by the Court, when, after the war of 1859, railway building again be-came possible as the Emperor relaxed his stranglehold on development, Brassey was in the greatest demand. As part of Imperial policy to federalize the rambling collection of nationalities, lines were planned from Bohemia to Trieste and from Vienna to the Danube and the borders of the two states of Moldavia and Wallachia, which were to become Rumania.

Into the limitless sea which seemed about to open up, a number of sharks of various sizes moved, and the Empire was rapidly made to understand the significance of the words 'finance company'; of which species the Crédit Mobilier, which had financed the Austrian railways of the fifties, is the classical example. The resources of its founders, the brothers Pèreire, were used for loans upon the securities of public works—as a social utility—sidetracking the traditional methods of banking and making possible the marketing of continental securities on a far larger scale. The speed with which such transactions could be done helped the multiplicity of short-term loans on which contractors relied.

Something of the same sort of organization had grown up in England, notably after the 1857 panic, though the need for it was never so great as on the Continent where the banking system was less flexible and developed. Overend and Gurney, the billbrokers, were at the head, with an enormous turnover in railway business. Ninety-day bills, loan piled on loan, made up an apparently resilient structure and returned amazing profits until too many similar organizations sprang up. 1863 saw the birth of the International Finance Society, followed by the General Credit and Finance Co. numbering Brassey, Samuel Laing, Blount, Drummond Wolff, Charles Devaux, and W. P. Andrew among its directors. The former was a bankers', the latter a promoters' company, with strong French connexions. A horde of others followed, many of whom were trying to sell off their bad contracts; such curiosities flourished as the Crédit Foncier of London, run by Count Legrand-Dumonceau for the Christianizing of capital, which involved the money of many good Catholics in shady undertakings and bankruptcy. Yet the finance companies astounded the world, for European railway building was at its peak and depended on them. Mileage was doubled in the decade 1860–9, paralleling the rush to arms of France, Prussia, and Austria and the turn of ships from wood to iron; and since capital did not exist in large enough quantities for the investment required, the finance companies who claimed to solve all this, enjoyed a fantastic heyday.

In London Bank Rate ran high (over 5 per cent) for most of 1860–5; yet investment *had* to go on. Contractors were encouraged to pledge themselves deeper and deeper on shorter and shorter loans, until they became hopelessly entangled. The finance companies, in principle, 'lent on securities of less certain risk and at longer dates than commercial banks had been willing to do'.(c) The result was a far more complex and expensive structure, which was viable only so long as the railways could be finished and run profitably—which did not allow for folly or war, failure to complete or failure to sell.

The control of such enterprises moved away from individuals, and Brassey and Peto remained isolated—and vulnerable, because they neither became a company nor limited their liability, feeling that their type of organization did not lend itself to such limits, and bound by an integrity which denied them the safeguard of selling their business out to the public.

The flood of railway promotion in Austria gave the finance companies their head. It was hardly surprising to the Crédit Mobilier that the International Finance Society floated a Danubian loan in 1864. Brassey was soon at work for the Emperor on the 165-mile Lemberg–Czerno-witz line, a continuation of the Carl-Ludwig Railway from Vienna, across the northern frontier of Hungary, while on the same loan Peto and Betts took the Rustchuk–Varna contract connecting the Danube with the Black Sea across the Dobruja. Brassey had begun the official approach in 1862 and after two years' negotiating the terms were not easy; in spite of the loan to come Brassey was to lend his name to the formation of the company which would eventually take it over, and undertook to accept half his payment in bonds at par if the public issue was not fully subscribed. This was an appalling hostage to fortune, particularly as the bonds were not expected to sell until the railway was finished, but the Danish war had not yet opened Brassey's eyes to this sort of danger and his faith in the lines he had so far completed was so great that he never doubted he could sell at a profit in the end.

Work began in 1864 and proceeded steadily; the next year he embarked on 128 miles in Poland, from Warsaw to Terespol to connect with the Russian system. In India the Punjab railway was under way and in the Argentine, he realized a long-held dream—an experiment as important as the Grand Trunk had been.

When Brassey visited the U.S.A. in 1855 Americans had fired his imagination with the vision of the railroad as the river of civilization. Even in the States, though, this dream remained largely unfulfilled, until, after the Civil War, the Union Pacific was begun.

The surface of Latin America had only been scratched by the entrepreneurs; enough to show what vast resources remained to be developed; the mines and guano of Peru, the nitrate and copper of Chile, the fertile pampas of the Argentine and the hinterland of Brazil. The few railways which were working before 1866, all served local needs, like the São Paulo Line to the coffee plantations.

The genius of early development was William Wheelwright, an American who established a fleet of trading vessels in Valparaiso. He conceived the idea of linking the West Coast with Europe by a fleet of fast steam vessels and in 1848 came to England to build four ships, first of the Pacific Steam Navigation Company. Through this enterprise he acquired interests in the coal mines of Talcahuano in Chile and was able in the forties to build for an English syndicate the first Chilean railway from Caldera to the Copiapo silver and Coquimbo copper mines. He surveyed the Valparaiso–Santiago route (though this was built by a later American, Henry Meiggs), planned to extend the Copiapo line over the Andes, and finish it from Cordoba in the Argentine pampa to Rosario on the River Plate. When the Transandean was refused by the Chilean Government, who thought it impossible, he came to London to raise money for the Argentine section, and agreed to meet Brassey; for when the Valparaiso line was being considered Brassey had had an agent competing for the contract, as well as looking for other lines. Through him he had learnt of Wheelwright's monopoly of the coast trade and success as an entrepreneur and decided to offer him a

99

partnership. Wheelwright agreed; Brassey took an immediate liking to the anglicized American; his boldness was strikingly similar to his own and his dreams of an economic power, imperial in their extent.

Railways in the Argentine so far had had only a paper existence. As early as 1854 the American engineer, Alan Campbell, surveyed this Rosario–Cordoba route, not a difficult undertaking since it lay like a ruler across the 270 miles of level pampa. A contract was given to the Spanish promoter, José Buschenthal who, however, failed to raise the necessary loan in Europe, and in 1857 it was handed on to Wheelwright. His own disputes in Chile and the political troubles in Buenos Aires swallowed the six following years.

For Argentina was not yet a nation. An era of military dictators, mass slaughters, and revolution ended with the collapse of the Caudillo, Rosas, in 1852, but for ten years more the Confederation remained a name only: a collection of impoverished rural provinces tacked on to the rich city of Buenos Aires. President Urquiza, who followed Rosas, saw railways as a means to unite the Confederation, but the city saw no reason to bleed itself for the unproductive hinterland in the name of a nationalism which did not exist.

Urquiza's job was made more difficult by being forced to agree with Great Britain on the repayment of the defaulted Baring loan of 1824 before he could get any money in Europe for his public works; and by a disastrous and prolonged war with Uruguay he destroyed his sole support, the Army.

While his emissary in London, the glib-tongued Alberdi, threatened to look in the U.S.A. for his loans and proclaimed that even the prospect of railways was already making a nation, the tension exploded into war between Buenos Aires and the other States. For two years fortunes fluctuated until at Pavón in September 1861 General Bartoleme Mitre emerged supreme. A compromise Confederation was achieved and within a year the Government felt able to launch a programme of guaranteed railways, similar to that in force in India.

For the line from Rosario to Cordoba they granted Wheelwright and Brassey a wide concession; a league of land on either side of the line for its entire length with the exception of 20 miles from Rosario and Cordoba, on condition that the contractors peopled the land, half of which was conceded for ninety-nine years and the rest made absolute in part payment for the work. To this was added three square miles in Rosario itself and part of the harbour; and to attract the

European capital without which nothing could be done, a guaranteed dividend of 7 per cent.

Raising the £1,600,000 capital in London was, of course, at that rate of guarantee, easy. Indeed the flow of money into Buenos Aires was so rapid that Mitre paid off the Government's public debts in sterling. Argentinians however preferred their money in land, and only the Government featured largely among the South American shareholders, holding 17,000 out of 65,000 shares; the rest was taken up by investors in London, Brassey, Peto, and Wheelwright among them.

On April 20th, 1863 work was begun by Mitre in Rosario, amid municipal celebrations. After a benediction the President dug the first spadeful, and followed it with an elaborate speech. 'The railway will populate the desert and give peace and order in place of misery and war. It will ultimately pierce the Andes as does the Union Pacific.'(d) The desert had seemed implacable, full of wild Indians and disorder but the railway carried population, industry, justice, culture, law, and defence. Beside such benefits what was commercial reckoning?

The line progressed easily across the rolling plains; in places the going was so steady that the sleepers could be laid on the bare earth with a simple drainage trench running beside. And as the line crept towards Cordoba, in spite of war with Paraguay, prosperity did follow. Rosario had been a small town of 25,000 people. The Central Argentine Railway, as it was called, transformed it into the second port of the River Plate. In the years before 1870 it tapped the wheat production of the whole of Santa Fé province and exports rose from 40,000 to 1 million bushels a year through the harbour which the contractors developed.

Brassey left the actual building entirely to Wheelwright, whose work was often brought to a standstill by the ruthless conscription of his men for the Army. Otherwise, it brought no worries, and in April 1870 was finished and inaugurated. Sarmiento, the great intellectual, whom some called the saviour of his people, now President of the C.A.R., saw it as the fulfilment of his political beliefs. 'Paths of communication among us form part of the political system. Our party could take as its emblem a school, a telegraph, and a railway, the agents of peace and order. If our people fail us in filling so vast a land, the world will ask no more of us than security and protective laws to give in a few years millions of men from its superfluous population.'(e)

Velez Sarsfield, the new President, at the inauguration, was even more effusive. 'It will seal the fortunes of this province and the harvest will not be transitory but unquenchable fountains of riches; the start of a radical change in the whole being of the Republic. Give thanks to the company which has built this monumental work, showing that it is not guided by the principles of self interest.'(f) And Mitre, from his retirement, added a valediction for the 'greatest enterprise of the age'.

In this Brassey believed. The Central Argentine was perhaps the experiment nearest to his heart for he set it on colonizing the empty and fertile lands which the Company had been granted.

Wheelwright had written to him in April 1864:

'You are conferring upon that vast and prosperous country such infinite benefits, and to you will belong the credit . . . it is but the beginning of a line that will penetrate into Upper Peru and finally reach the Pacific Ocean and bring together nations of the same race and blood that have for centuries been isolated by the Andes. . . .

'We go into the heart of a country abounding in wealth, possessing a soil and climate unsurpassed. Some there are who will urge the political insecurity of the country but in spite of revolutions and dissensions, the country has gone ahead in a most rapid manner.

'The European element of population will in a few years exceed the natives; these are the best tests, for who would go if prosperity were insecure? The yearly immigration is augmenting at an extraordinary rate.

'As to the cost of the work . . . you will find all the calculations will be fully realized. I have given you an honest opinion as to the great value of land and if we can but manage it properly and not be in too great a hurry to sell, except a small part for the encouragement of settlers, much more will be realized than we contemplate.

'Out titles are clear and investigationable. We have at least the halo of British protection and that is the only true way of seeing it. . . . W.W.'(g)

The letter rings like a charter; there was no limit to the progress or profit of which the two dreamt, and if their aims were a cloak for an economic imperialism directed from London concerned only with the interest on loans it should not detract from their achievement.

It was true that the railway did not, and at first could not, pay the interest on the loan, but that was taken care of by the guarantee. The great shock came when immigration did not follow in the millions of which Sarmiento spoke. Between 1864 and 1870, only 400,000 entered the Argentine from Europe; and great and significant for the future though this influx was, it did not bring the contractors the glory or the profit they had hoped for from selling at £1 an acre 2,800 square miles of the most fertile land in the world. Brassey employed William Perkins, a Canadian of great resource, to set up several colonies on the line of the railway, but they did not all prosper and colonization received a severe blow from the report prepared by the British Consul, MacDonnell in 1872, describing a dangerous and brutish existence, and accusing the bankers, Thomas Bonar & Company, with some truth, of gross misrepresentation in their immigration prospectus.

Three years before that, Brassey had formed the Central Argentine Land Company to take over his interest for £100,000. Real profits did not come till twenty years later, but Brassey's beliefs suffered no real setback in his lifetime; by 1869 the Argentine was changing out of recognition and he could see that he had been part of that progress. The way in which a great country was being shaped seemed wholly admirable. No unease that it should be tied with the bonds of public debt and railways to the exporting of wheat to Europe disturbed him.

A conscience for his ambition and the restless profit-seeking of European investors would have been a far more remarkable advance on the philosophy of the century than his methods were on its economy. Certainly without Brassey and Wheelwright the development of northern Argentina would have been delayed twenty years.

By contrast, the Southern Railway from Buenos Aires, which also attracted English capital and was built by Morton Peto as far as Chascomus on the way to Bahia Blanca was different. It covered with a network a thickly populated area, served small towns and was able to give up its guarantee and stand on its own feet as a profitable concern. It passed rapidly into the management of men like Edward Lumb, who had lived thirty years in the Argentine, or George W. Drabble of the highly successful Bank of London and the River Plate, and under their direction became a purely Argentine enterprise.

The C.A.R. did not, though it carried the sugar of Tucumán and the timber of the Gran Chaco. Much as it contributed to the making of the nation, it was run badly by a London board who cared only that the guarantee should cover their inefficiency; Argentine money made up the deficit. Even the employees were English, and British enterprise, not for the last time, created anti-British feeling. But Brassey did not live to see, much less understand, the nationalist hopes his work helped to create, and in the year 1866 it provided the one ray of light in his world-wide undertakings.

10

THE YEAR OF THE LOCUST

O n March 20th, 1866 George Carr Glyn wrote to Brassey: 'There is a better feeling of peace—war between Austria and Prussia is now unlikely. Glad to hear you think your affairs are satisfactory.'(a) Rarely have two men who might have known better been so wrong. Yet Bismarck was not the begetter of the crisis. His Six Weeks' War against Austria only made the financial crisis more difficult for Brassey and Peto with their great undertakings in Eastern Europe.

The germ of disaster had been growing since the warning of the 1857 panic, hinting at a world underlined by instability, had been disregarded. The inevitable occasion came from the United States, where a 'smart' operator, James McHenry built a railroad. Shady fish swam in the murky waters of American railway policy long before Jay Gould, Drew, and Fisk battened on to the Erie Company and McHenry possessed their enterprise without their saving virtue of success.

He resurrected a moribund idea: the Atlantic and Great Western Railway, which should connect the New York and Erie system with the Ohio and Mississippi Railway, and which, when it was built, he would sell at great profit to the Erie Company. The promoter, Don José de Salamanca, pledged the good name of Queen Isabella of Spain and, on the credit thus provided, McHenry attempted to build his road for nothing, by mortgaging each section as it was finished and using the money for the next. In spite of the Civil War the line was pursued on a pyramid of increasing expense until finished in 1864. It rapidly became clear that it was three times overcapitalized and that a line which depended on through traffic yet had no control over either terminal was not a commercial success. As Cornelius Vanderbilt, crudest and most

magnificent of railway kings, said later: 'Building railways from nowhere to nowhere is not legitimate business.'

But it had to be made so in London, for the rapidly depreciating
shares of McHenry's railway were lodged with the highest banks and
finance companies of the City and Morton Peto himself had been
foolish enough to join McHenry's board.

Peto and others visited New York at the Company's great expense and
saw President Grant himself, but failed to persuade the almost bankrupt
Erie to buy a yard of McHenry's track. With no remittances and no
earnings, the banks who were implicated had to advance interest or see
their shares valueless; McHenry was bankrupt but could not be suffered
to drop. In that year, 1865, the bankers Masterman, Barned, and
Kennedy found it expedient to prepare for the crash by becoming
limited companies, and Overend and Gurney, the linchpin of the whole
interlocking overblown structure, with a deficit of £4 million, were
also incorporated and sold out their business to the public. Only men
like Peto who believed in the railways they built could not see the
truth; and Peto was involved, not only with McHenry, but in the
London, Chatham, and Dover Railway, perhaps the shakiest undertaking in England, which, in order to raise its nominal capital of
£16 million, had spent a quarter in collecting the rest and wasted
enormous sums on its London extension, competing for a terminus
with the South-Eastern.[1]

Throughout 1865, following the collapse of the Bombay cotton
boom, which Brassey had so shrewdly foreseen, markets grew more unsettled. In the pyramid of interconnecting companies, whose only
cement was the multitude of interwoven loans, it needed now only one
to fall to set off a chain reaction of disaster.

McHenry's contractors, Smith, Knight and Company, had plunged
heavily, financed by Overend and Gurney, into Mexico in the service
of the Emperor Maximilian, and when that misguided man was shot by
his subjects were left hopelessly bankrupt. Smith, Knight dragged down
into ruin their controlling company the Joint Stock Discount, and in
April the bankers, Barned and Company. Peto and Sir William Jackson
thought it wise to sell off their surplus plant at auction. Before the
movement became public and completely out of hand, the directors of
Overend and Gurney tried to hold the panic by taking Barned's shares

[1] They ran the line in from Kent to Victoria and Ludgate Hill and forced the
South-Eastern to open to Charing Cross and Cannon Street.

in McHenry's railway, in return for a flood of new 'acceptances', discountable for cash, but it was already too late.

Their firm had fallen into evil hands. Thomas Richardson and Samuel Gurney who built it up from a small discount bank to the largest dealer in credit in the City were dead.

Their sons were foolish: 'a child who had lent money in the City would have done it better'.(b) They made money fast by lending on securities of less and less worth until even their safest assets were speculative and hard to realize in a crisis. More and more they became participants in their undertakings until they had utterly overreached themselves. After 1861 the firm was losing half a million a year.

Henry Gurney, sleeping partner but head of the family, eventually woke up to this, but he, and the brothers Chapman and Robert Birkbeck made a grievous mistake when instead of pooling the family resources and ability to put the firm right they sold it to the public as a limited liability company and paid themselves £500,000 for the goodwill of the firm. There was nothing actually criminal in this; only when the family began to sell off their estates to meet the £4 million liabilities, suspicion spread. Even before the shares began to fall, their debts had been increased by the despairing attempt to save Barneds. Finally an action against the Mid-Wales Railway for recovery of securities failed and judgement was given on May 4th in a way which could only make public the failing condition of the firm, and which cast doubt on all its securities by making 'Lloyds bonds' or promissory notes from railway companies, illegal.

Ninety-day bills flooded in during the first week in May; Bank Rate was sharply raised to 8 per cent on the 8th, Overends' shares were marked steadily down, and on the 10th they closed their doors. Black Friday followed: 'the wildest agitation ever known in the City'; the end of an era.

Peto stood out for a moment, assailed by creditors. To underwrite the enormous cost of the London, Chatham, and Dover extension he had taken a large block of shares and left them with Overend and Gurney as security for the loan. Now the thread was utterly entangled. He claimed £380,000, the Company counterclaimed against him for £6½ million. In the end they settled for £1 million and no stain was lodged on the integrity of the great Baptist contractor, but he was finished; he resigned from Parliament and his organization was destroyed by delay and lack of work, leaving more than 30,000 men unemployed.

But Thomas Brassey survived. It was not a matter of getting £30,000 from Glyn nor of the friendship of Blount. Though the odds against him were exceedingly great they were not so utterly debilitating as those which lay against Peto; and, more important, were of a different kind: demanding a sense of calmest proportion and of infinite assurance, a mixture of the speculative risk, for which he was famous, and a faith in himself which had never before been tested to this extreme extent.

On the Victoria Docks, he faced a deficit of £600,000; a heavy loan from the General Credit Co. for the Danish railways was due in September, and the urgent repairs and renewals after the war brought this to £800,000; on the Evesham and Redditch Line, for which he had been paid in shares, he had a wages bill of £45,000 per month; approximately the same on several sections of the Great Western and again on the Warsaw and Terespol; he had to pay his men on the Queensland Railway where the State Government showed no hurry to settle his bills; Barrow Docks were losing £45,000 a year and the London, Tilbury, and Southend had reached its nadir of uneconomic return; but the worst of all was the Lemberg and Czernowitz line. For on this Brassey held £1 million of bonds which were almost worthless after the outbreak of war between Austria and Prussia at the end of May.

Quite apart from paying the 5,000 men at work, the magnitude of this was as if he had taken over all Overend and Gurney's holding in McHenry's railway.

Like the Duke of Buckingham, his contemporary, who avoided bankruptcy by living six months abroad so that his revenue paid his debts, Brassey was advised by George Carr Glyn to retrench and wait for better times; at least to stop work on the Lemberg and Czernowitz while the war was fought out. He would not listen. On his side he had great assets of which the banker did not know. Credit was indeed impossible to get: but from his personal fortune he had an income worthy of a great landowner and to it he added a lump sum of £252,000 borrowed from the trust he had been building up for his children (now over £1 million) and £45,000 from Joseph Locke's daughter, Phoebe.

Only courage could restore credit which in the long run, he had to have, however immune he was for a few months. And if there was one argument above all to disregard caution, he could see how Peto, who might have recovered from a single bankruptcy, was being irrevocably smashed by the interruption of his works and the dismantling of his firm.

He was 'largely committed'; in fact on the very balance of disaster; but if the world-wide organization were allowed to run down there would be no starting it again. So he gambled everything on finishing the contracts in hand, on making viable his paper holdings which were his depreciated payment.

On Black Friday night at a gloomy supper in the Westminster Palace Hotel, he looked up suddenly across the table at Wagstaff: 'Never mind—we must be content with a little less, that is all'; then changed the subject and talked of the survey of the Isthmus and the great project of the Panama Canal. Only in private he gave way to doubt: for he was sixty-one and it was hard to start again.

Nothing was allowed to alter; his orders were drafted in the same tone as the Foreign Office circular, 'there is no general want of soundness in the country'. Throughout bewildered Europe, his agents carried on, bound by allegiance though they thought him mad. Money poured out for three months in wages to his army of men from his private pocket; and the Lemberg–Czernowitz Line went ahead.

The Austrian Government guarantee was to come into force on the completion date, January 1867, or before, if the line was ready. With Prussian armies moving into Bohemia on a broad front supported by five main railways, against the rusty machinery of the Empire, this seemed remote enough. In June the front line round Olmütz lay close to the railway and skirmishing parties patrolled along the line between Cracow and Lemberg. The men had enough materials to finish it, and were working well beyond the fighting area, but they had to be paid. Officially, from Vienna, Brassey was told that no escort was available, and that he could expect no assistance.

Victor Ofenheim, one of the directors, was able to get as far as Cracow with the money but there all trains were halted. No one knew what lay ahead and all locomotives had been taken off. He discovered an old engine in a shed which no one would drive, but eventually bribed a man with 100 florins and a promise to support his family if he was killed and they set off at 50 m.p.h. up the track with no idea whether the line had been cut or not. They flashed past the outposts of both armies, lying flat on the footplate to shelter from the shooting, and swept triumphantly into Lemberg with the pay.

They perhaps turned the whole flank of disaster. If work had been suspended for lack of cash in June or July the men would have gone home to the harvest and the line would not have been finished before the winter. As it was, it was done by the end of September. The Six Weeks' War was then over and Bismarck was prepared to be lenient, almost generous, in his terms to Austria. The railway saved not only Brassey, who could sell his £1 million of bonds above par when the guarantee came into effect four months early, but helped the Emperor in the work of reconstruction and the boom which followed. Franz Joseph was suitably grateful: 'Who is this Mr. Brassey for whom men work with such zeal and risk their lives?' he enquired graciously, and an Iron Cross winged its way across Europe and was passed on to the contractor's wife.

Things were already better. The London market, perennially forgetful and still at heart buoyant with competitive energy, revived as the summer passed. Bank Rate fell steadily from 10 per cent to 5 per cent.

Brassey had never been so sanguine as Peto and had never undertaken what he could not perform. Where Peto had spurned limited liability as a matter of personal duty, Brassey did without it because he knew he could. He had not sold before he built, nor speculated on the works of others, and he survived. Within a year he was able to get rid of the unprofitable lease of the Danish railways and stand the great personal loss involved in losing both his own and Peto's deposits. He had paid back his loans, public and private, and to all appearances stood where he had done before; vindicated to a world where he had never been more famous for his foresight, endurance, and faith.

II

THE HAPSBURG DREAM

THE RECOVERY was an astonishing achievement, yet already the old man seemed a survival—a giant left over from simpler days. He became legendary as the finance company era closed, for 1866 was a far greater break than other years of crisis in the nineteenth century. As Brassey lived on he realized that no one could follow him in quite the same way; perhaps only the tradition and loyalty of his agents kept the firm, not merely in being, but as active as ever, as his energies spilled over in the last field still open, the floodtide of railway building which the reconstruction of the Hapsburg Empire provided.

The Emperor Franz Joseph, having failed to subject Hungary as he had wished, saw in railways a way to link, to Austrian advantage, the Dual Monarchy which events and war had forced on him. Schwarz and Klein, the State railway promoters, planned massive development out of whose promotion a new Mania grew, backed by the Government loans which now occupied the bankers and financiers of Europe.

In 1867 Brassey contracted for the 272-mile Kronprinzrudolf Railway from Vienna to Trieste and in 1869 for the Vorarlberg line in the Alps, and he continued to build from Czernowitz across the Principalities of Moldavia and Wallachia[1] to the Danube to fulfil the old Hapsburg dream of unity. In these years were sown the economic seeds of the *Drang Nach Osten* which was to culminate in the Berlin–Baghdad Railway.

The Rumanian lines, from Czernowitz to Suczawa and then to Jassy and Galatz on the Danube were the product of long negotiations. Before 1861, when a concession was actually granted, it had been hoped to carry the Carl-Ludwig Railway on to the Danube at a cost of

[1] Which in 1859 were united under Prince Couza as the new kingdom of Rumania.

£6½ million and after a careful survey Brassey said he was ready to take the Moldavian Section. The concession was given to Prince Leo Sapieha, Chairman of the Carl-Ludwig, but the Rumanian Government was just one year old and its credit in the capitals of Europe did not run to such a sum even on a 5 per cent guarantee of interest.

Brassey and G. C. Glyn suggested that the line should be built in sections, each paid for on completion, but the youthful nation wanted it all at once. Shares were issued and not taken up, mainly because there was no link with the Austrian system. In July 1861 Brassey wrote to Prince Sapieha:

'The serious defect is that it has no connexion with your Carl–Ludwig Railway and I fear you will have considerable difficulty in obtaining the support of the public for an isolated railway in the Principalities. If a company could be found for the entire line from Lemberg to Galatz, it would I think be favourably received. . . . I suggest that your Highness endeavour to form a combination with Baron Anselm Rothschild and your friends in Vienna. Should my co-operation as a contractor be thought desirable you may consider I will accept a third of the contract price which may be agreed upon in shares of the company.'(a)

So Brassey disposed of the royalty of Europe as his position warranted. The waters were undoubtedly deep and Rothschild would have nothing to do with it. Nothing more happened until June 1863 when another survey enabled Brassey to dictate terms with a 7 per cent guarantee to the Government. He submitted this to the International Finance Society but even they declined the hazard.

There can be no doubt that Brassey was out to make a heavy profit; and in spite of the enormous risk, as his Lemberg–Czernowitz line grew nearer to the border, the worst drawback, isolation, vanished.

However, a rival now appeared, the egregious José de Salamanca, who would build the whole line and relieve the Government by raising a quarter of the capital as well. Prince Couza's Government fell for it and tried to raise Brassey. Giles, Brassey's agent, told him bluntly: 'Let them have the concession. I return to England and I wish your Highness good morning.'

Salamanca had only one worry. He was a promoter not a contractor and there seemed little chance of making a killing if no line was actually built. Moreover Brassey's prestige was worth money. The two met in London in 1864. Salamanca proposed to issue £4 million in bonds bearing guaranteed interest; this would be enough to build the line; and the shares, sold at a premium when it was finished, would be the contractor's profit. This bore a distinct resemblance to McHenry's way of doing things. Brassey replied: 'Mr. Salamanca, before we can issue the bonds the shares must be paid up. I am not prepared to say we can get these shares placed.' (b) Since a bona-fide sale was impossible, the Spaniard had no answer.

Brassey then proposed that they pay up the shares themselves half and half. Offended by such honesty Salamanca broke off angrily. He took up the work but could make nothing of it; only serving to debase the credit of the Principality.

In 1867 Prince Couza approached Brassey again. The Lemberg–Czernowitz was finished and the line to the Rumanian frontier at Suczawa under way. By waiting patiently, Brassey had the Government on his own terms. The final contract was signed in June 1868; with a $7\frac{1}{2}$ per cent guarantee and a cost of £14,000 a mile (70 per cent higher than the original estimate of 1861) with an additional subvention of £2,500 a mile if necessary. It was a bad bargain for Rumania after the first white hope; yet the work was done rapidly at the end; before Brassey died the line had reached Jassy, and Roman on its way to the Danube. And Brassey was honest if somewhat hard; the last 140 miles fell to the tender care of Doctor Strousberg who, after amassing an immense fortune in jerry-building Prussian railways, made the mistake of giving an absolute and immediate guarantee of $10\frac{1}{2}$ per cent on this line—on a loan which lacked every semblance of proper management. But that debacle came afterwards, in 1871, and the efforts of Bismarck and the German aristocrats involved to cover up the mess did not disturb Brassey's rest. The line to the Danube was the last.

In Peru he began work on Callao Docks, 'one of the finest monuments of British work', and entered into stiff competition for labour with Henry Meiggs. Eighteen acres of dock and pier spread out under the direction of the engineer, Hodges, and the work lasted till 1874. And, as old men dream, Brassey turned his last energies to the almost mythical Euphrates Valley Railway.

The alternative route to India had been, until the Suez Canal, ardently desired and even after was attractive as a military route in case the Canal were shut. Something of the innocence of the early projects for girdling the globe always hung about it, yet serious negotiations with the Turkish Government for a concession did take place. In 1866 the

Sublime Porte granted a concession from Scutari via Aleppo and Baghdad to the Persian Gulf, a distance of 1,700 miles. Comparisons were made with the Union Pacific and its profit on through traffic alone. Clearly no one but Brassey could build such a line. The difficulty was money: the Government of India was not prepared to pay; the Sultan could not raise it if he had wished; and, for all the advantages, no British Government could think of putting so great a burden on the National Debt, as the guarantee of such a line. A Select Committee investigated the idea solemnly in 1872; but by then Brassey was dead; and the railway to Baghdad was left for a quarter of a century and another nation to pursue.(c)

Such dreams did not mean the approach of senility. Blount, now a pillar of and shortly to be Chairman of the Société Générale de Paris, was an earnest supporter of the Euphrates scheme. Brassey advocated a Channel Tunnel and no one laughed. Nothing seemed impossible to the man who in 1870 had built one mile in every twenty of railways in the world.

He travelled widely in the last years. In Paris in 1867 he was ill after strenuous sight-seeing, but travelled on to Cologne and then to the Mont Cenis to see how the Italian tunnel was going. Though its completion eight years ahead would mean the end of his own Fell Railway over the mountain which was due to open in the autumn, he was full of pleasure. In Italy crowds greeted him, and banners waved bearing the words 'Viva il re degli intraprenditori!' In October at the opening of the Fell Railway, the weather was bitterly cold. Brassey's special train broke down and he stamped about angrily in the snow waiting while his staff telegraphed for another. When he got back to the hotel at Lansleberg he was tired and depressed at not being able to open the railway on time. In the night he developed bronchitis and was with difficulty carried over the mountain to Turin for a doctor.

Meanwhile his family set out, prepared for the worst. Instead of waiting, Brassey moved on feverishly to Milan and passed the crisis of his fever in Venice; he was already recovering when the sorrowing sons arrived, while conducting the affairs of the Danubian railways.

But the tough body could no longer stand so much. In June 1868 he had a paralytic stroke; the effects wore off and he refused to abandon work. The Moldavian Line obsessed him. After so long, and when the line had reached the border, he had to complete it. So in October 1869 he set out once more on his last European tour. He was seriously ill, yet covered 6,000 miles in three weeks, constantly at work, with business waiting for him at every stop.

To those with him he seemed possessed by a restless spirit. Having travelled through Styria to watch the work on his Kronprinzrudolf Railway, he turned aside for a few days to the warm and sunny Adriatic, and met Morton Peto in Trieste. Peto, fighting for recovery, had a grandiose scheme for regulating the Danube and for a 300-mile railway in East Prussia. Money was the only trouble, the Governments were keen, it appeared. . . . But Peto was a shadow of past days and Brassey had learnt the lesson of 1866. He hurried on, ferried down the Danube and by cart to Bucharest, where he talked railway politics with Prince Couza and negotiated the final arrangements in Jassy. The local boyars entertained him lavishly on their vast estates and pressed him for allotments of the miraculous shares. In between Brassey inspected the works and then travelled back to Vienna in Ofenheim's private coach: nearly the whole way on his own railway.

Back in England the disease advanced quickly, and by the spring of 1870 his doctor told him that the cancer was fatal. In a broad, tolerant, Anglican way he was resigned and undisturbed by doubt. He did not become weak; even in the summer he used to visit contract sites in England and would 'recognise many of the old navvies whom he had not seen for years and address them by their names. He would never omit to shake hands cordially with old gangers and when he met them at the works he would pull up for a few minutes to talk over old times.' And so navvies came and wept openly by his bedside in Hastings with the family for whom the old man was the fibre of life itself; and after harsh suffering he died on December 8th, 1870.

His will was proved at £3,200,000. His investments covered every field of Victorian progress. He had stuck by them because he believed in them, railways, telegraphs, shipping lines, docks and harbours, waterworks, gasworks, and insurance. Besides this, the trust funds amounted to £2 million. The size of such a fortune in 1870 is not easily measured. Of others who were counted millionaires, Samuel Gurney left £1½ million in 1856, Samuel Jones Loyd, Lord Overstone, died in 1883 leaving £2 million. In modern terms it might be put as £60 million. Yet Thomas Brassey left more to Victorian England than a colossal fortune.

'To a man so modest, who had the courage in the days of Cobden to prove well paid labour to be cheap, success was not, perhaps, an unearned increment.'(d) Among his contemporaries he stood out as a pioneer employer, a promoter of great integrity and a visionary with the ability to clothe his dreams in steel and stone; whose life was synonymous with the Railway Age; who, not first, but in the largest manner, carried abroad the Industrial Revolution.

The death of Thomas Brassey was not the end of an age of British contracting. If a limit was set, it had been in 1866, perhaps the crucial year of the century's enterprise, when the wide cosmopolitan operations of a small network of promoters and financiers collapsed. The reaction to the Overend and Gurney crash came in many ways—in a new channelling of funds into Government loans rather than directly into railway building, in an absorption of contractors' enterprise in wider activities at home, in docks, harbours, gas and water services, and in new areas abroad. The great Railway building age was over in Britain, and in Europe, where mileage increased chiefly in subsidiary lines; but in Eastern Europe, the Balkans, Africa, and America, it had another forty years of vigorous life; and became now the subject of far more intensive competition from contractors and financiers of every nationality.

After 1866, Austrians, Germans, French, and Americans were working in the international sphere. De Lesseps, having cut the Suez Canal, turned to Panama; Baron Hirsch began his system of Balkan Railways to Istanbul; and Americans like Henry Meiggs reached a monopoly in parts of South America. The British contractors who came after Brassey had therefore to compete or confine themselves to home affairs. Many chose the easier way in the building boom of the 1870s which absorbed the surplus of men, while the 'Government loan business' took up the surplus capital. For twenty years after 1870 no British contractor operated widely abroad. Sir Morton Peto carried on with railways in Eastern Europe, John Aird pioneered gas and water services on the Continent, and Government Departments continued to build railways in India, Canada, and Australia; but not till the 1890s did the spirit of the 1860s recover, a parallel perhaps with the general position of British enterprise abroad.

When it did, it was circumscribed in ways which Brassey would not have understood. The flexible groups of entrepreneurs were fewer and more difficult to bring together. Instead, the contractor came to depend on the bank, and the banks, after 1866, and even more after the Baring Crisis of 1890, where less and less inclined to participate in ventures which, like those of Brassey and Peto, had been farsighted but for many years extremely shaky. By contrast, continental banks became prime movers: the Credit Anstalt in the Balkan Railways and the Deutsche Bank in the Berlin–Baghdad.

At the same time the contractors' wide range was cut by military necessity. Who built a railway or a port became a matter of strategic as well as economic significance. There is a vast difference between Brassey's lordly dealings with the Danube Railway in the 1860s and the complicated ten-year diplomatic manœuvres which Lord Cromer had to carry out against French opposition in Egypt before the Aswan Dam could even be planned. It was perhaps remarkable that British contractors did recover, and that, by 1900, they were again indisputably the foremost in the world.

This pre-eminence depended on certain technical advances, such as the development of structural steels, and the knowledge of the science of structural statics; as well as the extension of the Empire, which opened up new areas in the 1890s; but chiefly on the ability of the second generation of contractors like Sir John Aird, Lord Cowdray, Sir John Jackson or Sir William Arrol. It was the more remarkable because in almost every other great old-established Victorian industry, the second generation of industrial leaders lamentably lacked the energy, foresight and ruthless drive of their predecessors—a grave factor in the gradual decline of British industry in relation to the rest of the world which occurred at the end of the nineteenth century.

TWO

Sir John Aird

1

A SAMUEL SMILES STORY

SEVEN YEARS after Waterloo, in a harsh industrial depression, a Scots crofting family from Ross-shire walked the 500 miles south to London to find work. A fellow Scot, a Mackintosh, employed them on the digging of the Regent Canal and in a fall of earth in a cutting the father was buried alive, leaving his sixteen-year-old son, John Aird, to support his mother who spoke nothing but Gaelic, the English tongue having only recently penetrated to their remote Highlands. John Aird found work with the Phoenix Gas Company and a sordid cottage in their stable yard in Blackfriars Road, 'a very squalid part of London with a knacker's yard adjoining for the preparation of cats' meat from dead horses'.(a)

Among the thousands of the poorest living on the edge of starvation he was lucky to have a job. Competition among the first gas companies was fought by reducing workers' wages, and conditions were frequently intolerable. Nevertheless, carrying some quality of independence from his rural upbringing, he tried to raise himself. Night after night he sat up teaching himself first to read and write and then learning the rudiments of engineering. He won a reputation for shrewd thoroughness and moved into the office, having taken ten years to claw his way out of the hopelessness of the underpaid. He was then offered the job of Superintendent at the Gas Company's works at Greenwich; a position of some security and status.

The gas works lay in the poorest part of the town, on a low promontory made by the junction of the River Ravensbourne with the Thames, surrounded by the small cottages of the workmen. Inside a high wall were the Manager's house and offices and the factory buildings. Along the river bank stretched wharves for the colliers and barges bringing coal and taking on the coke. Through the filthy water of the Thames, bearing the sewage, the dead cats, the dogs, the refuse of all London, moved the river traffic, the barges and fine East India-men, the first steamers, the elegant clippers and paddle craft up to the Pool and the East India Dock. On the far shore spread the flat marshes of the Isle of Dogs on which his second son, John Aird the younger, was to build the two largest docks in the world.

Manager of fifty men in the factory, Aird could live with assurance; in modest comfort, with a bottle of sherry to entertain the partners on the monthly inspection, decent clothes, and friends not only among the middle-class tradespeople who now looked up to him. Samuel Smiles knew the family and saw in him the conclusions of *Self Help*— and Dickens, then living at Gravesend, knew them well.

About 1840, Aird who had done some engineering work for the Company, chiefly in laying new mains in Greenwich, asked permission to do outside work of his own. He was in the habit of handling his employees as if he were a contractor, and the transition was easily made. By 1846, when his two elder sons were sent to boarding school, Aird was a man of position, respected by the local shopkeepers whose bills he paid promptly and the residents on the Hill, whose houses he increasingly frequented. He began to lay mains for the East London Water Company, and was called out to Hertfordshire to bring water to Moor Park for Lord Ebury. He invested in building land in Green-wich and put up small terrace houses on the edge of the town. But as a contractor he was still a novice with a quite rudimentary organization. Only when he reckoned on enough work to allow him to stand alone, at the age of thirty-nine, he resigned from the Gas Works and offered himself as an independent contractor with a small labour force of a hundred men.

Several London water companies tried to engage him, but he sensibly refused to bind himself and continued to lay mains as he chose.

He was fortunate to strike a decade when his speciality was needed as much as Brassey's, because, parallel with the railways, almost as important in social history, grew the demand for the amenities of lighting and water, first perhaps in London but rapidly in the 1850s and '60s in provincial towns in Britain and on the Continent. If trans-port was the first requirement of an industrial machine, gas lighting and pure water were as much the needs of its people; for the results of the new order were to enlarge towns into cities, cities into urban conglomerations where candle and rush-lights were as ineffective for streets as they were for factories. Above all, new drainage and mains water became essential for the towns, spawning houses across the landscape, as primitive drains flowing into the river became through the water supply a source of poison for the whole population.

The days of wooden water pipes hollowed out of tree trunks, of gas mains made from musket barrels, crudely soldered together, were over. Industry, after the Napoleonic Wars, perfected the production of pipes of any diameter from the standard gas to the 36-inch trunk water main. The demand for expansion was so great and the pressure of railways on the larger contractors so urgent during the Mania that Aird could never do enough. By 1850 he had not only entrenched himself in this specialist field, but had multiplied his organization till he ranked as a major contractor.

Eight water companies supplied most of London: all eight drew their water either from the tidal reaches of the Thames or the lower stretches of the rivers Lea and Ravensbourne. From the Napoleonic Wars onwards, developing from a mere scandal to large-scale public poisoning, the Thames grew steadily fouler; and as the water closet replaced the medieval cesspool, all the sewage which had previously gone into the ground reached the river. To this, as London became industrialized, was added the chemical waste of factories, a host of poisonous products which primitive sand filtration could not remove. The tide moved the torrid mass up and down, and the new paddle steamers stirred it up from the bottom at regular intervals. Parliament found the stench of the river in the summer intolerable; and the water companies continued to pipe the mess all over the metropolis. The cholera of 1849, which killed one per cent of all the consumers of the water boards was needed, rather than the legislature or the 1850 Board of Health Report, to compel the companies to seek sources at least above the tidal limit at Teddington Lock.

Then every company moved at once. Pumping stations had to be built, reservoirs constructed, mains laid, filtration plant designed on a scale unparalleled in the world. Three major Companies, the Southwark and Vauxhall, the Grand Junction, and the West Middlesex, decided on a place a little above Hampton and all three employed Aird, until eventually something like 100 million gallons of water a day reached the City through his works; and supplied perhaps $1\frac{1}{2}$ million of its population.

What he had learned here he took abroad; for much the same reasons as Brassey moved to Europe. With his special knowledge and experience, he saw an almost entirely untouched market on the Continent. He had done some main laying in Holland a year before the Hampton works were begun, and after the 1848 Revolution, he was building waterworks for Rotterdam and Amsterdam and engaged on very large contracts in Copenhagen and Berlin. At the Danish capital he built a waterworks and then, to cure the problems of sewage disposal of a city on the waterfront, Aird designed the first outfall sewer ever built, stretching one and a half miles out to sea. He lost very heavily, almost running out of reserves in the process, when the tunnel ran into sulphurous rock. Probably only the complaisance of his bank, Currie's, in Cornhill, saved him. But the sewer was finished on time and if he got no benefit from the Danes, he had won a European reputation which was his qualification for the work in Berlin.

When the Great Exhibition Hall was raised by Sir Charles Fox in 1851, Aird had laid the mains for the gas and water, and again when it was rebuilt at Sydenham as the Crystal Palace. Fox and Thomas Crampton, the engineer, became the nucleus of a financial group which formed the Berlin Water Company in 1852 and they took Aird into partnership; his first contact with this type of enterprise. In the same years he was laying mains and building works at Hamburg, Altona, Schiedam, and at Archangel and Moscow.

The 1857 panic, however, which ruined Hamburg, set back public works for a few years in Germany and when they were resumed Aird's monopoly had gone. In its place he and his son, John, established the same degree of importance in London's gas as they had in its water a decade earlier. As impartially as he had worked for the water companies, he built for the private and highly competitive gas companies. Then, as London expanded, and the companies fought for the new areas, he supplied the whole of Kensal Green for the Western Gas Company, and formed his own undertaking, the Crystal Palace Company in 1858. Being now actor-manager in the business, he became a close friend of Stephenson Clarke, the coal-mine owner, whose fortune had reached vast proportions with the increased demand for coal; and then as new work came in after 1860, Aird passed his side of the business to Charles, the elder son.

Aird was now acknowledged to be the first expert in gas work in England.

His new offices, in Belvedere Road, Lambeth, matched the fine villa outside Lewisham, well furnished and richly curtained. Twenty clerks sat in the Head Office alone, while outside stretched quays and sheds beside the river and stabling for a hundred horses. There was hardly a gas or water company in the country for whom he did not work, Staffordshire, Oxford, Rugby, and Eastbourne among them. Out of piety for his homeland he tendered for the Loch Katrine water supply to Glasgow but failed to win it, though he did construct works at Lochnabo and Buckie. He tendered for the Tay Bridge, and perhaps the disaster which overcame that venture might have been avoided, but he found the promoters' conditions—that the contractor had to be responsible for ironwork in an unusual degree—were too onerous, and withdrew.

He was employing about 30,000 men. Subcontractors worked regularly for him, among whom were Mowlem and Burt, who began as paviours replacing the streets after the mains were laid. In 1858, when the gas stokers of the Imperial struck and plunged most of North London into darkness, he called for volunteers from all his contracts, raised 2,000 navvies and broke the strike with them, keeping the supply of gas at full pressure for a week until the men were forced to return. He was no longer in a position to sympathize with the grievances of men whose wages were cut down by a competition of which he was part.

John Aird, the younger, was in complete charge of the main laying department, and took over the general management of the Berlin work. He was, his brother Charles noticed, 'a great help, having tumbled into the pipe laying work so readily that he had almost complete charge of it at the age of 21'.(b) In 1856 he married Sarah, the daughter of Ben Smith, a wharfinger at Deptford Green, a man of some wealth and a power along the river. Perhaps his later dock connexions stemmed from this, though in all other respects Sarah had little enough influence on his life.

Since his father continued to hold on to the main part of the firm John felt compelled to carve out new provinces for himself; he projected a gasworks in Palermo in Sicily in 1859, built the waterworks at Warsaw, partnered Brassey and George Wythes at Cagliari in Sardinia, and in India in the vast Calcutta Waterworks. Adding to his world experience, he worked in Ottawa, moved on to build a gasworks at Pará, in Brazil; gave Bahia Blanca (the terminus of Peto's South Argentine Railway) gas and main drainage; and finished up in Singapore.

At home, his father toyed for a short time with railway building, more as a side speculation than with any real desire to enter the field of railway kings, but his energies were shortly devoted entirely to the new works rising out of the formation of the Metropolitan Board of Works; London Drainage and the Underground Railway.

A large intercepting sewage scheme had been suggested twenty years before the Board of Health campaign, but, like the water problem, had to wait until absolute necessity moved Government to interfere. As the water supply improved, even more sewage poured into the tidal waters of the Thames, and Parliament under the dual pressure of the cholera of 1853 and the stench of the river outside its own windows, created the Metropolitan Board of Works. The first result of planned progress was Sir Joseph Balzagette's scheme for two unified sewage systems for the City: one south of the Thames to Crossness Point; and on the north a low level and a high level sewer meeting to discharge at Barking Creek; both ends being dreary marshes far from the town.

Between 1858 and 1863, Aird worked on the lower and Brassey on the higher. The two tunnels were to take the whole of London's storm water, as well as its entire sewage. For the first time, Aird could regard himself as Brassey's equal. While the latter worked through the northern hills of London from Hampstead to the River Lea, he had the more difficult task (largely at river level), of digging through the West End.

The construction of the Thames Embankment from Waterloo to Westminster Bridge, part of the Board's scheme for improving London, was also given to Aird and on this he made his first connexion with the firm of Lucas Brothers who then joined with him on the Underground.

The first Underground, the Metropolitan, dug on the shallow 'cut and cover' system had been completed after ten years from Paddington to King's Cross and, in spite of the discomfort and filth suffered by passengers as a result of running steam trains in a continuous tunnel, was wildly successful.

By 1863, as the main lines south of the river reached far into London, to Charing Cross and Cannon Street, the problem of communications in the centre grew, not for the last time, intolerable. The streets were still quite unfitted for any large quantity of horse-drawn traffic and a twofold answer slowly evolved: cheap suburban trains and a rapid extension of the Underground system.

Working with the Lucases, Aird carried the District Line, which was still an isolated railway in the west, to South Kensington and West-minster. He built the Metropolitan out to Hammersmith and connected it with the West London railway and then took the contract for the St. John's Wood line up to Swiss Cottage which was opened in 1868.

The Overend and Gurney crisis passed almost without trouble. He was not committed to any of the undertakings which nearly ruined Brassey; all his overseas works were completed and he was able, thanks to his private savings, to take over several of the works left unfinished by Peto and to give employment to many of the men whom the failure threw out of work. Thereafter, he took less part in the firm's activities; and when he died in 1876 had virtually retired.

2

AIRD THE YOUNGER

J OHN AIRD the younger controlled the firm after 1870. He himself
had been entirely responsible for perhaps the largest single works
done by them in the sixties, the Beckton gas-works and the
Millwall Docks.

Beckton, the largest gas-works ever built, proved him to his father
and the family, among whose seven sons he had always been the most
thrusting and prominent; and its completion enabled the Gas Light
and Coke Company to become the largest gas company in Britain, if
not the world. The invention of the Bunsen burner, in 1859, had made
it possible to use gas for heating, cooking, and water heating for the
first time as a practical proposition, on a far larger scale than the ex-
perimental machines shown at the Great Exhibition. Demands for gas
rose continuously until the warring companies reached a point of
exhaustion, not so much of finance as of pure lack of their raw material.
The biggest, the Imperial, was under a weak management and its
ablest competitor, the Gas Light, under the forceful direction of
Simon Adams Beck, planned a new works large enough to give them
a hold over all the others.

Almost automatically the contract was given to Aird. Brassey,
after his brief experience with his own works, was not interested; and
no one else had the knowledge or the necessary plant. The Beckton
Works near the River Lea, named after the Chairman, were to be a
model of progressive planning, to be laid out as an architectural
spectacle as well as an engineering miracle. Something of the promoter's design was indeed achieved on the site, exposed to every
wind, and surrounded by marshes, and infertile land.

Four great retort houses were created, with space left beside for

Sir John Aird

Sir Ernest Cassel

Cartoon of Aird in Egypt

Millwall Docks

more, and the gas for the first time was pumped by the weight of the holding cylinders themselves. Massive 48-inch mains carried 1,000,000 cubic feet of gas a day to the City and Westminster.

Beckton was finished in 1870, more quickly than Beck had believed possible, and was a turning-point in the history of the Company, if not of the whole gas industry. It was the best and biggest and a symbol of efficiency. The huge new supply made it possible for Beck to drive through a policy of amalgamation; because the other companies had as yet no extra supplies, nor with Aird booked, and skilful delaying tactics used against their Bills in Parliament, had they been able to start. The City Company was forced in in 1870, and then the Great Central, crippled by large-scale embezzlement. The Equitable and Victoria Companies followed and the Western in 1872. Beckton was always the bargaining point and to back up Beck's negotiations, Aird continued to extend his original work.

The greatest triumph came in 1875. The Imperial, loth to lose its prestige, spent nearly half a million on new works at Bromley which were out of date before they were begun, too far away from the industrial and residential areas to compete, and not even near completion when the critical financial situation of the Company forced them to ask Beck for terms.

The Gas Light and Coke Company now served all London north of the Thames except for small areas of Fulham and Chelsea and part of the East End. Beckton was again enlarged by Aird in 1877 at a capital outlay of more than twice the original cost. Then in the year when the first Electricity Bill came before Parliament (1882) Aird and Stephenson Clarke were at last invited to join the Board.

But the gas industry was entering on its slow decline and they were too late to check it. Clarke was old. Aird was soon busy on the Nile; and old men ran the Board well into the Edwardian period who were in bigger jobs than they could handle; their weakness ramified in indecision and overspending and they were faced with the progressive expansion of electric light which could only be met by turning more rapidly to heating and gas by-products than they were prepared to do. It was, still, the real tragedy of the British gas industry that it had been so well and widely built by men like Aird, that electricity was delayed from those things for which it was best; in 1896 no more than three London parishes possessed it, and in the year Queen Victoria died only 200 miles of streets were lit with electric lamps. Britain lagged in this as in her heavy industries, well into the twentieth century, a long-term effect undreamt of by Beck or Aird himself.

Still in his father's lifetime, John Aird widened the firm in other ways. A form of partnership had existed with the Lucas brothers; in 1870 this was resolved into an amalgamation which left, for reasons of convenience, three firms; Lucas and Aird, Lucas Brothers, and John Aird & Sons, each with a separate account at Farquar Harries Bank in St. James. The merger was partly a response to the 1866 crash. The Lucases were experienced contractors who had among their works rebuilt Covent Garden after it had been burnt down, Liverpool Street Station, sections of the Underground, the London, Chatham, and Dover Railway, and Blackfriars Bridge. The managerial structure which they composed was able to cover all fields of contracting from railways to harbours, gas-works to canals. With an interlocking financial structure they were stronger, at a difficult time for contractors, and they were, with their varied resources, able to offer far more advantageous terms. Lucas and Aird could build anything; and this stage lasted until the end of the century.

However, personalities prevented a union as close as they desired. Thomas Lucas, the elder brother, suffered from ill-health and did not take a large part after the amalgamation; and Charles Lucas, who by age was senior to John Aird, found him less tractable than his brother Charles, who was an old friend and a constant guest at their home, Warnham Court, near Horsham. Like the elder Aird, he had begun at the bottom as a small builder in Norwich; he had risen rapidly; employed as subcontractors the future giants, Wimpey and MacAlpine; and was a harsh, domineering man who clashed frequently with his equally stubborn and far more fiery counterpart.

John Aird, at thirty-five, was not a complacent partner. With the advantages of his father's rise to cut him off from real poverty and given an entrance to the firm as soon as he showed ability, he had been for twenty years in a position of responsibility. He had enormous respect and love for his father, but Agnes Aird was subject to attacks of nervous depression in later life and he was never very close to her—nor at any time in his life did he show the family affection for her which characterized his elder brother. Charles, whom he had always looked down on as a weakling, proved to be an able if pedantic administrator and was brought in as a partner in the gas enterprises. But in 1876 he had a nervous breakdown after hearing that a contract had failed and John had no scruples about pushing him into retirement. The only other son to enter the firm was Alexander, who turned out a spendthrift and was pensioned off to a fruit farm in Kent.

Even as a child, Charles had noted his brother's dominance. In one of their frequent quarrels John had seized a knife and nearly slashed the older boy's hand off. 'He was quite different from me. As far as I can remember he was a somewhat dull boy, very hasty tempered, had not the least idea of doing anything to educate himself, and never cared for reading'. But he left Charles behind, not from learning 'but simply from extraordinary force of character, of mastery over all about him; even men of great position in the busy world who had far more culture and education, would be glad to associate with him and seek his advice . . . he was always in the front of everything and meant to keep there, while I was prey to a strange diffidence . . . he showed a marvellous grasp of the ins and outs of different works but more marvellous still was his masterful power over men older than himself and of greater position in life. He firmly believed in himself and whatever might arise he stuck to that opinion'.(a) Nothing in his life ever gave him cause to alter it.

A contractor still alive remembers him standing on Craigendoran Station at the starting-point of the West Highland Railway which he had just finished. Looking up the Holy Loch at the track winding between the trees, the massive figure of the man with his strong head, dominated the wild landscape. A tall, florid giant with prominent features, blue eyes, a deep and commanding voice, and a beard which he wore longer and more splendid as he grew older, Aird made a striking impression.

This was only one of the outward signs of what he believed to be the role of the great contractor. He modelled himself, consciously or not, on the ideal of the Renaissance prince, then a fashionable doctrine. A contractor should appear to be three times as rich as he was, and should live always in the greatest magnificence. In a sense he was a superb showman, which was not a façade hiding a weakness but the expression of a great if crude vitality.

He moved the firm's offices to a huge baroque building in Great George Street opposite the Foreign Office; leased Wilton Park, near Beaconsfield, and had installed in his own large house at 14, Hyde Park Terrace, a private theatre, to which plays were brought to him to

save the journey and inconvenience of going to the theatre. At
Wilton he had a wind director placed in the hall and if it changed by
no more than a point the butler was instructed to alter it. Almost
meticulous in his pursuit of the grand manner he would at his many
dinner parties present every woman with a gift, chosen with care and
great expense, of which the finest were a selection of exquisite fans.
Always he loved to be at the centre of parties; yet he did not aspire to
enter high society, partly because he was never really rich enough, but
mainly because he was not interested. He cared instead for his own
circle of friends; as brilliant perhaps and intelligent as the other.

By contrast, to his family he was aloof, determined, and severe. He
hated to be argued with and his temper shortened with age. Yet he
could be a delightful and informal companion; he liked to play the
flute though he never performed well, and enjoyed nothing more than
showing off his skill in the traditional sword dance. He restored Wilton
with taste and made it comfortable, even at that date no mean achievement, but he brought up his children not to be impressed by anything,
and in the process he was unfair and often despotic, preferring his
younger son to the elder. Knowing their abilities more than sympathiz-
ing with their ambitions, he never troubled to hide his low estimation of
their business knowledge and gave them no chance to manage the
firm as long as he was still capable of control. They were not on his
intellectual level and he despised them for it.

Perhaps intellectual pride was his only real extravagance. He
enjoyed the company of the artists of his day, like Alma-Tadema and
Dixey, and his picture gallery was well known; he patronized contemporary masters and made it almost a point of honour to buy the picture
or sculpture of the year at the Royal Academy. He took Alma-Tadema
to Egypt for no other reason than to paint him a picture of the finding
of Moses. But the whole taste of his generation and himself was less
magnificent than their fashionable and scrupulous reconstructions of
Ancient Rome, more tawdry and sterile than he understood or wished
to.

To be an intellectual was a luxury, as estates were to be for Cowdray,
and war for Norton-Griffiths; which he could afford because he gave
nothing else of himself away. His wife, Sarah, was small, very thin and
dark, gay, flirtatious, and attractive but she never influenced him in his
business, and not greatly in his private life.

Although he bought Highcliffe Castle and gave large parties there, he was not interested in estates or the country and its sports. He became Member of Parliament for North Paddington in 1887 and made a hobby out of politics; as near as he came to enjoying any sport. Made Lord Mayor, he wielded some influence in the borough, where gestures such as that to celebrate the Diamond Jubilee, when he gave a commemorative book to every child in the constituency, were long remembered. He held the seat until 1905, a staunch Conservative (though his father had been a Liberal) and a follower of Disraeli, more out of unthinking temperament than any profound political decision. He spoke frequently on employers' liability in a fair but illiberal sense in the early years but, growing bored, rarely addressed the House after 1890. He remained a back-bencher, silent on the important issues of the day.

In business he was a master of his craft. Possessing an absolute ability to shut off his private life, he worked intensely hard for short periods. He had an innate judgement and foresight of possibilities. To the end of his life he was prepared to alter even the basic premisses of his work if occasion demanded, as it did several times on the Nile. His ideas were wide, his sense of mission Olympian, but his methods were precise. His writing was tiny, his signature the smallest imaginable, and he controlled the firm from its minutiae to its grandest designs without relaxing or wavering, until, crippled by a stroke, he retired absolutely. He was the complete autocrat who never in his life met a greater force and who never had to temper his will to the overriding demands of necessity.

The firm was moulded in this cast; he was fair to his men, but not loved. His father had broken strikes and his attitude to labour scarcely ameliorated. But his financial direction was shrewd and sensible, building the firm up to the foremost in the world for perhaps fifteen years; and in his dealings in Egypt he rose to the stature of a great financier.

3

LUCAS AND AIRD

As might have been expected, Aird became the dominant though the junior partner. Although the contracts for the next twenty years owed much of their size to the Lucas's experience and even more to their financial connexions (which Aird, up to now had lacked) they bore the stamp of his personality as much as the surviving records show him to have been the driving force. What was most significant for the future in the partnership was that Aird came to know the Barings and Rothschilds and through them and their world of closed tightly knit co-operation, Ernest Cassel.

Dock work was the chief expression of the contractors' partnership. They had the plant, the newly perfected steam dredgers, trucks, and mechanical navvies which were needed in the colossal excavation of large docks; they had the resources to build dock walls, deal with stone or concrete, lay the railways, build sidings and stations, erect warehouses, granaries and cranes, lay water, gas and later electric mains; there was no side of the work which they could not include in their tender. And as Brassey in England built railways impartially for the competing private companies, Aird and Lucas built docks through twenty years of cut-throat war between the two major London dock companies.

Just as the protests of dissatisfied consumers, and recommendations of Royal Commissions had failed, against the philosophy of the age, to persuade Government to any effective regulation of the private gas or water companies, no coherent shipping policy was administered on the Thames below the Pool of London in the nineteenth century, other than the creation of the Thames Conservancy. Competition and private enterprise produced both the best and worst results of an unregulated economy; at times the cheapest dock rates were given to shipping lines to attract their custom; but the services fluctuated in quality and companies held on to the last minute before being forced to make improvements by the competition of their neighbours.

What effect the negative Government policy had on the growth of London as the largest port in the nineteenth-century world is impossible to gauge. An authority like the Mersey Docks and Harbour Board might have attracted more traffic and would certainly have saved great waste, but it is more likely that it was the expanding trade itself, and the constant growth in the size of ships, which governed the development as it would have ruled that of a guided monopoly. Lucas and Aird were able to provide the response to the need; they would have built bigger docks if they had been asked—their effect was that by building them quickly they caught new trade, and by doing the job well they kept the cost and later repairs low, so that harbour dues remained an attraction for the shipping of the whole world.

The first London Dock, the Howland wet dock, had been dug by hand in the seventeenth century. Slow changes culminated in 1806 in the foundation by Act of Parliament of three companies, the East India, the West India and the London Dock; each of which had restrictive privileges and built what for the time were large and commodious docks.

An opportunity to amalgamate them was lost in the 1820s when the privileges ran out; and there followed an era of unbridled competition whose first symptoms were the building of the large St. Katherine's Dock (the last built solely for sailing ships) and the amalgamation of the East and West India Companies. As a direct competitor, Brassey and Peto had built their Victoria Dock; then in 1864 the newly formed Millwall Freehold Land and Dock Company commissioned Aird to build them a dock to beat all the rest. They bought up, secretly through agents, and at agricultural values, 200 acres on the Isle of Dogs, south of the West India Company's dock, and succeeded in pushing their Bill through Parliament before the others had woken up to the danger.

Aird began work in June 1865 with the engineer John Fowler and finished in the very short time of three years. A dock area of 36 acres, the wide 80-foot entrance, the first dry dock to be connected with the main work, a fine and coherent railway system and the first granary to be built in the Port of London should have made Millwall a commercial success. It never was; partly because the rates were set too low in the original Bill, partly because, although it cornered the Baltic grain market, it did not get the very large trade on which the rate had been calculated. Only the speculative rise in the value of the Company's land around made it viable; at first and for many years it remained a thorn to the others, competitive without being profitable.

The threat, however, moved to action the sluggish East and West India Company which, since their merger, had done nothing whatever to improve their facilities. The South-West India Dock which this Board planned, turned out a triumph of false economy and bad design, with no more notice taken of the increasing bulk of ships than of the advent of steam; yet for a short time it achieved what Millwall had failed to do, the status of premier dock of the port, a famous haunt of the clippers of the tea and wool races from China and Australia.

The volume of trade coming into the port continued to rise very rapidly through the nineteenth century. By far the greatest time of increase was between 1860 and 1870 when traffic more than doubled. In a dock-owner's market the greatest plans were proved the best, and in 1874 with unlimited confidence, the London and St. Katherine Board went ahead with a plan which had originally occurred to Brassey, to extend the Victoria Dock right through the Isle of Dogs to Galleons Reach and cut off the four-mile detour round. The old Victoria was no longer large enough and the engineer, Alexander Randall, designed one which, when opened, was the finest in the world. Lucas and Aird built it in five years; using a degree of mechanization not previously seen and which was not exceeded until the Manchester Ship Canal ten years later. By permission it was called the Royal Albert and in dutiful succession its older partner became the Royal Victoria.

The Royal Albert could take ships of up to 12,000 tons, (though such giants were not built until the twentieth century) but it was so well constructed that with limited dredging it could have been and later was enlarged to accommodate vessels of up to 25,000 tons. It was essentially a transit dock. Warehousing on a large scale was becoming outmoded and lines of single-storey sheds flanked it instead of the old-fashioned tall buildings round the Victoria. Not surprisingly, it took all the steam traffic from the inefficient South-West India.

Faced with collapsing revenues, and a traffic which was still not large enough to give both companies plenty, the East and West India Dock Company at last decided radically to improve their facilities by building a wholly new dock. The Suez Canal had diverted much of their old Eastern trade to Mediterranean ports; their warehouses were now liabilities in the face of changed needs and the competition of wharfingers; and in 1880 the large Australian Line threatened to transfer to their rivals. Unable to reorganize their old dock, since it would mean a three-year closure and loss of business, they adopted a bold scheme—for a wholly new dock down river at Tilbury. They bought up the land before announcing the scheme; made the contract with Kirk and Randall while the Bill was still in Parliament; and opened work only five days after it received the Royal Assent.

The contractors however were slow to work and soon asked for more money. The Company paid but its engineers became dissatisfied. Disputes over the nature of the blue clay in which they were digging followed. The contractors were turned out in July 1884 and the work was given to Lucas and Aird, who finished it in two years.

This masterpiece lay next to the London, Tilbury, and Southend Railway station, and embodied several new and untried ideas; a tidal basin open to the sea, a main dock with branches, a system of graving docks which could also give an emergency outlet if the main entrance was blocked; and cranes so shaped that the trains could run between the wheels. A large hotel was built to house the passengers and friends seeing them off, and the dock was surrounded by offices and 50 miles of railway sidings.

Tilbury Dock lay right at the arrival point of ships in the Thames, where the largest vessels could enter regardless of the tide, saving often a day or more and towing and pilotage. But it was disappointing. The tidal basin, as Aird had feared, became a mud trap and the dock branches were soon too narrow; and the Board's over-sanguine hopes of traffic were shattered. Sheer envy of the Royal Albert had begun it; now the wharfingers and lightermen boycotted it. The Board could only buy traffic by ruinous concessions. Aird's price was more than double the original contractor's estimate: more than the Royal Albert; and the first contractors began a prolonged and costly lawsuit. For five years after its completion Tilbury fell into the hands of receivers; but in 1888 all competition was annulled when the East and West India announced amalgamation with their rivals to form the London and India Joint Docks Committee. Coherent organization came eventually in 1903 with the Port of London Authority.

Aird's work on the Thames lasted for twenty years and did not leave him or the firm much time elsewhere. He and Lucas planned a small but important industrial network in Hull—a 66-mile network of railways seawards from Barnsley, mainly for mineral and goods traffic, a work which served rather to inflate the importance of Hull than to pay any large dividends.

It was followed however in 1885 by the West Highland Railway. For the first time Aird returned to his homeland and he made the work a major piece of publicity—a gift of prosperity and advancement to the Highlands, a return perhaps for the systematic depopulation of the preceding century. Significantly, the contract was signed only a year after the 'Crofters War' in Skye and the Hebrides; when the militia had been called on to subdue the rebellious Scots for the first time since Culloden; and while work began at the termini of Craigendoran, near Glasgow, and Fort William, the Government was legislating, a century too late, to provide for the Crofter's Commission.

The original, and for Scotland obviously the best, scheme, had been to build from the Glasgow end, up Loch Lomond to Crainlarich, across Rannoch moor to Ballachulish and Fort William, then up the Great Glen to connect with the Highland railway near Inverness. But since this cut 50 miles off the Highland Company's route to Glasgow, they fought and defeated the Bill in Parliament. The next Bill, passed in 1887, went only to Fort William and another proposed extension to Mallaig, opposite Skye, was defeated by the local landowners who, having efficiently depopulated the land, had no desire to restore it.

The North British Railway Company, who finally built the line, took on Aird at a tender of £2¼ million. The plans had been altered (fortunately for the scenery) to cut out the heavy gradient through Glencoe, and instead the line now ran past Ben Nevis through Corrour and Roy Bridge to Fort William; then down to the Caledonian Canal. Curiously, the route followed exactly the scheme of Telford's for a turnpike road traced sixty years before; now exactly 100 miles; perhaps the finest scenic route in the British Isles and still the best way to see the wild moorland and lochs of Rannoch and the remotest reaches of the Grampians.

The first sod was cut near the Ben Nevis distillery by Lord Abinger and the Mackintosh. The line was built as cheaply as possible, because of the sparse traffic expected, but across the marshes of Rannoch, Aird had to use the now traditional method of laying great bundles of brushwood and logs surmounted by thousands of tons of ash and earth to make the embankment for the track. He took great pleasure in it, spending months at a time on the site and devised a suitable ceremony for its completion. A train containing 400 dignitaries left Glasgow and entered Fort William through a triumphal arch of heather, decorated with flags and medallions, which was opened by Lord Tweeddale, Chairman of the North British, with a golden key while pipers played it in.

He wanted to carry it on, but the Highland Company defeated every attempt to link with Inverness, and in 1895 that idea was bargained in return for the Mallaig route. And at last, stimulated by the work of the Crofter's Commission, the Government was moved to help the Highlands. Since the 41-mile railway to the coast was expected to develop fishing and crofting in Skye and the Hebrides, they guaranteed 3 per cent interest on the capital cost and granted £30,000 to build Mallaig a pier and a breakwater. The benefits which contractors had been able to give India, forty years before, at last returned, too late, to Scotland. Aird was already at work on the Nile and the contract passed to Robert MacAlpine of Glasgow.

Meanwhile by virtue of their great dock experience, the firm was invited to take on the Manchester Ship Canal. Fired by the cutting of the North Sea Canal which made Amsterdam a port, Manchester aspired to take the trade of Liverpool, which in the mid-nineteenth century was very nearly as great as that of London. The Mersey Dock and Harbour Board fought the proposal tooth and nail, ably abetted by the procedural knowledge of Lord Redesdale, Lord Chairman of Committees in the House of Lords who, by a curious coincidence, was also Chairman of their own Board.

At last, after ten years, having got their Bill through the Commons, Manchester felt able to issue to financiers a prospectus for the canal. The estimate for the work had been £6¼ million but Lucas and Aird offered to do it in four years for half a million less. However, the Manchester promoters were out of their depth in high finance and failed to get the response their pride had promised them. Their Bill contained a specific prohibition on the payment of interest during construction which was hardly an inducement to invest in the scheme. Aird offered, so great was his confidence, to pay the interest while they were at work. He had based his original offer on an agreement with Rothschilds, who now refused to put up the cash unless the interest were paid by Manchester itself. Again they promoted a Bill giving them power to do so and, giving evidence before the Lords, Lord James de Rothschild said that the scheme must be sound 'if the greatest contractors in England are prepared to undertake it on such terms'.(a) But when the shares were issued, the promoters were too mean to pay Rothschilds the commission on the whole sum; and in default of suitable publicity, both the London and provincial markets largely rejected them. The issue had to be withdrawn and the promoters were forced to start again.

Such a signal shaking of confidence was bad for Aird also; and when the promoters, having sacked their Chairman, came back with a spirited campaign in which large numbers of citizens of Manchester were induced to buy shares to show local support, he declined. Though this time Rothschilds and Barings made their support conditional on the appointment of a trusted contractor, it was T. A. Walker, the builder of the Severn tunnel, who succeeded. Perhaps the fact that he took not only Aird's price with half a million paid in ordinary shares in the Company, but offered to pay the underwriters their $3\frac{1}{2}$ per cent commission on the total loan, helped. Aird had enough business without buying even so great a work at a cost of £140,000 of his profit before he began.

Walker's contract went badly, until he himself died of Bright's disease in 1889. His successors moved from failure to disaster; the works were successively flooded, frozen over, and set back by storms; and the canal was completed only in 1894, the first major work of Sir John Jackson.

4

THE NILE

CHARLES LUCAS died in 1895. His brother had retired some years before. Aird himself was nearly sixty; and after the failure of Manchester, he was progressively less concerned to build small works in England. Also, he was aware of stiffer competition; of new men like Jackson and Weetman Pearson, building up highly efficient companies against him. There were no new gas-works. Even in dock works, his speciality, Pearson was proving himself at least as able a contestant. Aird had refused to buy the work in Manchester; when the Highland work was finished something was required both magnificent and rewarding. He could not delay his choice for long.

Abroad, the traditional sphere of the great contractor hard up for work, foreign competitors were stealing the market which had been Brassey's by prescriptive right. From 1868 to 1888 the Hungarian, Baron Hirsch, had been building the Balkan Railway to Constantinople, in the service of the Credit Anstalt, only the largest among his works all over the world. In the nineties the Deutsche Bank under Georg von Siemens took over the continuation across Turkey, which in the next decade became the controversial railway to Baghdad. Aird was therefore pleased beyond measure when he was cautiously approached by one of the great financiers of the day with an interesting proposition in Egypt.

The strategic implications of Empire led Britain almost against her will into Egyptian affairs. Bankrupted by their extravagance and a desire to improve the condition of their country by grandiose public works, the Khedives of Egypt fell steadily, in the nineteenth century, into a colossal debt with various European states, Great Britain and France at their head. As revenue less and less sufficed to pay the interest on this pile of loans, bondholders of all nationalities clamoured for action against the failing government. To offset this, Ismail sold his Suez Canal shares at a knock-down price to Disraeli's Government. Later the Caisse de la Dette Publique was set up, a tripartite commission like a receiver to control Egypt's finances in favour of the payment of the debt. However, by 1882, France had become so ambitious on behalf of the bondholders that her old ambition in the area seemed to be leading towards occupation.

The 'government loan business' had ruined Turkey as well as Egypt. As the traditional object of British strategic diplomatic plans in the eastern Mediterranean weakened, Egypt seemed to become an alternative, perhaps a more important way to defend the Middle East and, in particular, India against the old menace of Russia. However, the British occupation of Egypt in 1882 was the result of diplomatic and military confusion between Britain and France rather than of over strategic ambitions. At first the only object of the British administration was to neutralize Egypt, satisfy the bondholders, and retire from an embarrassing position. But it was necessary to make reforms which would produce enough money to pay interest on the loans. These were slowly woven in with assumptions and necessities of defence, and the occupation turned steadily towards an African policy of aggrandisement. There followed the recapture of the Sudan (lost with Gordon in 1885 to the Mahdist forces), the annexation of Uganda, and the Fashoda affair. This ambiguity is the background to the contractor's work on the Nile, as it was a key to the pressure for annexation and division of a large part of Africa.(a)

Unwilling though the administration was at first, it was efficient and became dedicated. But it remained a superstructure which changed neither Egyptian institutions nor its customs and left only two achievements, financial reform and irrigation.

Egypt's greatest need was water. The annual Nile flood had governed for twenty centuries the prosperity and life of the land; and irrigation by the ancient basin system (by which the water was let into the land for forty days and then drained out) was not improved on before the nineteenth century. However Mehemet Ali, Turkish Viceroy of the province of Egypt in the 1820s, gave an impetus to perennial irrigation by storage and canals, giving a constant flow of water all the year, and the Barrage which his engineers built on the Delta held back enough of the flood eventually to irrigate large new areas of Rosetta and Damietta for cotton.

Evelyn Baring, later Lord Cromer, the first Consul-General in 1882, realized that more money was needed immediately to prevent large and permanent famine conditions; and at the same time to repair and keep up the neglected barrage. To these requirements the Caisse de la Dette turned the blank face which could only be achieved by a committee of different nationalities bent on screwing out the last penny for the bondholders. Two projects, one for a Nile dam, and one for using the Wadi Rayan, the great depression west of Cairo, as a reservoir, were summarily dismissed and Cromer had to face bitter opposition even to spend money in preserving the Delta barrage from ruin.

However, the infant Department of Irrigation engendered able minds; William Willcocks, Colin Scott-Moncrieff, and William Garstin among them. Several had been trained in India where great weirs had been built, such as that across the Godavery, two and a half miles long, holding up 12 feet of water. Perhaps in no other country was there such engineering potential; and from these came the plan of the Dam.

Willcocks, having explored the whole reach of the Egyptian Nile to find a suitable spot for it chose Aswan as the best possible site. An International Commission, consisting of Sir Benjamin Baker, already the most eminent engineer in Britain, Monsieur Boulé of France, and Signor Torricelli of Italy, was appointed to consider his plans. The Commission, which was designed to make it easier to persuade the Caisse to provide the money, was laughable in its discords. Boulé wrote of the voyage up-river; 'Baker sits in his chair and scarcely ever opens his mouth. I do all the talking and that fellow Torricelli does nothing but make macaroni'.(b) Nevertheless, they reported in favour of Aswan as a site for the dam. And though the Caisse refused any funds and though the British Government saw no reason to return to Egypt some of the great profits it had drawn from the Suez Canal, the project did not die.

(It was, however, cursed with the archaeological sympathies of Boulé; for Willcocks' original plan was to dam the Nile to a height where the ancient beautiful temple of Philae was submerged for a large part of the year. Boulé gave his assent only on the condition that Philae remained untouched.)

Military necessity and imperial strategy forced a decision. In March,

1896, two thousand miles to the south, Menelek, Emperor of Ethiopia, defeated an Italian Army at Adowa and endangered what the Cabinet and Lord Salisbury saw as the whole defence of the Nile. The decision was at once made to recapture at least a part of Sudan in order to secure the Egyptian border.

It was made clear to Lord Cromer at the same time that the Egyptian Treasury was expected to pay for the cost of the expedition which was to do it; yet, without the permission of the Caisse, Cromer could not touch even the surplus he had painstakingly at last achieved in his budget. And though General Sir Herbert Kitchener, who was given command of the force, was a rigid economist, the expense was bound to be heavy, particularly as his advance was to be helped and maintained by the construction of a railway from Wadi Halfa to Khartoum.

Cromer solved his problems with the simplicity of genius. He would build the Dam, and the profits of Egypt's redeemed agriculture would pay for the war. But how to raise the money first? As Kitchener and his army moved slowly out of Egypt, Cromer wrote discreetly to some of the major financiers of Europe, in particular to Lord Revelstoke, a family connexion (as he himself was a Baring), senior partner in Baring Brothers and a director of the Bank of England. In spite of the Baring crisis of 1890 he was personally irreproachable, and his best advice was to contact the brilliant Ernest Cassel.

Cassel, younger son of a Jewish banking family at Cologne, had come to England in 1870 and had made an astonishing reputation by his skilful reorganization of the largely overblown finance house of Bisschofsheim and Goldschmidt. Working in the inner network of Jewish connexions, he raised himself with his friend Jacob Schiff to a position of great power and wealth by disentangling webs of investment and litigation, beside which McHenry's railway was an open casebook. He moved steadily upwards until at the time of the Baring crisis he was able to give considerable help to the Bank of England itself. In the three years before Cromer's approach he had begun the Central London Underground, and financed large loans to China and Uruguay. In 1896 he became executor to his old friend and mentor, Baron Hirsch—which gave him not only interests in the Middle East, but the entrée to the circle of the Prince of Wales whose close friend he later became.

Cassel moved with great caution. French interests were so heavily involved in Egypt, with their holding in the Suez Canal being only the

Metropolitan Railway, Westminster

Admiralty Pier. Dover Harbour

The shield in East River Tunnel

largest of their investments, that he could not move without concessions to satisfy their control of the Caisse. German commercial
enterprises also were probing every corner of the Middle East and
would have to be considered.

Between the summer of 1896 and the end of 1897 Cassel was able to
manœuvre the competing forces into a private agreement which enabled Cromer, on December 5th, 1897, to address definite proposals to
Lord Salisbury: Egypt, he stated, could not reconquer the Sudan alone;
he was hoping to sell the Sudan Railways contract to the Rothschilds,
but the administration of the Sudan would inevitably be a heavy charge
on his revenue, even when Kitchener had succeeded. There was therefore no choice but to build the dam. 'And now, a financial combination has been found which will not only reduce the annuity payable on
the works to £150,000 but will also permit that the charge be postponed until the completion of the reservoir.' He concluded, 'I hope the
matter will be reconsidered—I have never submitted a proposal with
more confidence'.(c)

The genius of Cassel's proposals was that they could be swallowed
by both the home Government and the Caisse. They involved a
complete intrusion of international finance into Egyptian affairs on a
scale beside which the operations of the Caisse itself were insignifi-
cant.

In essence the Dam was to be built on hire purchase. The Egyptian
Government was to pay the contractor in promissory notes as the
progress of the works made necessary. Cassel's company, the Irrigation Investment Corporation, would then buy the notes from him for
cash and deposit them with the Bank of England. The Bank would
sell them to the general public as trust certificates. From the date of
completion of the dam (in five years, 1903), the Egyptian Government
would pay £78,613 every six months for thirty years; which would
come entirely out of the additional revenue expected as the result of
irrigation. As Cromer wrote, 'the risk that the Government is taking is
practically nil, even for the first year after completion'.(d) He expected
increased revenue of at least £2 million a year—on which Winston
Churchill, then serving with Kitchener, commented, 'they were
offered what was, upon the whole, the best investment in all history'.(e)
Equally, Cassel, who received his payment from the Bank of England
immediately the certificates were sold, expected a handsome profit.

However, this was only part of the scheme. Cassel was then to found the National Bank of Egypt. So far the only bank was the largely French-controlled Ottoman Bank which alone had the right to issue notes. Cassel's bank was not to infringe this privilege, nor to be a Government bank, but the leading merchant and commercial organization in the country. He arranged its subscription through the French Suarès brothers of Cairo. Suarès wished to bring in the German bankers, Bleichroder, and Warschauer, but made the mistake of offering them a premium so high that Cassel immediately vetoed it. In the eventual subscription Cassel held half the shares and complete control, making it, as Cromer said, an Anglo-Egyptian institution.

The third prong of his proposals concerned the Daira Sanieh estates, a quarter of a million of the most fertile acres of Egypt, growing sugar and cotton, which Ismail had illegally acquired from his reluctant subjects. They had formed the security for one of his largest European loans and were administered by an offshoot of the Caisse. The whole, with its sugar factories and buildings was now sold by the Khedive to Cassel, Suarès and two Paris financiers for £6½ million, to be paid in full in October 1909. For this Cassel paid a deposit of half a million which was used at once to pay for Kitchener's railway. In the intervening years Cassel hoped both to run it at a profit and sell it steadily piecemeal to the Egyptians themselves; thereby recouping an enormous sum out of which to make the final payment.

An even longer term part of the plan was the proposal to form the Agricultural Bank of Egypt (founded with a capital of £3 million in 1902). And his triumphs of the same period: the foundation of the State Bank of Morocco and the National Bank of Turkey, cannot be divorced from this original scheme. So great a design was neither purely imperialistic nor capitalist—it had its moral implication in the restoration of land to the common people of Egypt and in the restoring of national prosperity. It was the type of manoeuvre which could only have flourished at a time when diplomatic and financial networks were highly sensitive and carefully interlocked in an international economy. And it depended ultimately on finding a contractor who could build the Dam to the exact schedule which the scheme imposed.

Cassel approached both Aird and Weetman Pearson. Pearson offered to build both Aswan and the Assiut Barrage for £1,875,000, Aird would do Aswan alone for one and a half millions. Perhaps Cassel chose Aird as the more experienced and because he knew him better; perhaps it was that Aird's reputation would help the public sale of the certificates; perhaps because Sir Benjamin Baker, the engineer, preferred to work with him than with the younger, still unknown, Pearson.

Baker and Aird and their subordinate engineers visited Egypt in January 1898 shortly before the Cabinet had made its decision. Their plans were already settled when on January 26th Lord Salisbury wrote giving permission but adding the stringent condition, which Cromer had expected, that the Government would expect all the administrative business of the Sudan to be paid for out of Egyptian revenue.

On February 22nd, Aird signed the contract with Hussein Fakry Pasha, Minister of Public Works, to complete the dam and the Assiut Barrage within five years. Cromer had prudently stayed away from Cairo to prevent any commercial suspicion. He wrote his congratulations privately to Cassel four days later. 'Let me now express to you how pleased I am that this matter at which we have been working for years has been satisfactorily ended. Of the benefit to the country I entertain no manner of doubt'.(*f*)

There followed in the spring, and through to the end of the year, the crisis of the Sudan: Kitchener's victory at Omdurman, the French expedition under Marchand to Fashoda in the extreme south; the diplomatic crisis; the French withdrawal and the reconquest of the entire country. Cromer, faced with the cost of it, had reason to be grateful that work at Aswan was well under way.

The Aswan Dam was perhaps the greatest single work ever planned and carried out by British contractors. The design which Benjamin Baker took from Willcocks and slightly altered was for a reservoir dam with sluices which allowed the first of the flood water, laden with silt and debris, to rush through, and could then hold up and store the clear water behind for the next six months. When the water became needed it was let out to flow downstream to Assiut where the Barrage would hold it up high enough to flow into the canal system of Upper Egypt which was to be irrigated.

Sluices were the only way to let through the immense volume of water and the huge wave of red mud flowing down from Ethiopia. There were to be 140 sluices on the bottom level and 40 above; they had to be extremely large and one of the problems was to design a gate which could be shut or opened against the pressure. A massive steel door, running on two sets of rollers like ball-bearings, which could be raised or lowered at will, was designed by Stoney, a British engineer.

The dam itself, originally planned by Willcocks as five separate sections joining the five islands at Aswan, was changed by the Commission to a single wall 84 feet high, one and a quarter miles long, stronger, more magnificent, and probably more expensive. The specification allowed £1½ million for Aswan, £½ million for Assiut and the canal

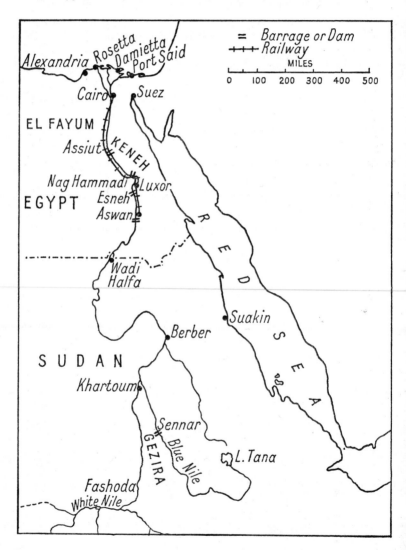

works; but cost had become in, the wake of Cassel, a less important matter.

The engineers and contractors were powerless in the face of the archaeological furore over the temple of Philae. They offered a sop; they would fortify it (it was in fact in danger of falling) so that it would resist the annual flooding for ever. But Boulé of the Commission was adamant; he was in a minority but he found world-wide support. Baker then offered to raise the Temple vertically, (as is now proposed with Abu Simbel), but the Egyptian Government, in haste for the dam, to remove any objections from Cassel's mind, and following several years of good flood, gave way and agreed to the lower height. It was a lamentable decision and they were shortly disillusioned. They had bargained away a reservoir of 2½ cubic kilometres for one of one cubic kilometre. Churchill, who visited the site on his way up to Omdurman was moved to write: 'It is from the irrigation system that Egypt must depend for revenue to develop the Sudan. The State must struggle and the people starve in order that professors may exult and tourists find some space on which to scratch their names'.(g)

As Kitchener's army advanced, Aswan became the terminus of the narrow-gauge railway from Luxor. To the south, into the Sudan, the land was harsh and wild, bluff yellow sandstone cliffs and dark rock mountains blocking off the narrow valley of the river from the desert. Northwards, after the cataract, the Nile flowed quietly past the green palms of Elephantine Island into the changing, softer landscape of Egypt. At the site itself a tongue of hard granite, famous in the ancient Empire for its quarries, pushed out from the western desert, making a ridge which the river had never worn away and over which it poured making the First Cataract. On the ridge, and out of the warm, pink-coloured stone, the dam was to be built,

In May 1898 Aird, his agent, and the government engineer, Maurice Fitzmaurice, examined the site. Aird was frankly disturbed as he watched the vast and turbulent river and the surrounding empty desert. 'It would be hard', wrote Fitzmaurice, 'to imagine a more desolate and uninviting spot. The five main channels forming a torrential cataract as they fell over the granite crest into the lower reach gave the impression that five years was none too long'.(h) By the autumn the Government had bought the land, workmen from Lower Egypt were imported, and a small township of 15,000 men with a hospital, shops and churches, and water supply had grown up.

Everything had to come up either by railway, delayed by the heavy military traffic for Kitchener, or by river in barges; all food from Cairo and Alexandria and the vast plant and quantity of material which Aird sent out from England. Wisely, he decided to be over-mechanized in case his labour supply failed or his schedule was delayed. All the cement and coal had to be shipped out but the granite came from the Aswan Hills, quarried two miles away and dressed by skilled Italian masons.

The construction plan involved a time schedule projected five years forward to coincide with the yearly flood. The channels between the islands were to be dammed successively by *sudds*, a double rampart of stones, earth, and sandbags, leaving a gap between which could be pumped out and excavated to receive the foundations. The dam would then be built to a height which could resist the flood and the works moved on to the next channel. Because it was the first time a dam so large had been built, Aird and Fitzmaurice went about it with the greatest care.

The first three channels were closed by the summer of 1899, several of the walls having been swept away by the force of the current, until Aird was forced to lash loaded railway trucks together to hold the *sudd* down. Immediately they were pumped dry the work began, and a three-track railway was laid across to carry in the materials. Excavation on the river bed at once turned out trickier than anyone had imagined; much of the granite was rotten and Aird had sometimes to dig 20 feet lower than he had bargained for; his men blasting the way down and trimming the surface by hand. So great was Fitzmaurice's persistence that he had the surface brushed and cleaned with rags to inspect it for cracks or fissures which might later undermine the wall.

The flood of 1899 was extremely low, and work could be continued much earlier than Aird had expected. He took a chance and decided to build the foundations in all these three channels and the wide central one as well. The whole volume of the Nile was poured into the narrow western passage.

He very nearly failed; finding more and more rotten granite in the centre, until he was left with only three months to build the whole masonry high enough against the flood. He was using almost exclusively Egyptian workmen, superb labourers of Luxor, for the excavation and he now paid them bonuses, put them on day and night shift by electric arc lamps, brought in more machinery and more men, until between

May and July the dam was built to a height of 79 feet across the four channels. In a temperature of 160°F in the sun this could not go on, even for his demanding authority. He stopped night work when his exhausted men could go no longer, cut the *sudds* and continued to build slowly until the flood struck the wall and poured steadily over the top in August.

Anxiously, he waited for it to lessen. The excavation had already been five times as much as he had expected and he was scarcely in a position to face the cost if the wall broke anywhere. When the river fell the dam stood unchanged; and the flood again proved to be one of the lowest on record, allowing the remaining channel to be closed in February. While this was dug out the wall continued to rise; until by the flood of 1901, it stretched in an unbroken line from one bank to the other.

Meanwhile the lock for ships to pass upstream was cut in the western end, well beyond the range of the sluices. Four locks were made in the channel, the largest lifting ships up 50 feet. Philae was underpinned and preserved; and from England, built by Ransomes & Rapier, came the 200 sluice gates, their rollers, the lock gates and the hydraulic machinery. The entire dam, surmounted with its dressed granite top was finished in June 1902, a whole year before the Duke of Connaught, Queen Victoria's youngest son, was scheduled to open it.

This year's crop was Aird's bonus for his gamble on the low flood. His costs, due to the deeper excavation, were half a million more than the estimate and they were soon to be repaid. The superb inauguration followed; the Khedive Abbas came in his royal barge, the Duke and Duchess of Connaught in their yacht, Hussein Fahkry Pasha, Lord and Lady Cromer, Willcocks, Garstin, Cassel, Baker, and Aird. Among the crowd of guests was Churchill, fresh from the Boer War. In the flowery oratory of the speeches, only Cassel's name was not mentioned; his instinctive hatred of publicity kept him in the background. Baker said the dam was the end of the old taunt that all British works in Egypt had only been to maintain the creations of the French; and Cromer, with a pride which permitted the aphorism, claimed that 'it justified Western methods to Eastern eyes'. The Khedive took the silver key, turned it, and the electrically operated sluices rose; the magnificent jets of water sprang out to fill the million acres already fertile with the cotton crop.

At Assiut, success was equally swift; though again Aird was

presented with a gamble. The design of the Barrage was quite different: a 12-foot wall built of local limestone, raised on an apron of masonry lying on the sand and mud of the river bed, made the weir high enough to send the water into the wide Ibrahmieh Canal for the whole district of the Fayoum and Upper Egypt. In normal times the flow would be controlled by sluices and in flood the river would flow freely through them. The river bed was shifting and treacherous but by the summer of 1902 the masonry was finished and the sluices ready to be fitted. Then in yet another low flood the Nile refused to enter the Canal and the whole crops of Upper Egypt were threatened with disaster.

The barrage had never been intended to regulate the flood and there was a clear risk that the massive force of the river might undermine the foundations and destroy it completely. Against the failing of the crops Aird had to balance the loss of a million pounds and three years here and at Aswan. The engineers could do no more than advise. He had to make his own decision. On August 15th the gates were lowered. Slowly the Ibrahmieh Canal filled. The swirling river tore up the bed below the apron behind the barrage and the whole contractor's force was centred on filling these holes with stones or anything which could be dropped in from barges lashed against the current, almost under the waterfall itself. After weeks of struggle the river fell; the crops were saved and no permanent damage was done.

Aird had achieved a great name in Egypt. He considered building a railway across the desert from Suakin to Berber to connect the Nile with the Red Sea but the scheme was defeated by the hundreds of miles of uncharted land. He and Baker were able to overcome the only danger produced at Aswan, when the ceaseless hammering cataract of water from the sluices threatened to wear away the foundations as the jets tore out lumps of granite from the riverbed and battered the face with them. He defeated it by an apron so thick that the water slid harmlessly down it.

But before this was even finished, the Egyptian Government was regretting its weakness over Philae. Its appetite grew with eating; more land must be irrigated and more water must be stored. Perhaps also they reckoned that the archaeologists would not be able again to raise so favourable a cloud of opinion as the first time. Meanwhile foreign capital, chiefly British, was surging into the country in the wake of a series of large budget profits created by the dam's prosperity.

The Egyptian capitalists themselves, many of whom had made fortunes out of buying Cassel's Daira Estates and hoped to multiply them by irrigation, now looked to the dam for hydro-electric power and new industry. After 1905 the heightening grew from a hope to a political and economic necessity.

The next stage began, effectively, again with Lord Cromer. His Annual Report of 1907 set out the imperative need for more water and suggested solutions: among which were several new reservoirs, but none of the suggested places seemed so good as Aswan itself. Not only Egyptian opinion was behind the demand. Willcocks was a born publicist as well as an imperialist and he flooded the market with schemes which ranged from the recreation of the ancient Lake Moeris to the cutting of the Sudd in the south of the Sudan. The cash side of this he solved simply: 'the strong men who understood the construction of the Aswan Dam will not long stand wavering and undecided'.(*i*) Perhaps most important for the future, Cromer's report contained that made by Garstin three years earlier—the first comprehensive scheme for utilization of the whole of the Nile.

Willcocks was correct; the strong men were ready. Cassel's interests ramified into every part of the Egyptian economy. To his earlier plans he had now added the Mortgage Company of Egypt, founded in 1908, and the Société du Wadi Kom Obo;[1] but he was no longer needed in the same way. So great was Egypt's revival that the heightening could be done directly from its own funds. Moreover, Cassel was at his peak, pursuing in Berlin a British share in the Baghdad Railway, and at home closer and closer the friend and trusted financial adviser of the King. He was also becoming worried by the political climate of Europe; seeing the clamorous rise of German ambitions which only seven years later he was, almost single-handed, to try to pacify.

Aird, however, was ready; at seventy, active and quite untroubled by the complexity of the task. There was clearly no other choice of contractor and any doubts as to his capabilities were silenced by his prior claim, having built the dam in the first place.

Benjamin Baker however took two careful years to decide whether it was an engineering possibility and only then produced the design which answered all the most searching questions of a slightly hostile

[1] Which bought 800 square miles of land below Aswan and irrigated it by pumps direct from the river, below the Dam.

Commission; because Philae, although now officially condemned, could still raise trouble; and Aird himself had several threatening letters while he was at work to submerge it. Perhaps more important was that Professors Atcherley and Karl Pearson, two of the leading theoreticians of the day, said that the heightening was impossible.

The most difficult problem was that created by the climate; between the 150° Fahrenheit of the hottest day and 40° of the coldest night, the contraction and expansion on the length of one and a quarter miles was considerable. If this were restricted by an extra wall, moving perhaps in a different way, enormous strains might develop. The new masonry could not be given the same properties as the old which had taken five years to settle down.

Baker's answer, probably the supreme decision of his career, was to keep the two separate; wait till the new wall was ready and then bind it to the old, making a single unit. Iron rods would hold it with a six-inch-wide gap which would be filled with broken stones; later, liquid cement grout would be injected to fill all the gaps.

Aird undertook the work with the scrupulous care and attention it needed. This time he was not working against the clock, and the contract took five years, not being finished in his lifetime. He did however begin it and his firm carried it out. The constant danger was that the muddy Nile water would get into the gap and vitiate the entire project, because unless the seal was made absolute, the work could never be regarded as safe. Slowly the new wall was laid against the downstream face, like a blanket; the original crest was removed, and 26 feet more built. And on New Year's Day, 1910, as if to warn of the dangers latent in the river's power, the Menufieh Head Regulator, which had formed part of the Delta Barrage for nearly seventy years, was totally destroyed.

The disaster called out almost the last flicker of Aird's energy. At low Nile the damage was not serious, but, if the flood came before it was repaired, the entry to half the Delta, the most cultivated and fertile area of Egypt, would be open to the red, muddy torrent. This gave Aird exactly seven months. Without bothering about a contract, he ordered 5,000 men from Aswan to the Regulator under Murdoch Macdonald, a Scots engineer who had been on Aird's staff and was now Director-General of Reservoirs. While they excavated new foundations, Ransomes made a rush job of twenty-seven steel gates and shipped them to Alexandria. A new channel was cut and Macdonald spared nobody in the work, earning himself the title of 'The Man of Granite' (a reputation which lasted through his long work on the Nile till he finally came out of retirement to unravel the affairs of the last of the great individual contractors in 1930).

On December 23rd, 1912, the Aswan Dam was again inaugurated. The village of Aswan, four miles below the dam on the river bank, was now a town. The original dam had mellowed; and within the next few years provided the most telling memorial to Sir Benjamin Baker; for the join could scarcely be seen. Even now, though, its great stature was only a third of the volume of the great pyramid of Cheops.

This, though the most important, was not quite Aird's last work on the Nile. From 1906 to 1909 he built a barrage at Esneh between Aswan and Assiut. Like the latter, it was a simple weir with sluice gates; on a rather smaller scale. Under Macdonald's general control it was finished eighteen months ahead of schedule and brought basin irrigation, sugar, and cotton to the whole of the province of Keneh; another link in the chain begun at Aswan. As the great dam loosed water in the dry season Esneh and Assiut held it up to flow into the canals.

Irrigation and financial reform, borne of the partnership of Cromer, Baker, Cassel, and Aird, put Egypt on her feet and freed her largely from the grip of the Caisse. But it did not change the old and corrupt social structure. By drawing all authority into his own hands, Cromer had begun gravely to weaken the power of the Royal House; against it, and him, rose the clique of new rich, bound by no ties to the mass of the population, and a generation of politicians more corrupt than the old. Meanwhile, the Fashoda crisis led to the reconquest of the Nile as far as the Great Lakes and Uganda; and instead of Egypt being given back her sovereignty, the course of world events before 1914 made it strategically imperative for Great Britain to hold on. Perhaps the only lasting and satisfactory result lay with the Irrigation Department which, having won its first battle, grew to control exclusively and impartially for Sudan and Egypt alike the whole 3,000-mile course of the Nile. This more than anything, perhaps alone, 'justified Western methods to Eastern eyes'.

5

EDWARDIAN END

Lᴛʜᴏᴜɢʜ encountering serious opposition at home from
Pearson, whose firm was growing rapidly, the older contractor
was able to keep his position. Pearson won the contract for
Dover Harbour in 1897 against Aird's tender; the first convincing proof
that his long supremacy in dock works was over. However, Pearson
committed himself to nine years' work there and Aird took another
contract to build for Bristol the docks which would make it a modern
and competitive port.

At the end of the nineteenth century, the city of Bristol began to
build docks whose development culminated in the Royal Edward
Dock at Avonmouth. The pattern followed that to which Aird was
used; a 250-acre site was bought for industrial development, and on it
from 1902 to 1908 he built a 30-acre dock of immense size. The main
basin contained next to the entrance dock a graving dock, another
lock into the old docks, and two short arms which could later be dug
to make a work like a second but more practicable Tilbury. Four
million cubic yards of earth were excavated, almost entirely by
machinery; the firm of Ruston and Proctor having produced a more
efficient steam digger. The only difficult part was the entrance;
because the plans provided for two piers, over 1,000 yards long, which
had to be sited on the rock below the shifting, treacherous, Severn
mud. To get through it, Aird cast monoliths in concrete on the sea
front as Pearson did at Dover, but his were far larger, measuring at
the base 30 feet by 25 and, when lowered, as they sank through to the
rock, were built up to a height of 60 feet.

Around the dock spread warehouses, sheds and railways; development at which Aird was practised. The King himself opened it in

July 1908, with the contractor and the engineers. And by 1910, the traffic which ten years earlier had been 300,000 tons a year, had risen to over 2 million.

This was almost the last public function which John Aird attended. He had never spared himself at home or in the violent heat of Egypt, even in his seventies, and some months before the inauguration had a stroke which left him partly paralysed. He retired almost entirely from the firm except for the decision on Menufieh, leaving it to his two sons, Malcolm and Charles, and his son-in-law.

They were unfortunate enough to make a disastrous contract at the same moment; and since he had never allowed them any control in the firm or given them the insight into his methods, they were heavily handicapped. Perhaps they were disabled by the knowledge that their father never thought them capable of carrying on, and perhaps also by a certain lack of interest in the matter altogether.

Whatever the reasons, the firm had made a contract on information which had been received while Aird was still active, but too concerned with the heightening of the Dam to evaluate it properly. The Tanjong Pagar Dock Company, who controlled the commercial port of Singapore, decided to make the very large improvements necessitated by the size and quantity of ships then trading in Far Eastern waters. They borrowed heavily from the Government of the Federated Malay States, and their engineers in London, Coode Son & Matthews, invited tenders, on information supplied from digging trial pits in the bay itself. The Airds' tender was worked out on the Singapore engineers' information, since they did not actually visit the site themselves. It was just under a million pounds. The chief work was the new Lagoon Dock of 24 acres with about one mile of quay wall, with a minimum depth of 30 feet inside. There was also a big wharf reconstruction and the building of the Keppel Graving Dock.

Aird himself distrusted the specification. If he had not been too old and ill, he might have gone out to look for himself. As it was, he warned his sons that the sand in which the foundations were to be sunk might be shifting; but the crippling effects of his stroke were at their worst and he was disregarded. The contract was signed in February 1908: it was too good and too important to miss, particularly in the face of the sort of competition which was becoming evident from new firms like Sir John Jackson, and Topham Jones and Railton.

Work began satisfactorily and by the end of 1908 the tidal area of the dock was closed and pumped out. Sir John Anderson, Chairman of the Tanjong Pagar Dock Co. noticed that 'the plant and appliances provided by the contractors are most complete and leave nothing to be desired'.(a) A year later, half the south wall of the dock was fully built and the rest under construction; the entrance had been begun and a blockyard was turning out the now almost standard concrete cubes for the foundations of the east and west walls.

Then in 1910 'progress was much delayed by questions which arose between the contractors and the Board in connexion with the walls at the east and west end. Towards the end of this year work was almost entirely suspended'.(b)

Quite simply, the building of the dock walls became impossible under the conditions of the contract. The designs of the engineers had been wholly inadequate and their information from the trial pits misleading. The contractors had to dig through mud of variable depth to reach the rock which was then blasted out to receive the foundations. On the south wall the depth of mud was 40 feet, which was dealt with by the usual timber trench method which had been agreed in the contract. On the other walls, however, the mud increased to 60 feet, at which depth the pressure made it impossible to dig the trench as the mud pushed in steadily from underneath.

The Aird brothers asked for a revision and were refused. At the beginning of 1911, they stopped work altogether. The Dock Board at once confiscated all their plant and machinery and continued to build the dock themselves for three months, until they gave the contract to Topham Jones & Railton. The new contractors specified a new and more costly method, that of sinking monoliths, and finished it in June 1913.

The Airds, meanwhile, having been paid less than half a million and lost their whole plant, took the case to court. There followed one of the longest civil trials in the history of English litigation. The best counsel of the day were briefed, Upjohn and Lyndon Macassey for the Airds, Sir Robert Finlay and others for the company. For twenty-nine days, between October and December 1912, at a cost of about £7 a minute, they argued out the complexities of engineering science.

There was no doubt that the Singapore engineers' information had been wildly inaccurate, or that it was impossible to continue the walls by the timber trench method. The Airds, however, to recoup some of their losses, claimed that this was a clear case of deliberate fraud, and sued for damages for misrepresentation and seizure of their property.

Giving judgement, Mr. Justice Parker allowed that the contractors were entitled to rely on the information supplied from the trial pits. But though he found confusion and inaccuracy he could see no specific intention to defraud; the claim fell, the Airds settled out of court for about £300,000 compensation, and the Tanjong Pagar Company kept the plant and materials. This virtually finished the Airds as contractors. Their total losses still amounted to over a million pounds. Conscious perhaps that they should have investigated the site themselves, the brothers liquidated the firm. They were rich enough; their father, having spent widely all his life, still left a considerable fortune.

Sir John Aird lived long enough to see the failure at Singapore but not its expensive conclusion. When he could no longer walk he retired to Wilton Park, and his butler would push him through the gardens in a bath chair, occasionally stopping to take from the back of the machine his medicine, a bottle of champagne on a bed of ice. There were no regrets; he had lived exceedingly well; his name, in Egypt at least, was such a symbol of magnificence that when his daughter was travelling there after the First World War, she had to alter her name to Berkeley, to avoid being charged double as an Aird. Never having aspired to society or looked for warmth from his family, he missed neither. He was spared the collapse of Cassel, who having lost his beloved daughter, was ostracized by society for his attempt to make peace with Germany, by a bitter and outrageous campaign during the war; 'a dejected and pathetic figure, a sermon if you like, on the vanity of great wealth', as a contemporary wrote; and he escaped the collapse of the world within which he had worked, dying peacefully at Wilton, January 6th, 1911.

THREE

Weetman Pearson, Lord Cowdray

IN MARCH 1912, the directors of the most powerful offshoot of the House of Rockefeller, Standard Oil of New Jersey, gave a dinner at the University Club in New York. John D. Rockefeller Junior, and W. C. Teagle, the Vice-President, presided at a function with an object rare in the history of the great American Trust—to apologize to a competitor.

Weetman Pearson, first Lord Cowdray, had built up in Mexico, in the teeth of incredible difficulties and a cut-throat war with one of Standard Oil's subsidiaries, an immense oil enterprise and consolidated it under the title of Mexican Eagle. When Pearson began to drive his competitor into bankruptcy, the Standard Oil directors realized it was time to change horses, and with their customary politeness to an able opponent went about it in some style. A stranger company of Greeks bearing gifts would have been hard to devise.

Their opening move was a straightforward offer to buy out the successful Mexican Eagle. They discussed it amicably and finally both agreed to drop it. Standard thought the price too high; and Pearson felt the Mexican situation was too unstable and revolutionary for a take over on such a scale. They liked and respected each other, and parted friends; and remained at peace through the next ten years of revolution, disaster, and war. The Rockefeller seal of approval had been set.

Perhaps no other man, who at first knew nothing of the oil business, has ever gambled so much as Pearson—who, from a position as the foremost contractor in the world, entered the strange obsessive search for oil, the temptation of 'black gold', the long, nightmare, often despairing search for productive wells and the bitter competition for possession and distribution; who fulfilled the test of Kipling's 'If' and placed his whole fortune on the test, and pursued his object with cold determination and perseverance to success.

He never admitted to a gamble; would never admit that he was not in control of his fate; and perhaps the extreme moral courage which he showed in the fifteen years when oil was his life was due in part to the need to justify an adventure so uncharacteristic of his calm and Olympian mind.

1

A YORKSHIRE DYNASTY

THE PEARSON FIRM was part of Bradford, having built much of the town in the 1860s. George Pearson, contractor, held flamboyant sway in the not uncivilized group of industrialists whose large houses in the suburbs were monuments to the second generation of prosperity. His father, Samuel Pearson, by intense hard work building in Huddersfield in the forties, by driving himself and his men with blunt toughness, had turned an ordinary talent into a fortune of £20,000. He was no Brassey, but at heart a countryman, living in a farmhouse and cultivating the fields which his works were beginning to invade.

George Pearson had no ties with the land to hold him back. With a charm and poise which he exploited, a clever tongue and a good tailor, a handsome face, a talent for women, and enough wit to disguise the gaps in his business ability, he rose in Yorkshire society, where the sons of the pioneers did not always follow in their rude fathers' footsteps. His undoubted energy and speculative insight were valuable—the firm worked for Brassey on the Lancashire and Yorkshire Railway but George Pearson was too shrewd to tie himself solely to railway development when the boom was starting to fade and, as further contracts came in, the family moved to Bradford, setting up in considerable style; more indeed than the state of the firm warranted.

George Pearson married Sarah Weetman Dickinson; and Weetman Pearson was born to them in 1856. His parents' marriage was not happy; the boy grew up in the ambiguous atmosphere of a house dominated by his mother's strength of will and a life outside ruled erratically by his father; whose bold front like an over-ambitious façade carried a faint hint of bankruptcy. They lived a comfortable provincial existence, but his mother fed him with greater ambitions, seeing in his quiet determination the virtues her husband lacked, and arming him unconsciously against the vices which at times nearly drove her to the social suicide of running away.

Before these tensions became explicit with his maturity, Weetman Pearson led the sheltered life which was, curiously, judged a fit preparation for following his father in the hazardous business of a contractor. From private school to boarding school at Harrogate there was no question that he was a contractor by birth. If proof was needed, his chief promise was in mathematics; and the rest was also fitting; perseverance, deep thought, and a slow, steady ability to overcome obstacles, surprising in a boy. He visited London briefly and then, at the age of sixteen, went straight into the firm, learning to survey. Having seen him schooled and apprenticed, his father judged him a man, leaving him in charge of a small steelworks when he went to Paris and giving him a waterworks contract to manage. In 1874 Weetman was put in full charge of the firm's brickyard.

His father's trust was justified; Weetman showed a meticulous care, quite foreign to George Pearson's ways, noting in his diary the jobs for the next day, schooling himself against error and waste of time, learning with a thoroughness which came close to pedantry. These business habits coloured his personal life; keeping an account book for his father's pocket money was a model exercise for a young man, but, perhaps seeing him too assiduous, George Pearson sent him in 1875 on a tour of the United States to look for business openings, particularly in the market for bricks and glazed tiles, in which the firm supplied most of Yorkshire.

This American tour opened his eyes to the world as the first glimpse of London had not done. Genuinely on his own, he followed habit carefully, heading his diary with a meticulous inventory of his clothes. Yet slowly the routine of careful observation took on a more human note. From Brooklyn to Montreal, Niagara to Chicago, he visited brickyards and unashamedly drank in the heady vigour of a commercially buoyant society. Chicago, he called, four years after the great fire, 'the wonder of the world'. Then to St. Louis and the long river journey down the Mississippi, lonely after Northern hospitality and finding the Southern women aloof and unapproachable; to New Orleans and back by Atlanta to Washington.

This tour had great importance in his life. In the same way as

Brassey (whose memory was still vivid and whose life, written by Sir Arthur Helps, had recently appeared), his ideas were stirred by the American genius. 'I returned', he said, years later, 'with an intense admiration for Americans. I marvelled at their progress during a short hundred years as a nation . . . some of their methods were instructive and their energy and ambition infectious.' In 1878, as a reward for his success in learning the business he went abroad again through Europe on a latter-day Grand Tour to Rome, the Holy Land, the Greek Islands, Smyrna, and the Golden Horn. It brought out another side of his character: without being sublime or poetic, he contrived to appreciate in a sensible way, commenting, of Jerusalem, 'it is considered the correct thing, to weep, on first beholding the sacred city, but we refrained'. And at Constantinople he shrewdly noticed that the new iron bridge, built by an English firm, was unfinished for lack of funds: 'It has not been touched for one or two years and quite four-fifths of the work is done. It is simply another proof that while the present Empire lasts nothing can be done to develop the country. The bulk of revenue . . . goes into the private pockets of the pashas . . . we came across a Turkish contractor for stores to the Government who said he knew the pashas well . . . he generally made a profit of 100%.' (a) There would be little for him to learn when he came to deal with countries where corruption was endemic and heads of state looked to foreign capital as a relief from their personal as well as public embarrassments.

He was already a junior partner, and when he was twenty-one his father gave him charge of the main drainage of Southport, a difficult and wearing job, one of the hardest of his life. The works lay in sand and shifting subsoil, yet he rarely turned to his father and the obstacles taught him not least how to get his men to work well in unpleasant conditions. Although brought up exclusively among those of his own background, the years in the brickyard had given him the assurance with his men, which, above all, he admired in the life of Brassey; who now and always was one of the guiding influences in his life.

When he came back from Palestine old Samuel Pearson had retired and he took a half-share in the business. His life changed—so far he had been dependent, now he began to make himself and the firm into something more stable and important than the family had yet known. For it was inefficient by the standards which he was beginning to appreciate, and, more seriously, its bank account was far more heavily overdrawn than its prospects could warrant. George Pearson's easy optimism masked the fact that he had failed to build up reserves; and if a crash like 1866 came again and the bank called for more security Pearsons would go bankrupt.

This instability was a hard thing to change. It was still inconceivable that the family should turn itself into a limited company and off load the responsibility on the public; and it is perhaps harder to revive a declining firm than found a new one. The conflict with his father which had been a tacit opposition to the faults of a facile and too successful provincial mind became open as he set himself to lay his own foundations with painstaking labour. With his particularly close sympathy for his mother he fought her difficult battles and, partly for her sake, he stayed at home to gain control of the firm.

The Southport contract, and the £1 million drainage scheme he carried out at Ipswich helped; one more major contract at King's Lynn left him in a position where he stood beyond his father's authority. And by winning this independence he came to a decision which can hardly have presented itself before: whether to redeem the business in Yorkshire or move to London and enter the sphere of national and possibly international undertakings.

The building of King's Lynn docks where, cutting costs to the bone, he drove a traction engine and worked beside his own navvies, taught Pearson, who had lacked all specialist engineering training, the rudiments of harbour work, dredging, underwater foundations, and sea walls, the rip and scouring of the tides and currents and the use of concrete and of machinery on a far larger scale than before. For years after, he was to work, filling in the whole day, taking no holidays, but never again so hard physically and mentally. When it was done, he was already mature and, as if to complete a phase of his life, he married.

The parallels with Brassey's life are striking—none more than in the wife he chose. Annie, daughter of Sir John Cass, one of the big mill-owners of the district, came from a better family as Bradford reckoned it, but this was not a matter of prestige. Pearson needed a foil, a strong managing influence, like his mother's, which would run his house and family while he devoted himself to his work. He loved the attractive girl round whom flocked the young men of Bradford and her acceptance gave him the confidence which he had lacked with women. He was shy, yet persevering, always respectful, and she saw in him the source of a power which could be moulded into greatness and a life beyond Yorkshire and the society they both found constricting. What was perhaps a blend of convenience and affection grew with time into a warmth and closeness which all his absences and the driving urgency of his creative life never disturbed; a match of powerful personalities prepared to make allowances and search out each other's strength.

He, she, or both of them, decided to take the firm to London. George Pearson could carry on in Yorkshire, but the real rewards lay in the South, in having headquarters in the financial capital of the world; it might take years to restore the firm at home. The Deptford Sewer, built for the Metropolitan Board of Works, was their test case—when it was completed, the office was moved to Delahay Street, and the family to Camden Hill.

Success did not come, as it did to Brassey, within months, on the march of the great railway age. Pearson worked incessantly for five years, catching up on sleep on bank holidays, tidying up the office with his wife after the clerks had gone home. From these days dates the saying which became a Pearson classic: 'We can't deal with that now—leave it for Sunday.' When he took stock, from the new office at the heart of Westminster, the firm was at the top. In 1886, he wrote to the Yorkshire Banking Company, who held the firm's account:

'As you are no doubt aware, the business we are carrying on requires a very large amount of capital. From the position we have gained and now hold as one of the leading firms of contractors in the kingdom, we have occasionally good contracts offered with little or no competition and such contracts we *cannot* decline. What we have to do is to be ready for them . . . but a sudden reduction in an overdraft is rather liable to upset one's calculations'.(b)

A year before, the bank had refused to increase his overdraft from £25,000 to £30,000 without full security; but a succession of major works, Sheffield Main Sewer, Milford Haven Docks, Halifax Docks in Nova Scotia, and the Empress Dock at Southampton, between 1884 and 1888, firmly established the new reputation and wiped out the instability of the old.

As the firm, so the family: Harold was born in 1882, followed by Gertrude, Clive, Geoffrey. It was a time of steady development in Pearson's life. So far experience had been almost savagely practical; now he had to acquire the theoretical mastery, financial understanding, and wide outlook of a major contractor and, as always in his life, he did it slowly with great thoroughness, so that when it was once learned there was never any need to do it again, or again question the basic rules and assumptions from which he worked.

2

ANATOMY OF A CONTRACTOR

T HE CONTRACTOR'S world changed very rapidly in the last quarter of the nineteenth century. In a way, the risks had become much less: before the old Queen died Aird had entered Egypt on terms which would have been impossible in Brassey's day. Risks in building were being constantly diminished by engineering developments, the use of concrete and machinery and the almost new science of structural statics; risks in financing the undertaking were cut as the more violent fluctuations of the world economy ran down. The Baring Crisis of 1890 showed that the interlocked web of international finance was stable and that Governments and institutions could not be allowed to go bankrupt in the old ruinous way.[1] To a large extent the system of tendering for a contract which was slowly becoming universal, safeguarded the contractor against the grosser liabilities and the Governments against the more flagrant fraud; but with this went a narrowing of margins. Accuracy of specification, the growth of qualified supervision, meant that the contractor had to be more skilful and less speculative, more business minded and less imperious. And correspondingly as Governments, even of the poorest countries, became financially acceptable and were able to borrow freely in London, Paris and, later, New York, the greatest need which the mid-nineteenth-century contractors and credit companies had supplied, that of access to capital, diminished.

Pearson's own finance depended on the bank and on his reserves. The irksome discipline on his overdraft taught him to enter contracts with the greatest care and to supervise with an accuracy Brassey and Aird had never achieved. Not till 1892 did he open a second account, with

[1] Except on the periphery—banking failures in Argentina in 1891 and in Australia in 1893 showed that only the centre had achieved stability.

Williams Deacons Bank, and in that year, when he had contracts worth £5 million, he wrote to them saying that the firm was 'probably the first firm of contractors in regard to the work it has on hand and the third or fourth in wealth'.(a) He had not lost money on any undertaking since 1874. Assets by 1898 were nearly £1 million, excluding goodwill and 'the only firm now of similar standing is John Aird and Sons'. In 1900 when Williams Deacons refused to increase the overdraft by £1 million without extra security he opened a third account with the Capital and Counties Bank. 'As our business grows we must increase our banking facilities. The firm pays all accounts monthly, has no acceptances and no creditors except bankers.'(b) As if to emphasize the lesson he added that half the share capital was not paid up—he and his family owned the rest and would bear the shock if the firm got into difficulties, rather than shelter behind the Companies Act.[1]

This supremacy was achieved in ten years by the simplest principles. Pearson had the great gift of financial acumen; figures moved into place for him and he cut through the most complex subtleties with a cool analytical logic which Henri Deterding, head of Shell, later found as his first point of contact. He could reduce an entire railway to terms of wheelbarrows and shovels, yet keep balanced the interests of a firm with undertakings in five continents. Each contract was kept separate for accounting as well as administration and was made to pay for itself after the initial outlay, so that, Pearson having raised the money for the first stage, regular payments kept the working smooth. In the pre-1914 world economy Pearson could count, far more than his predecessors, on continuity of payments, and only once, in the Hudson Tunnel, had to abandon his works for lack of money. The history of Pearson finance and of the 'Pearson luck' is one of steady accumulation with remarkably few losses.

The same simplicity underlay the mechanics of tendering for contracts: a shrewd, speculative approach, tempered by slow deliberation. Pearson never rushed a tender, even when pressed for time, and it was an education to his sons to watch him prepare it; to divide 100 miles of railway into feet of earth moved, brickwork needed, hours of

---

[1] His election to Parliament precluded the firm from tendering for Government work so he turned it into a Limited Company before the Dover Harbour contract in 1897. Edward Pearson his brother, B. C. Cass his brother-in-law, and Edward Moir, the firm's engineer, were the other directors.

manpower, even if it was to be done by machinery; then view the whole five-year sweep of the work. He took nothing for granted and when he ceased personally to make every tender of the firm, often did his own independent estimates.

Of the three main types of tender, which had now become standardized, 'measure and value' (in which a full specification of all items was laid down for the contractor to fill in his costs separately and *in toto*); 'cost plus profit' (where he built it without a fixed estimate and took a percentage profit on the whole sum spent); and 'lump sum and contractor's risk' (a fixed sum which included his profit and made no allowances for delay, errors, disasters, or bankruptcies); he greatly preferred the first, judging the second to destroy any urge for economy, and the third too unsafe if it could be avoided. The knowledge needed in a measure and value tender[1] could only be the product of years' experience and hard work; to it, Pearson added his foresight—when the first rumours of a big work were heard he would be on the site, deciding whether to go for it or not: and if he did, he kept his invariable rule never to look over his shoulders at other competitors but set down his own price, which cost him some dubious contracts but never lost him money.

Brassey's philosophy was no longer needed to demonstrate the importance of a fair wage for his men. Pearson extended his own liberal economics to belief in a share in the firm's profit for his employees, paying it by way of bonus, either for work done well or exceptional success. In public he talked of Labour and the Ideal Wage; and his fairmindedness filtered down through the firm. Throughout a period of militant trade unionism, of syndicalism, war, and the General Strike, the firm had only one stoppage: a demarcation dispute in 1903, when Pearson paid 10/- a week and £1 for married men to all strikers who had been with him more than three years. However remote the apex of the pyramid (and he employed nearly 45,000 men[2]) he never lost the touch of the Yorkshire brickyard, the tractor at King's Lynn. It was remembered that he had nearly died of the 'bends' among his workmen in the Hudson Tunnel.

Whether in England or abroad, with migratory Irish or static Columbian Indians, he looked after his labour well. Schools, hospitals,

[1] The Dover Harbour specification list was 146 pages long.

[2] The difference in size between his firm and Brassey's, being entirely the result of increased mechanization.

missions followed the camps; sanitation, pure water and his doctors helped to check yellow fever on the Mexican Gulf. He safeguarded them with pensions and the Aged Navvies' Fund; for piecework and the bonus and long employment were rare enough in pre-1914 England, confined to the most advanced industries, and Pearsons were, by contrast to most contractors, model employers. In return he demanded whole-hearted support. He once asked an old navvy 'how long have you been with us?' 'Twenty years.' 'You look very hale and fit.' Pointing to the engineer in charge, the man said, 'I have need to be, if I have to work with him!'

He was a pioneer of business efficiency without being a dogmatic theorist, constantly on the search for the principles which today underlie time and motion study. He never scrupled to take a man out of a job he did unsatisfactorily, but preferred to find one he did well rather than sack him. He hated waste with an obsession which led him to scrutinize all the firm's accounts minutely and almost pedantically; for the overheads of contracting are enormous, so much that he preferred to run a contract at a temporary loss rather than see it stop and founder on reconstruction. Where time mattered to such an extent he was decisive, abandoning his normally slow process of judgement; at Dover Harbour when the price of stone rose steeply, suspecting a cartel against him, he bought a quarry, mined it, and continued to work it at a profit for years. His mind never broke off short but pursued the matter logically; when building the dry dock at Halifax in 1886 he chartered a ship to take his equipment across cheaply, then took other freight to make up the cargo and finally found himself in open competition with the Cunard Company on the Northern route. Characteristically, he met them unabashed: 'You must buy me out or I buy you!'

However careful his supervision, he had to have good agents whom he trusted with full responsibility. The telegraph and telephone could not absolve him from their mistakes and they needed to be trained far more intensively than when he had begun, in new techniques, in the use of concrete and new machinery, in the understanding of structural statics, and to come to terms with the phenomenon of organized labour. So he chose men more qualified than he was himself, reserving the right to pick another man's brains, to criticize and to be right. By nature he was generous in his attitudes and like Brassey he rarely interfered but watched for trouble so closely that he could sometimes forestall the man on the spot. He stuck by fools if they tried and, with too much humanity to be a martinet, preferred to pay to get rid of a bad bargain; but idleness was inexcusable. Later he chose the motto, 'Do it with thy might', and unlike many, it summed up his outlook.

He missed little and scolded little. During the building of the Tehuantepec Railway one of the locomotives was derailed and lay on its side near the line just before Pearson was due to inspect the section. The men sweated to clear up the mess and eventually one bright fore-man suggested they build a hut round it. When Pearson came he only looked and said—'that hut is too close to the rail', but they knew that *he* knew. And he gave praise always where it was due, seeing the qualities in others which he strove to perfect in himself. When he was negotiating for this railway he spent three hours outlining the contract to a Mexican lawyer. 'That man never reacted—never a word or nod, so I decided I had wasted three hours, except that I had clarified it in my own mind. To my surprise and admiration I got a contract in draft which was word perfect.'

He knew where to go for help. Others built his steel bridges because he did not fully understand their construction. The engineering firm, Lobnitz of Renfrew, built him the largest dredgers in the world and massive shields for his underwater tunnels. He chose men like Edward Moir, Edward Body, Clarendon Hyde, and Frederick Hopkinson, ruled them, trusted them and when he knew they could do it, gave them a free hand. Hopkinson built the docks at Hull for him in 1906—'Quite different from what I should. I can't budge him, but he'll make a job of it'—and he did.

A round, short little man, Pearson had least of any the physical attributes usually given to empire builders, yet without exertion he commanded, possessing great dignity and a strikingly dominant personality, having no need of the high heels and raucous voice of the dictator. Partly this lay in his personal mannerisms, in his careful, methodical movement, his habit of distilling the answer to a question so that it arrived clear, unhesitant, and by its late unexpectedness, frighten-ingly final. Even at dinner it might be a full minute before he replied and if the question was trivial, out of no impoliteness, but his own sense of proportion, he gave no reply at all. Like Bonar Law, because of intense concentration, banal chitchat did not exist, and this detach-ment gave him a measured aloofness which demanded respect or laughter—and laughter was impossible, the stare of his pale blue eyes being too disconcertingly straightforward.

If his public face was imperial, his private smile was delightful, dissolving his dignity for his family at least. His close friends were few but all his acquaintances were friendly for he was almost impossible to quarrel with. Perhaps the front was a response to his size yet it revealed no inner tension; he was the rarest of small men, who never felt ill at ease merely by having to look up to talk to others taller than himself. His habits, like his mind, were meticulous, his writing neat, his figures carefully drawn—and having worked once in a boiler suit he never lost a preoccupation with scrubbed hands and nails.

Everything but his family was peripheral to the creative impulse which showed itself in the firm and its works. This was his life: if he had been a socialite, an intellectual, a pursuer of hobbies, there would never have been time for the sheer quantity of building with which he filled fifty years. It was not merely application to a duty—literally nothing interested him more. Some arts appealed, though he never really appreciated music and spent the hours at Covent Garden which his wife loved, abstractedly working out the answers to the next day's problems. When, later, he could afford it, he bought fine pictures in fashionable taste, but the real collecting was his wife's; whose passionate appreciation of craftsmanship and beauty, and an unsurpassed gift for spending large quantities of money well, led her to the great, though then much disregarded, *maîtres ébénistes* of the age of Louis XV and XVI. His collection of Mexican antiquities reflected his real interests, derived from his work.

So, more than most men, there were office hours, cut off from family life but always encroaching. He might be worried; go down to the Whitehall office on a Sunday with his secretary and sit quietly at his desk—then in a burst of activity move all the furniture round and suddenly, the problem solved, turn with a light smile—'let's go home'.

Annie Pearson had accepted this when she married him, judging with unusual maturity for a girl of nineteen his blend of persevering courage and calculated caution. He had seemed secure but not dull in his self-possession, reaching great heights with his simple creative ambition. She was the perfect foil, complementing, buttressing, helping where she could. She furnished the offices: and in Mexico in the early days boiled the water and found clean food with a calm efficiency without which he might have died of tropical disease.

Lord Cowdray

President Porfirio Diaz

Lord Cowdray, President and Madam Diaz on the Tehuantepec Railway

Cowdray House in Mexico City

When he was away for half their married life she never complained; not though every house they ever lived in was a prey to workmen and builders satisfying his craving for domestic improvement and expansion of estates.

As prosperity came, they moved again, in London to Airlie Gardens and when his baronetcy came, to Sussex, where he bought from Sir Edgar Whitehead (inventor of the torpedo) the house and estate of Paddockhurst, 6,000 acres stretching past Three Bridges. They spent all their time out of London here and loved it more than any of the later estates. Draining and altering, laying out new gardens, levelling and supplying water, engrossed him for seven years. Everything was done in the best and most modern way possible; bathrooms in profusion, polished granite stairs, marble window-sills and bronze grilles over the radiators.

Lady Pearson ran the house thereafter; paid, engaged, and dismissed servants, organized parties, dinners, wines, menus, so that when her husband came home he needed never to be worried by domestic troubles. As they moved up in society, she made the way, ambitious and persevering, and if she had just been snubbed by the cold refusal to dine of a country peer, he at least was not told of it. If he was snubbed she was fury incarnate—they were little-minded, who could so ignore him.

He knew, perhaps, more than she suspected of her heart-burnings and single-mindedness; years later when even the war and women's suffrage had not educated public opinion to the liberal feminist standards always held by the Pearson family, he said in public, 'to have one by you who shares with head and heart the successes and the failures, who gives due encouragement but has the courage to administer the home truth, who is never afraid of responsibility, prepared to start life afresh should need arise, such a partner is beyond praise or price'.

He was a true radical though politically undemonstrative beside his wife. Only the weight of the whole family deterred Annie Pearson from chaining herself to Whitehall railings with the Suffragettes. Pearson preferred to work out his beliefs within his own sphere. He found the House of Commons dull beyond bearing and endured it only for the sake of a sense of duty to his beliefs and because he held a difficult seat which a successor could easily have lost. His beliefs: that the rich should be taxed to provide services for the whole community;

in a co-operative process of wealth-making; in old age pensions, industrial insurance, and sickness benefit, were too advanced in the 1890s for him to bother with an active part in Parliamentary life, even if there had been time for it. For the rest, he was a Liberal Imperialist, a friend of Lord Rosebery, and a sound supporter of the Party funds.

His true philosophy lay in his work. 'Undoubtedly he enjoyed the making of money and the sense of success which went with it, but his main pleasure was in the making of things, in seeing great undertakings grow under his hands and in devising expedients to meet emergencies and overcome difficulties'. This utter absorption produced the 'Pearson touch', the Pearson luck; the elaborate planning which led by careful timing to the style and artistry of performance. With it went immense zest; the enthusiasm of a powerful energy properly channelled and directed. He had no illusions about luck, and being sometimes very lucky, was the arch enemy of the sanguine: 'Dame Fortune', he wrote to his daughter, 'is very elusive; the only way is to sketch a fortune which you think you can realize and then go for it baldheaded. The headaches, fears, ceaseless work, the endless disappointments, all become incidents that have to be overcome and forgotten. Then Fortune, wooed in such manner, usually succumbs'. To his son Clive he put it even more simply:

'Qualities required in my business:

1. Practical knowledge which the foreman possesses.
2. Commercial knowledge which a trader must have to succeed.
3. Technical imagination, analytical knowledge, and the qualities that prevent improbabilities being undertaken or considered.
4. Ability to get round you trusted and competent men of all grades . . . . Do not hesitate for one second to be in opposition to your colleagues or in overriding their decisions. *No business can be a permanent success unless its head is an autocrat*—of course the more disguised by the silken glove the better'.

3

FIRST FLUSH

IN THE years when Aird was building the new London Docks, the years of the Manchester and Rotterdam Ship Canals, the Suez Canal, and the supremacy of steam-powered iron hulled ships, nearly every harbour and port in the world became out of date. By the late 1880s Pearson was in a position to look for work overseas and was caught in the boom which lifted the firm in five years to a position which he described as 'now probably the first firm of contractors in the country as regards work'—second in its assets only to John Aird & Sons. For twenty years after, dock work remained half of Pearson's business; following and taking over from Aird, he became the world's expert and the King's Lynn experience served him well.

The first was a fine dock for Milford Haven, built in 1885 when the town was hoping to capture part of the American trade by cutting off the Channel passage and 300 miles of the Atlantic, but it never materialized and the town was left with its pride and £120,000 worth of docks which could accommodate twelve liners. The Halifax, Nova Scotia, Dock followed, a work which could take any ship afloat, cost quarter of a million, and entailed three years of excavation in solid rock.

The Empress Dock, begun at the same time at Southampton, did take the American trade. Over five years, Pearson erected a thirty acre deep-water dock with 800 feet of wharves. It was a hard contract: a vast excavation of mud and clay by hand, before the rails could be laid for steam navvies to do the rest, was followed by disaster when part of the north wall collapsed and finally, when nearly finished, the east wall fractured and had to be completely rebuilt. Pearson lost his bounty for time and £30,000. However, he was learning the dock business properly, and in 1889 was able to do the tricky underwater opening up of Alexandria Harbour, made necessary by the size of ships using the Suez Canal. A sunken reef made the entrance dangerous in stormy weather and Pearson had to drive a channel through it 30 feet deep and half a mile in length. No ordinary dredgers could do it and he made his first contract with the firm of Lobnitz who built one at Renfrew capable of taking out 400 tons of rock an hour. Pearson was never deterred by the fact that machinery did not exist—if the job was possible it could be made: and this one worked satisfactorily for three years until the work was done.

His early railway work was not so satisfactory in profit or experience. By 1885 so many of the main lines of the world had been built that those which remained necessary were either of peculiar difficulty, or financially unsatisfactory. The Avila–Salamanca Railway, which cut 65 miles off the Madrid–Lisbon line was both. New Castile, the wild lonely land of the Spanish plateau, vast plains and small white villages under a flaming sun, storms and snow in winter, was as inhospitable to foreign contractors as in Brassey's time. The work was unpleasant, with heavy tunnelling through rocky hills and deep cutting; peasant labour was hard to find and recalcitrant to employ, particularly in harvest time, and finally the promoters quarrelled with the Government and work had to stop. Pearson who had spent weeks with his wife in the torrid monotonous land suffering the privations of inexperienced travellers became acutely aware of the advantages of being his own actor-manager in such a contract, and insisted on it, when, ten years later, he made the Tehuantepec Railway under far worse conditions.

But the toughest work and one which went far to make his reputation was the tunnel under the Hudson River in New York. In the same way as his dock work it helped to make him a world expert; only here the techniques were almost unexplored and the dangers great; in the face of the new hazard of publicity.

Even in the railway boom after the Civil War the warring railroad companies had not brought a line directly to Manhattan Island from the west and the city relied entirely on the Hudson Ferry for transport to the New Jersey shore. Fog, snow, and ice played havoc with time-tables in winter, and since the cost of any bridge a mile long and high enough for ocean traffic was prohibitive, the Hudson had to be crossed by a tunnel.

The company which tried this between 1874 and 1880 never had enough capital and the American engineer-contractor, De Witt

Haskins, was plagued by failures until a fall of silt and water buried twenty of his men at the moment when money ran out; and the works he had finished, nearly a third of the distance, were abandoned.

Four years later an English syndicate with an eye to a large profit took the project up, and Sir Benjamin Baker, then at the height of his career, much as Locke gave Brassey his first break in France, offered the contract to Pearson, whose ability and cool head had impressed him. He transferred Ernest Moir, an expert on compressed air work from his own staff to help him, and Pearson began work at the end of 1889.

There were then two great obstacles to underwater tunnelling, in finally solving which Pearson and Moir were truly pioneers. Where the tunnel had to pass through soft material, silt or sand, the only way to keep it from caving in was to build an air-tight bulkhead farther back in the completed tunnel and raise the pressure forward to a height which would keep the silt from running in. The test was to keep the pressure constant; if it fell too low the silt poured in, if it rose too high it blew out into the river above and the roof might fall. It was this which had defeated the American attempt.

Secondly, working under the pressure of perhaps two and a half times normal proved highly dangerous to the men, for as they came back through the bulkhead decompression chamber into the ordinary atmosphere they might be seized by the 'bends', or caisson disease, as the change in pressure gave them agonizing cramp and frequently left them partially paralysed.

To try and solve the first of these problems Pearson used the 'shield', a device originally invented by Brunel the elder, and improved by Sir William Greathead. Pearson's model, built in Scotland, was a great advance on both; a circular steel drum with a cutting edge, moved forward like a punch by hydraulic jacks at the rear. In front it was divided into nine compartments, so that two men could work in each, with doors in the central wall behind them. Protected by the projecting rim they could dig away at the face without fear of the roof collapsing, and pass the earth back through the door.

Pearson hoped to assemble this when the parts had been shipped over, in front of the last bulkhead of Haskin's tunnel, but over the years the silt had flowed back so much that a large space had to be excavated. Silt flowed in continuously until a great funnel opened up and the river itself began to flow in. Divers found the spot and sealed it with a sheet of heavy canvas weighed down by tons of clay, and the pressure of water bound it so tight that the men actually mined through it as the shield moved forward.

Already with this first difficulty it was clear that Pearson was on trial, for the first time, by the New York Press, more than faintly hostile to a British enterprise so near at home. Now it was no more than exploitation of his setbacks for the evening headlines; later, in the East River, there was to be active campaigning against his success.

The size of the work established an epic scale—in erecting the shield alone, nearly a mile of pipes led back from the forge where the plates were riveted in a temperature well over 110° F. The death and sickness rate was alarmingly high, once touching 25 per cent and in December 1890 after a visit to the shield face, Pearson himself was caught by the 'bends'. He had been warned not to go down but refused to hang back when his men were exposed. For days he was paralysed from the waist down but his wife was in New York and nursed him with great care through the excruciating pains as his legs came back to life. When he could walk she took him south to Mexico to the sun and convalescence but he was never again allowed in the high-pressure region.

Moir's great work was to overcome this danger with the medical airlock, which he had used on the caissons in the building of the Forth Bridge. The patient was put back, above ground, into a room at the same high pressure, in which he nearly always recovered; then over some hours the pressure was lowered to normal. The results were completely successful, cutting the death rate to $1\frac{1}{2}$ per cent a year. While Pearson himself recovered, with the worst difficulties over, the shield was pushing forward 10 feet a day through the soft material with hardly any need for the men to cut in front.

Then, in 1890, when 2,000 feet had been added to Haskin's work, the Baring Crisis broke and the syndicate ran out of credit. At his own cost, Pearson kept the pressure up for three months, but was at last forced to shut down and box up the shield at the face. The apparent failure, however, did nothing to harm his reputation, for all the hard work was done; and when it was finally taken up again, the shield was found intact and ready to move forward at once. But long before this, he carved out his best fame in Mexico.

Early in 1889, Porfirio Diaz, President of Mexico, had sent to him in London to ask if he would be interested in the draining of Mexico

City. Pearson was preparing the Hudson plans and was unwilling, but when Diaz sent a personal friend to meet him in New York, he was more receptive. During the autumn he was preparing plans for the projected Aswan Dam, and missed the last boat home before Christmas. Rather than spend it in a frozen New York, the Pearsons took the Montezuma Express to Mexico City—she bent on finding the sun and he with more than a thought for business.

Ten years of Diaz' dictatorship seemed to have imposed stability in Mexico. In outside help he saw the only salvation, the only means to restore order in the state shattered by civil war and the infinite rivalries and disparate ambitions of the 'many Mexicos' he ruled. So the mestizo President, half Indian and half Spaniard, sold out to foreign capitalists with his eyes open to the risks he ran. The budget was balanced, historically a unique feat, and in 1889 a remarkable era of peace seemed to have begun.

Britain which, until the 1867 Revolution, had had far the largest share of Mexican trade and capital investment, only re-established good relations after long and tentative approaches in 1884, and by then, during Diaz's early years, the United States had encroached heavily on her pre-eminence. The power of 'Northern Imperialism' was becoming too marked for Diaz's liking; American interests controlled all the Northern railways and he feared that the whole economy would soon be subject. Out of this grew the Anglo-Mexican settlement, and this was one of the reasons why he sent for the English contractor.

Pearson went with no preconceived ideas about Latin American Republics such as the Bondholders Committee in London expressed to the Foreign Office, to get payment on the defaulted loans of 1820. He allowed himself ten days to make a satisfactory deal. The Commission set up by Diaz to negotiate a contract was not accustomed to being hurried, so he made them meet morning and evening and forced the agreement through until only three points remained—to be referred to the President himself.

Pearson met Diaz, and stated his demands, which were translated. Diaz asked him if he would decline the contract if he was not met and Pearson said yes, expecting a blank refusal. Instead, Diaz gave way 'provided you assure me on your honour that you will always treat the Government as we have done you'. On this basis, which slowly grew with mutual trust towards genuine admiration, the contract was signed.

Pearson had not forgotten the Turkish contractors of his youth. Normal Latin American practice was for the Government to impose impossible conditions. The contractor would then sue to have them modified, distributing bribes liberally until everyone was satisfied. 'It was an unknown thing for a contractor to stipulate for a fair clear contract and to abide rigidly by its terms', but this approach gained Pearson the friendship of the President on which his position in Mexico came to rest. Secure in the trust of the ruling clique, fulfilling his obligations with meticulous honesty, he was able to dominate the Mexican economy for a generation.

The Pearsons returned to England 'a little tired'; he had not yet decided how to tackle his problem. It had, indeed, defied engineers for three hundred years.

When the Aztecs built Mexico City on a site given them by their gods it was a town on the water, raised on piles above streets which were canals. The great plain which held the lake, 7,000 feet above sea level, is wholly ringed with mountains and there is no natural drainage. Gradually the main lake seeped away, leaving five smaller ones, and when the conquering Spaniards settled they chose to enlarge the Aztec city discovering too late that once or twice in every decade storms and melting snow caused the highest of the lakes to overflow and for months turn the new paved streets back into canals.

From 1607 to his death forty years later an engineer, Martinez, tried to drain the lake, first by a tunnel and when that fell in, by making a cut straight through the mountain wall. Cursed with a pusillanimous Administration he always lacked money and when he died the work was still hardly begun. For a century more, colonial governors pursued it until, with the sacrifice of fortunes and quarter of a million lives of slave Indian labour, they had opened up a chasm 14 miles long, sometimes 400 feet deep, along which today the train looks like a lizard on the side of a house. This fantastic labour, which could be set beside the Pyramids, did drain off the great floods, but not the lower lakes. Some danger remained; and as the town grew into a modern city without any form of drainage, cholera and typhus became endemic. Plans to relieve this were made before Juarez's Revolution, but the Treasury had no credit in Europe. Finally, Diaz raised a loan of £2½ million in London and after some difficulty with other contractors passed the job to Pearson.

The Mexican engineer's plan was simple and not to be improved on.

A canal, bearing the whole sewage and taking off the flood water, would lead from the city through the lower, Lake Texcoco to the north of the plain where a new tunnel was to be dug by other contractors. But it was 30 miles and Martinez's slave labour no longer existed. Pearson spent three months looking for other means because he disliked the idea of dredging—the cost of building and shipping the machines would cut his profit to the bone. Eventually he accepted the inevitable and set out to beat the time limit. In Mexico work was started with hand labour, a purely holding operation; in London he met Lobnitz and the two men locked themselves in his office for three successive days until they had a sketch of the machines he needed. He ordered four, more massive than any ever built, which could dredge to a depth of 50 feet, yet floated in a shallow basin dug by hand. As they scooped down, the canal would be made and the earth brought up carried by two giant arms on either side, reinforcing the embankment. This Wellsian contraption could dredge 4,000 cubic yards a day, but had first to be got up to the centre of Mexico. The parts were shipped to Vera Cruz, then an open harbour, subject to the fury of the 'norther' gales, and Pearson, who was back in Mexico City, waited impatiently for the single-track railway to bring them in.

For the floating of the first, *Carmen*, named after Diaz's wife, Pearson gave the inaugural fiesta which the contractor was expected to provide on every possible occasion of celebration. A banquet was laid on for the Cabinet and the local landowning aristocracy. After the toasts and flowing speeches, he told the President bluntly that there would have been two dredgers ready but for the railway delays— (the company, unsure of shipments at Vera Cruz in bad weather, stockpiled cargoes to be able to run a daily service throughout the year). Diaz called the managing director over. The bland official replied, he would inquire. 'Don't inquire—send the material.' A trainload arrived within three days. This was the extent of Pearson's influence; exerted at this stage only to get the job done. His interest was clearly that of the country, but it made for jealousy; one member of the Commission with American connexions was already putting legal obstacles in his way; and Pearson's rule in Mexico was long enough to feel the repercussions.

Once the four dredgers, *Carmen*, *Conchita*, *Annie* and *Lucy* were at work the canal progressed rapidly. Pearson found his bonus system worked excellently. Setting off a race between the four, with monthly prizes, he kept them moving night and day. Walsh and Ryan, his agents, took over when he returned, and for the first time J. B. Body, a trained engineer who had lived some years in the country, came into the Pearson orbit. He spoke fluent Spanish and interpreted for him to the President; and also he had wide investments and useful contacts in the provinces.

Behind the dredgers came a horde of Indians to smooth and trim the banks. They worked well under supervision and perhaps for the first time since the seventeenth century received a fair wage and just treatment. Dispossessed of their traditional lands under the iniquitous land laws, harassed and bullied by the State police, the *rurales*, sold into virtual slavery in the deathly plantations of Quintana Roo, they were more abused than at any time since the Spanish occupation. On some of the great estates slavery still existed openly; and Pearson, finding for the first time their labour good, in return may have nourished the dreams which flamed within twenty years in Zapata's horde of rebels.

There were other, special, difficulties, apart from a built-in jealousy of Pearson's favour. Payment could be made by the Government in notes, bonds, or silver. Paper, under the Diaz régime, was stable, the world price of silver was not. Mexico was the largest producer and the price of 50 pence an ounce in 1884 fell to 33 pence by 1892 and 22 pence in 1898. Careful planning by Clarendon Hyde was needed to avoid loss. At one crisis, Pearson had 50 tons idle in London and was reduced to planning a scheme for cheap silver cutlery for every table in England, when the market opened again and the pile disappeared in a month. There was, also, always the risk of a change of régime—and since he was dependent on an annual vote in Congress he was subject to the hazards of politics as well as the gamble of the exchange.

When it was finished in 1896 other great works had engaged him, but he was securely established in Mexico, bound to the President by friendship and mutual advantage. Relations with members of the ruling class, like the vast landowner Guillermo de Landa, had been cemented by courtesy and hospitality. Above all, he showed to Mexicans of all classes a courtesy and respect which were as unusual as they were greatly rewarded. The President was already on a lonely eminence, never able entirely to trust his cabinet, always afraid of military revolt. He found in the Englishman a like mind, a man who understood the Mexican temperament and never descended to the contemptuous attitude of the American entrepreneurs. Lady Pearson helped enormously. After the first few months of squalid hotels and camps she stood out and they bought a house and were soon living in the style which was expected of the President's friends, entertaining old Mexican society, and becoming associated with the country in a manner which took away much of the taint of 'exploitation'.

4

FLOOD TIDE

A DECADE of enormous activity opened with the 1890s. Working on tunnels, docks and railways, in thirteen years Pearson became indisputably the largest contractor in the world. By 1905 he was employing over 60,000 men. Aird, having concentrated on the Nile, was slowly letting his business run down as he grew too old to manage it; but John Aird & Sons had never been as large as Pearson & Son now became.

J. A. Spender, in his life of Pearson, gives a key to the work of this time. 'Money for its own sake was only a small part of his needs; what he loved was engineering, constructing and prospecting, and in proportion as he succeeded, he felt the greater necessity to break new ground, take large risks, and do what others had failed to do.'(a) Out of no mere bravado, he determined to excel; it was perhaps this energy, when nothing greater remained to do after 1905, which lured him away from the business of contractor into the dangerous field of the oilman.

Londoners had waited years for a road link across the Thames below Tower Bridge. Only the ferry, subject to all the delays of fog, storm, and tides, connected East London with the southern bank, condemning two million people to the hazards of antiquated transport. As on the Hudson River, bridges were impossible owing to the size of ships using the Pool of London and the docks.

Sir Isambard Brunel, father of the more famous I. K. Brunel, had driven the Thames Tunnel from Wapping to Rotherhithe in the years 1825–41. At that time it was a remarkable achievement, but the intractable difficulties of wet gravel, falls, accidents, and the sheer length of time involved, broke the engineer's health, and were not repeated. He had pioneered the shield; though his prototype was made of wood and iron and had to be moved forward in segments, instead of as a whole. Since then there had been the small Tower subway for pedestrians and the train tunnels of the City and South London Railway, driven from the Monument to Stockwell in 1890.

The London County Council now wished for a new tunnel at Blackwall—far larger and far more difficult, for long sections would have to pass through waterlogged gravel instead of the easy London clay, and near the Middlesex shore probably only five feet of headroom could be expected. The tunnel could not be made deeper because of the maximum gradient for horse-drawn vehicles, and the inclined approaches were already as long as they could allow. Two lanes of traffic and a narrow footpath—23 feet in all—made it the largest underwater tunnel then to be built, a mile and a half long, of which the greater part was to be lined with cast iron.

Pearson was seriously advised not to touch it: Brunel's agony was held up as an example; but the problems interested him so much that he did not need his wife's urging. Having gone over the site months before, he was first with his tender in 1890 and won the contract at a price of £871,000.

Men who had worked on the Hudson were again employed: Edward Moir succeeded in improving the design of the shield. Now 27 feet in diameter, the great tube was divided into twelve compartments in front and fitted with hydraulic machinery at the rear. As the shield moved forward, a complete ring of cast-iron segments was fitted in behind, under cover of the rear rim; the jacks were then placed on this and the shield pushed forward again—a movement which also served to clamp the iron ring tightly; and the gap between ring and actual wall of the tunnel left by the shield was filled with quick-setting hydraulic lime, to make a watertight joint. Finally the inside was cemented and lined with glazed tiles, while the men at the front were digging again under shelter of the forward rim.

Since the pressure in the tunnel was three times normal, even higher than in New York, the medical air lock was often needed and Pearson felt that two bulkheads, with two stages of decompression would be safer.

To get the shield in position, since it was a waste of time to wait for the long approaches to be dug, a massive square caisson was sunk on the Kent shore and the shield put together and encased in wood in a dry dock beside it. The shaft was filled with water and the whole mass floated; and as the water was pumped out it sank slowly to the bottom (facing a circular door which was then opened) ready for its 1,000 yard journey under the river. It moved steadily through the Kent clay until it hit a belt of unexpected limestone rock which turned up the bottom rim—as it could clearly not be withdrawn a channel had to be cut ahead until the next shaft, the last before the river bank, was reached—in which harbour the edge was cut out and replaced. It pushed under the river until, a third of the way across, the waterlogged gravel and shingle was reached. Immediately the air pressure bubbled out. From now on until the Middlesex shaft was reached the work was made most difficult; if the pressure was high enough to keep the gravel out at the top, it was 13 pounds too low to keep it out at the bottom, and if it was right for the bottom, it blew out above.

Moir fitted the compartments with baffle plates or shutters in front, which were screwed out in front of the shield and allowed the men to work in only one or two compartments at a time, top or bottom; even then the pressure was such that the engineers could sometimes see through the door stones and flints churning up and striking sparks. The doors were ready to be slammed shut at the first signs of danger. In 1895 several men were nearly lost; when the upper shutters were advanced, the pressure of the river forced the roof in and threatened to flood the whole forward compartment, but the men behaved admirably and battened it down within seconds.

They led an eerie life; and Pearson's bonuses were well earned. Under the constant eye of the L.C.C. he showed the greatest concern for the men's health and the sickness rate was low. But it was a hard work—visitors described the strange atmosphere—the cast-iron gloom with a line of naked bulbs running into the narrowing distance, the light glistening on damp running down the walls—the noise of dripping water and the hollow echo of voices, shrill and weird above the hum of machinery.

Progress with these shutters was slow and as the shield neared the Middlesex shore it came to the exceedingly narrow ceiling between the tunnel and river. Barges provided an artificial roof by dumping hundreds of tons of clay, forming a 15-feet bed; but it became essential not to have any more blowouts for fear of pushing this off and swamping the entire tunnel.

Eventually in May 1897, it was finished and the Prince of Wales drove through to inaugurate it. Pearson, who was to have been presented, sent his father up instead, since the titular head of the firm was not likely to have the chance again.

Six years passed before he took up tunnelling again. In April 1903 in New York, on his way home from Mexico, he fell ill from an obscure tropical disease, and filled in the time in bed by preparing a tender for the East River Tunnels. Perhaps it was an answer to the promoters' failure in the Hudson tunnel, and he was so engrossed he was still working on it when he had to have an operation at Paddockhurst later in the year. The tender was completed by Moir, and won easily—no American firm had the necessary experience, though there were several large enough to handle it. However, a British work in Man-hatten itself caused immediate comment; and hostile publicity dogged the work for the succeeding five years.

The terms of the contract gave a handle to this. The Pennsylvanian Railroad Company wanted four train tunnels to connect Long Island to their own Manhattan system. Under United States law it was necessary to form a new firm, S. Pearson & Son Inc., and Pearson shrewdly brought influential Americans into the Board—his friends Lewis Clark, George Wickershaw (later Attorney-General) and H. W. Taft, brother of the future President. The two last were able lawyers, who were already helping him in Mexican affairs.

The £3½ million price, however, was on a cost-plus percentage basis, and it was this which was attacked. If the cost turned out less than estimated, Pearson was to take half the profit, but if it was more, he should pay half the loss only up to a limit of $1 million. Without giving credit for the lowness of his tender, or the real size of the penalty, the papers seized on this as preferential.

Pearson had quite enough problems as it was. The four tunnels had to be driven under the East River through rock, of a particularly treacherous mixture of decomposed schist, which had to be blasted, and quicksand which lay in a layer as far as the river bed itself—above which was not the quiet Thames but 60 feet of turbulent Atlantic. For the first time the work had to be done in advance of the shield, by boring and blasting a hole through which it could move. Apart from the constant risk of the quicksand penetrating the fissures on the rock, this raised the curious danger of fire. Wooden scaffolding was needed, and when candles were used to find holes where air pressure escaped, the rush of air sometimes set fire to it, burning far behind the ironwork. making it red-hot and raising the temperature intolerably.

More machinery was assembled than on any such contract before. There were not only the four tunnels, but a 2,000-foot extension across Long Island so that the Company's trains could run straight into downtown Manhattan. Pearson decided to use eight shields and work from each side towards the middle. Enormous extra plant was needed and a power house on each shore, but he felt it justified by the equally great saving in time. The shields were lowered through caissons, as at Blackwall, and set off, at about 15 feet a week for the middle.

By 1906 they had reached the most difficult region, and blowouts through the quicksand were common, stirring up the turgid waters of the river and followed by claims for disturbance from the masters of tugs and ferries. The Press announced Pearson's failure, worked up his difficulties and even accused him of walling up dead miners in the tunnel to avoid the strictures of an inquest. He was eventually forced to dump another clay blanket and renew it continuously as the shields advanced. Perhaps the worst moment came when one shield sank nine inches in disturbed mud and had to be closed down and then lifted when the river bed had settled down.

Worried, and still not completely well, Pearson pursued it doggedly, in the intervals of Mexican business, taking no notice of publicity. When the Railroad Company wanted to freeze the quicksand by a new process he did a rapid, wholly empirical, calculation and said it would not work. They tried it, wasted time and money, and proved him right (though, since then, the process has been perfected); and as they did, so New Yorkers at last came to appreciate his endurance and courage. The tunnels were finished in March 1908—before any other part of the Company's undertaking. Pearson was vastly relieved; the use of his eight shields had earned a time bonus, but it had been a more speculative thing than the other works of the time. It gave him a name in America, and, perhaps more important for the future, gave him powerful American friends.

The railway work which he undertook in England between 1890 and 1905 was sporadic, and, though it was considerable in size, he never took as much personal interest in this: his was the largest firm and therefore he tendered automatically for any large works. None of them was as stimulating as the great pioneer undertakings.

Tampico Refinery

Dredger on Mexican canal

Oil rig

Petrero gusher

Tanker *San Fraterno*

The Lancashire, Derby and East Coast line, a £1 million contract, one of the very last main lines to overcome the opposition of the older vested interests, was built from Warrington on the Manchester Ship Canal to Lincoln and the coast, to tap the Derbyshire coalfields. Apart from the Bolsover tunnel, one and a half miles long, where unstable coal seams and flooding was met, the work was finished quickly and profitably.

A larger undertaking for the G.W.R. was not so successful. The opening of the Severn Tunnel had brought new traffic in from South Wales, and to connect this with their own system at Wootton Bassett, the Great Western planned a short cut. In 33 miles, Pearson had four large viaducts, over a hundred bridges, and three tunnels through the Cotswolds, the worst of which was of two and a half miles at Acton Turville, which turned out far harder than the estimates. Cutting through marble had been expected but not the steady flow of an underground river which forced him to build an arched subway under the track to drain it off. Pearson loathed litigation, feeling as Brassey did, that it lost more money than was gained, but having done the work well he expected some concessions for his extra £312,000 as well as the lost half a million pounds' profit on five years' work.

The G.W.R. denied liability. Sir Benjamin Baker, arbitrating, said that the contract had been for a 'dry' tunnel and awarded Pearson half the loss: but he reserved part, subject to points of law, and on these the Company won in the Lords after protracted and expensive proceedings. Pearson lost heavily and was angry, not so much for his loss as their intransigeance, and he never worked for the Great Western again.

Other works went more smoothly—including the Great Northern and City Railway in London. In this £2½ million project he was promoter as well as contractor, planning to link the Great Northern main line, north of King's Cross, to the Great Eastern at Old Street in the City. Though it was designed for main line trains, it was to be underground, from Finsbury Park, through Highbury, under City Road to Finsbury itself and Old Street. Pearson floated the company to build it and invested considerably. There were no technical difficulties except the unusual size of tunnel, much wider than the Underground; he used six big shields and even larger ones for the stations, through which the others passed on their journey in the clay. Pearson ran it for three years and sold it at a profit to the Metropolitan Company, but it never achieved the main line connexion he had hoped for.

From the days of the Spanish Conquest engineers and empire-builders had dreamed of cutting through either the Isthmus of Panama or of Tehuantepec in South Mexico. Though a longer distance, Tehuantepec was not impossible, and was surveyed as early as 1771. The 700 feet of the Sierra Madre forbade a ship canal, but was no great barrier to a railway, and schemes to connect the two oceans here were among the earliest railway projects. Like the Honduras and Costa Rica lines, they left a trail of bankruptcy and wasted loans behind.

The building of the Panama Railway delayed it for years, and the Emperor Maximilian used the concession to raise money. Captain Eads, engineer of the Mississippi delta works, proposed the spectacular but improbable scheme of a broad-gauge railway to convey ships bodily from coast to coast. Some track was actually built in the 1870's before President Grant and Jay Gould began to speculate in its shares. Delfin Sanchez built 66 miles on the Pacific slope with a German loan, and finally Diaz gave the contract to the American, Edward McMurdo.[1] McMurdo died in 1892 and an Anglo-U.S. syndicate under Chandos Stanhope, with another £2½ million loan succeeded in finishing the 190 miles.

The line was hopeless. Mexican governments had invested $19 million in a railway which scarcely worked, which could not bear the weight of traffic for which it had been designed and which alone could make it pay, and which connected two open harbours incapable of dealing with whatever ships might wish to unload. The condition of the track, the daily derailments, the rotting sleepers, crumbling masonry, wooden bridges, and hairpin bends were bad enough; but the port of Coatzacoalos had only two fathoms' clearance at the bar, and Salina Cruz on the Pacific was an open anchorage subject to violent storms and dangerous even in fine weather.

Pearson's work in Mexico, after the drainage of the capital, had proved his worth to the country. He had built, between 1895 and 1900 a fine modern harbour for Vera Cruz. The chief Atlantic port of Mexico, as he had found with cargoes before, was open to the 'Northers', winds of hurricane force which blew for several months a

---

[1] When Sanchez gave up, having wasted and embezzled the loan, he personally got $170,000 'for the profit he would have made if the railway had been built'!

year. Working with the Goliath cranes and laying the huge concrete blocks which were to be used later at Dover, Pearson built three large breakwaters, a half-mile jetty for ocean liners, wharves and warehouses, and enclosed and dredged a harbour of 540 acres, complete with the most modern machinery. Land was reclaimed for a railway station and powerhouse, and the sprawling, fever ridden town turned, with pure water and electricity, into a monument of twentieth-century progress. 'The town's water', as it was aptly said, 'had lost its capacity to ascend to the upper floors of houses.' Its restoration abolished yellow fever and helped to cut malaria: and since the work was unique—for no other contractor had left *useful* memorials—Pearson became the symbol of European progress working with the Mexican national conscience.

He and Body, now his most trusted aide in Mexico, surveyed the Tehuantepec Railway when it became obvious even to the Ministry that it was unworkable. It was a matter of some prestige—such enormous sums of public money should have created a truly Mexican monument and Diaz was considerably embarrassed. Pearson offered to help. His relations with the President were now very close. In 1897 Diaz was writing such letters as—

'My dear good friend,

[Talking of his son's marriage] Carmelita and I thank you greatly, as well as the inestimable Lady Pearson for the open and splendid hospitality with which you honoured our son. With grateful and affectionate good wishes; remember me always as your dear friend'.(b)

Together they planned to capture for Mexico at least part of the American transcontinental railways' trade: a large part of the shipping cargoes round Cape Horn: and to outclass the costly freightage of the inefficient American-run Panama Railway. Diaz saw the new line as a counter-weight to U.S. control in the North; he and Pearson hoped to maintain the trade even when, or if, the Panama Canal was cut. And Americans were aware of the danger. In 1896 the Panama Railway Chief Engineer told a U.S. Senate Committee:

'I do not think that you can over-appreciate the importance of protecting our future trade by checking the development of Tehuantepec . . . it is much easier to hold a line of traffic than to get it away from somebody else after they have got it once. . . . The route is much shorter than Panama to all Pacific ports of the U.S.A., Orient or Australasia. . . . And New York and Hongkong are 1,351 miles nearer'.(c) He believed it would be competitive even when the Canal was opened. And perhaps most important to Diaz the dictator, success here would prove that Mexicans themselves could build and run a first-class industrial enterprise.

Pearson, convinced he could rebuild the line, took great trouble in settling his terms. His vision of the complete undertaking with its fine ports and regular services was a concept worthy of Brassey and the Grand Trunk, but the expense to Mexico would be colossal; and since it would have to be found on a yearly budget, reinforced by foreign loans, there was greater security in the closest association with the Government. Pearson would take no contractor's profit; but he would be an equal partner and take his share of the profits of operation, $37\frac{1}{2}$ per cent for five years, slowly falling to 25 per cent after twenty-five.

So in November 1899 the Tehuantepec National Railway Company was formed. Pearson agreed to find half the nominal capital of $5 million and was prepared to subscribe more. He would find the shipping traffic and would run the line for fifty-one years. At any time the Government could buy him out at a percentage of his costs. Losses were to be borne equally, except that if they were greater than $5 million, his liability would cease.

It was a colossal gamble on his judgement, not only as a contractor, but as economist and politician. He called it 'far the most serious business we have ever undertaken'. Disaster was forecast, not only in America[1] but in Europe where financial houses remembered other Latin American railways, and the past history of this one. It was, after all, only thirty years since an American contractor[2] on what was left of a £6 million loan had built, in the rain forest of Honduras, a 60-mile railway which led from nothing to nowhere and had neither rolling stock nor stations. But the promise was glittering; Pearson conceived an enterprise which, like Brassey and Peto's attempt to corner the Danish trade, was monopolistic, yet if successful, would give him the willing and perpetual support of the State.

The first thing was to repair the line, and it was shortly clear that it would have to be entirely rebuilt. For the next eight years Pearson spent part of every year in Mexico, and was constantly on the line in

---

[1] C. P. Huntington, the 'Railway King', in particular among newspaper owners, feared for his transcontinental interests.

[2] Keith Meiggs, son of Henry Meiggs who ruined Peru with his railway ambitions.

his train with its roomy and comfortable 'office on wheels', incessantly
watching and directing, spending weeks at Railway headquarters at
Rincon Antonio: and he now began to be caricatured in the House of
Commons as the 'Member for Mexico'.

He thought the existing line followed the best route: rising gently
from the port of Coatzacoalos to a plateau where it crossed the wide and
turbulent Jaltepec River and continued through wild rocky cañons
and chasms to the village of Rincon Antonio; which became a town,
with marshalling and repair yards, workshops and the houses of the
European staff. At 825 feet the line crossed the Sierra Madre ridge in
two horseshoe curves and dropped steadily to Salina Cruz on the
Pacific.

Reducing gradients, straightening curves, putting steel instead of
wooden trestle bridges, and relaying the 190 miles of track was delayed
by every rainy season which from June to October closed the work
down. Torrential storms hurled sudden floods against the embankments
sweeping away the unfinished work. Malaria and yellow fever
plagued the workmen, and though never so serious as the epidemics
which broke De Lesseps at Panama, the sickness rate was frighteningly
high. At one moment, Pearson had to ask for Foreign Office help in
recruiting replacement labour in Jamaica. Flies, intolerable heat,
earthquakes, humidity and the insects of a tropical jungle made conditions worse than on any other contract he handled. Fresh water, good
housing and food was provided at Rincon Antonio; an American medical
unit was brought in; but on the line there were occasional troubles,
and the fact that he got the best out of peon Indian labour, notoriously
intractable, without serious dispute, is not the least tribute to Pearson
and the management of his agents, Ryan and Body.

Work started in June 1901; an unusually wet season followed and
Pearson wrote about the line almost in despair 'I have never seen such
a mixed lot of rails and fastenings . . . it is not uncommon to find two
classes of bolts with nuts of different sizes in the same joint'.(d) Still,
progress was made; in 1904 a decent passenger service existed and a
year later the railway was in full operation, waiting only on the ports.

Without these the line was nothing—for the local traffic was
negligible. Coatzacoalas was no great problem: the port lay on a
navigable river with deep water at the bar. Following Eads' method at
New Orleans, Pearson built two jetties so that the tide scoured it out
once the bar had been dredged. A mile of wharfage was built, with

warehouses, and the town given proper drainage, pure water and electric light. The magic of Vera Cruz worked again and the new town was called Puerto Mexico to fulfil its national obligations.

Salina Cruz was another matter. The bay lay open and in certain winds it was almost impossible for sailing ships to make it. Very large breakwaters were needed to enclose a harbour and it was in payment for this that the finances and time schedule of the undertaking became strained. In September 1902 a violent storm smashed up the works and blew a Titan crane into the sea; and American papers gleefully reported a loss of half a million dollars. The whole enterprise was held up three years for its completion; until at last, in January 1907, Pearson and his wife entertained 200 guests to a banquet, and a special train ran President Diaz, the Cabinet, and as many dignitaries as could be decently crammed in, from the Atlantic to Salina Cruz, where Diaz commended the 'energy and courage of Sir Weetman Pearson whose name will endure and be held in high honour in Mexico'. . . . and pulled the lever which loaded the first wagon of Hawaiian sugar. Pearson dwelt more soberly on the debt to his staff and the work of the peons, whose stubborn, stoic labour had awakened his deep respect.

Hawaiian sugar was the crown to the delayed success. Since 1902 he had been negotiating with the American-Hawaiian Steamship Company (using the Cape Horn route), the British Leyland-Harrison Line and the Cuban Line. Every visit to New York was spent in the offices of shipping companies where Pearson proved himself a skilful envoy; gave a degree of guarantee as a pledge of his faith in the route, with a veiled threat to form his own shipping line in competition; and when, after the contract was signed, the President of American-Hawaiian asked him where he had got his experience in commerce, replied, with some truth: 'In this office.' The other companies followed suit; and the traffic was ready before the line was open.

Mexico had invested heavily but was to be well repaid in the end. Pearson had refused to fix an estimate for the harbours and as late as 1906 would not accept a ceiling of £6½ million from the Finance Minister José Limantour. He was high-handed, expecting the Minister to see that his interest was identical with that of Mexico. A Dresdner Bank loan tided over the difficulties at Salina Cruz; but the final total of £7½ million for railway and harbours was more than Diaz had bargained for. Americans said that construction cost twice what the line was worth, but it was undeniably built superbly well.

The return on this money justified the outlay for seven rich years. The sugar contract provided nearly half the freight which rose from Pearson's best estimate of 600,000 tons a year in 1904 to over a million tons in 1912. As the bulk of this was international traffic the Revolution made no difference, but the line was killed by the 1914 War. As trade routes were disrupted, the total fell to 136,000 tons and the Company began a steady decline. There had been a reasonable hope, under Pearson management, of competing with the Panama Canal, but it had dissolved long before he was expropriated by the xenophobic Government of Carranza. He was only too happy to see his share bought out, though he had been prepared to carry on and try to restore trade. And his hold, even in revolutionary Mexico, was still so great that the Government paid him the agreed price. It was, they explained 'an end to Pearson tyranny', but 'the Mexican Government could not act with Pearson in the same manner as with the landowners who were enemies of the Revolution, because Pearson was backed by a great Power which had many Dreadnoughts and guns'.(e) The Pearson oil empire which gave some truth to this came after Tehuantepec, but it was a pointer to the future that the railway, from the beginning, ran on oil.

There were, of course, many other works; a 200-mile railway in China built for the Pekin Syndicate; the enlarging of Bermuda Harbour, for which Lobnitz built a dredger capable of crossing the Atlantic under its own steam; the remodelling of part of the Surrey Docks, of Cardiff Harbour, and Port Talbot, to accommodate modern vessels; the conversion of Seaham Harbour into a coal port for Lord Londonderry,[1] but the main occupation after Tehuantepec (of which Pearson said, 'If I had nothing else to do, I should be busy on this alone') was Dover Harbour. Tehuantepec symbolized something to Mexicans: Dover was near to Pearson's heart.

The need for some better anchorage than the Downs was an old one: Sir William Harcourt had been ready in 1886 to allot £2 million of the Navy Estimates for it, but economy shelved the idea. Eleven years later there was not only the need for a harbour safe from the new weapons, the torpedo and submarine, but the distinct chance of an

---

[1] A bad contract. Pearson lost £50,000 in a 'lump-sum' contract, when the main harbour wall was destroyed in a violent storm and had to be rebuilt on a far larger scale. The experience served him well at Dover.

enemy, not facing the traditional ports of the Channel, but the exposed East Coast; and Dover Harbour could no longer be delayed. Goschen, the First Lord of the Admiralty, finally gave the scheme approval. Not only the value of the contract (Pearson won it with a tender of £3½ million) but the fact that it was in the most urgent national interest, and on a scale which demanded visionary planning and the minutest calculation, attracted him.

The Admiralty required the largest artificial harbour in the world. The existing Admiralty Pier was to be extended 600 yards, a new eastern breakwater built 1,100 yards out from the cliffs, and a great isolated south wall nearly a mile long raised between them to create a deep-water harbour of more than 600 acres. Some work had been done already—while the Admiralty had delayed, the Harbour Board, in a bid for Atlantic trade, had commissioned Sir John Jackson to build the Prince of Wales Pier, and this was now fitted into the grand design.

The new harbour bottom was hard chalk, and once excavated and levelled would provide a perfect foundation for the concrete block walls. But the average depth of working was 66 feet at high spring tides; strong currents scoured the bed and Channel weather and gales are notorious: Pearson calculated on no more than 150 days' work a year. His mind was bent chiefly, though, on the most complex time-schedule he had ever attempted; the work on each of the three massive walls must coincide so that the whole finished together nine years ahead. The slightest delay on any work at any time might put off completion by as much as a year—and this meant, not only Pearson's profit, but, after the war scare at Agadir, the safety of the North Sea and the Channel defences.

From Paddockhurst and London, all the time he was in England, Pearson came down to watch progress. In 1898 a gantry was run out from the end of Admiralty Pier to begin the extension. Hundred-foot wooden piles were driven in and joined by steel girders on which two sets of rails were laid to make an immensely strong framework to carry the Goliath cranes and the train which carried the 30-ton concrete blocks to build the wall. Five cranes worked in line, the first excavating the chalk, the second carrying the diving bells in which men levelled the foundations, the third and fourth placing the blocks and the last building the superstructure.

While the steel skeleton ran out into the sea, land was being re-

claimed on the narrow shore beneath the Castle cliffs to build yards to
make the great blocks. Two were made here, one at Rye, and one near
Dover, and were in operation by 1900. Work began shortly after,
from the new foreshore, on the eastern arm which moved quicker
than Pearson had hoped; while the Admiralty Extension rose with
superb precision.

The isolated south breakwater, a narrow island, nearly a hundred
feet from top to bottom, presented greater difficulties. Independent
staging was tried and totally destroyed by storm. Pearson had to wait
until the two arms reached far enough to carry the gantries on. Finally
a continuous railway ran from end to end, and the wall was built,
leaving only gaps for the harbour entrance; a two-mile crescent of
steel and timber against the wintry Channel weather. Storms tested it
severely and one desperate night in 1904, when Pearson happened to be
there, he took charge of the men fighting to save the half-completed
end of Admiralty Pier. In the enormous waves he had to jettison
something to prevent the unfinished blocks from being torn away, and
for years afterwards the section was remembered: 'That's when the
Chief threw the locomotive in to prevent a breach!'

Dover gave him great pleasure by testing his organizing ability to its
limit. As the naval race with Germany inflamed opinions, Dover
became vital to the Grand Fleet, and the new North Sea strategy; for
there was no other defensible harbour between Portsmouth and Scapa
Flow. So the south wall worried him: and time also was loss of money
and, in the public eye, of prestige. When the price of cement was
raised against him, he bought up the Wouldham Cement Works,
enlarged it, and later sold it at a profit. When granite ran short, he
bought a quarry in Cornwall. Many of his worries lay with his employers—he loathed and distrusted red-tape and bureaucrats, would
brook no delay and preferred to settle matters with a telephone call
direct to the top. Equally, he hated trivialities and tiresome pecking at
the Admiralty when his own things went wrong.

'I deprecated the voluminous correspondence as it only led to
friction; for if we had a letter of complaint, we were bound to reply to
it in self-defence. Any small complaints ought to be expressed verbally
and they would be attended to'.(f) Still, it gave him a useful insight
into the workings of Government departments which served him well
when war came and he took over his own Ministry.

Some criticisms were made of the design before it was finished—the western entrance was not easy to make in certain winds; but the harbour was a triumph of skill and methodical organization whose worth was fully proved in action. Perhaps no other contractor could have completed it to the nine-year schedule without a single revision, either of estimate or obligation. After the War it seemed a white elephant of military necessity, its vastness wasted on a few Channel packets and leased to the Harbour Board who had no real use for it, since the Atlantic traffic never came to the inconvenient town and railway. But Pearson's interest survived and he tried to make use of it in his grandiose scheme for the industrialization of Kent in the 1920s.

Not all his Admiralty work ran so smoothly. He built the new Malta harbour between 1901 and 1909 and suffered a heavy loss. Storm damage to breakwaters was a fair risk, but in excavating for the Valletta docks, fissures appeared, and sea water poured in at the rate of 30 million gallons a day. Nothing like this had ever been experienced, even in digging the Severn Tunnel, and when the expensive pumping machinery had at last finished, Pearson was £265,000 out of pocket. The Admiralty refused to pay anything towards it.

He felt bitter and took the case to arbitration, where the Admiralty Director of Works decided against the firm on this, and on the penalties for delay. Faced with more endless litigation, he gave up, less endeared than ever to the view of responsibility held by public bodies.

5

A PLACE IN THE COUNTRY

PEARSON was not a politician in the House of Commons sense; he never sought political power, office, or prestige in the Liberal Party. Fourteen years as Member for Colchester made little difference to his life and he made hardly any impression at Westminster.

Through no fault of his own he entered Parliament in the wake of one of the first major honours scandals. He was persuaded to stand against the Conservative, Captain Naylor-Leyland, at Colchester in the general election of 1892 and had succeeded in cutting a majority of 291 (on the old electorate) to 61.

After the defeat of the Home Rule Bill in 1893 and resignation of Gladstone, the anti-Liberal drift continued in a worrying series of bye-elections. Then, in the spring of 1895 Naylor-Leyland unexpectedly applied for the Chiltern Hundreds and later declared himself a Liberal. The Tory Party organization in Colchester was thrown into confusion and Pearson easily won the resulting bye-election in spite of declaring that his business interests would prevent him from regular attendance in the Commons.

In July, Lord Rosebery, the outgoing Liberal Prime Minister, nominated Naylor-Leyland, who at thirty-one seemed totally unqualified for honours, to a baronetcy. The affair was far too near the knuckle to escape comment. Already Rosebery had been obliged to give peerages to two unlikely Members[1] as a consequence of promises given by Gladstone in return for subscriptions to the Liberal party funds. *The Times* now condemned this affair openly and Labouchère, writing in *Truth* went further: ' "It does not smell", said Vespasian of

[1] Stern and Williamson.

the money he obtained from a tax on the latrines of Rome; but the money brought in by this . . . reeks of corruption. It stinks!'(a)

Pearson's part was wholly blameless; and his accession helped to turn the Party away from these methods—against which also Rosebery tried to set his face. Men like Pearson and Lord Inchcape were soon worth far more in regular contributions than the occasional doubtful haul like this. Through fourteen difficult years he held the seat, enormously popular with his constituents, though, as he had told the selection committee, he was rarely in the country more than five months a year. He was silent in the House, and was later cartooned as being turned away by a doorkeeper who thought him a stranger, but when he spoke, diffidently and on rare occasions, his great industrial knowledge was effective, and his radical beliefs in the services which the nation should provide was stimulating.

In the inner circles of the Party, where his wealth and experience took him automatically, he was a Liberal Imperialist, supporter of Rosebery and close friend of Asquith and Sir Edward Grey. They trusted his business sense and his advice on labour and trade unions to which most of them were complete strangers. He was known not to be ambitious, his house at 16 Carlton House Terrace was a useful centre for party functions, and Lady Pearson was an excellent political hostess. Paddockhurst and, later Cowdray Park, were to see great garden parties. Above all he was honest and judicious in his opinions, and like his friends, Sir Alfred Mond and Pilkington, he felt it a duty to support his party as far as his purse would carry it.

By the 1906 election things had changed. Mexico claimed his time too much for him to wish to represent a constituency, and he made it his last Parliament; the Party needed every Member it could muster in the crisis brewing with the Lords and an absentee was a liability—though, as he suspected, Colchester fell at once to the Opposition. They made him High Steward of the Borough; and within three years, as Baron Cowdray of Midhurst, he was for ever in the 'other place'.

Parliamentary life was summed up for his wife in a few lines, echoed by many Members since, written shortly after his election in 1895. 'This life will be a break and will be anything but a joy to both of us, but having got here, here for a time I must remain. . . . It is a weariness to the business man. Dinners . . . the waste of time . . . are at present too much for a pampered man like me'.(b) Dilatory activity had no attractions.

He went on, to sketch the fine qualities of his wife, with great charm and the guileless simplicity of all his family relationships;

'When I possess such treasures in a wife, who can wonder that a stolid uninteresting slogger—having only one quality of mind and that concentration—like myself should have reached the present position of competency of means, hereditary honours and M.P. within 15 years of obtaining that possession of priceless value. The only question is when one can stop when so inspired. Further flights mean greater efforts, less leisure, more wear and tear. I say we are entitled to a rest, to taste the joys of a country life at Paddockhurst, to take life more easily so that we have a hale and hearty old age, to let the children feel that they have to go ahead and not that all has been done for them & this I beg to inform her who has so often impressed on me such wise considerations & to beg of her to insist upon their fulfilment'.(c)

Justified or not, the rest never came; in his heart Pearson never wanted it to. Work was his life, whether in the office, on the contract, or on holiday: even his estates were never more enjoyed than when major earthworks were in progress.

The prewar years brought the family an assured position—of which estates were the visible show. In 1908, at the nadir of his Mexican fortunes, Pearson paid £340,000 for Cowdray Park: 'It is a big venture', he wrote home, 'but even if the oil does not prosper and we do not become more heavily involved than our present commitments, we cannot, I think, be accused of undue rashness. May we enjoy it together for many years'.(d) Only the full Mexican story can show the extent of his faith at this moment. The magnificent ruins of the Elizabethan house were carefully propped up and the Victorian mansion improved almost out of recognition, fitted with marble bathrooms and central heating.

In Scotland he first leased, then bought, the vast estate of Dunecht near Aberdeen, 9,000 acres of moor and forest and a battlemented baronial house. Over the years the family grew closely associated with the grey northern city; later he crossed swords with the preservers of ancient monuments, who complained bitterly when he bought the crumbling ruins of Dunottar Castle and propped them up from falling into the sea.

In spite of the success at Court of men like Sir Ernest Cassel and Sir Thomas Lipton who had risen with the Prince of Wales, it was not easy for the self-made man—particularly a well known Liberal—to scale

Edwardian society, and the hardest climb lay not in London but in the country. From Carlton House Terrace, where they were friends of the Prime Minister, and hosts on a grand scale, it was a long journey to Sussex. Pearson never cared much—even of his peerage, given in May 1910, he only wrote: 'I am really glad it has come. I expect there will be a settlement with the Peers about their veto. In any case we will come in under the old régime'.(e) But by then their battle was already won, and the success belonged to Lady Cowdray. Her early persuasions had urged her husband to London and international work; after, at home, she had consolidated a place for the family. Great courage and skill, a blend of wit, diplomacy, and stubborness had been necessary. The American, Judge Gerard wrote of her: 'This most intelligent and interesting woman was an example of how much a wife can help a man in his career. I know that Cowdray depended on her judgement of people and on her advice in all things'.

They paid a certain price. Talking to the Judge once in a quiet interval of a shooting party, Cowdray said without boasting that he was one of the richest men in England, and added suddenly: 'Do you know that there has never been a day in my life when I have not been kowtowing to somebody?'(f)

But Society really did not matter to him. The Derby was an amusing spectacle, but he saw no need to go twice; his close friends were men like Asquith, J. A. Spender, Mond, or Americans like Gerard who had been Treasurer of the Democrat Party, George Wickershaw or H. W. Taft. At Dunecht he would mix his engineers with the local notables without thinking anything of it—fitting in all comers with a bland politeness, and when he wanted to, going to bed. For all his estates and shooting parties he was never really a countryman either; the hydro-electric plant which he designed at Loch Skene to provide light for the house was highest among the real pleasures he found in Scotland.

There were some splendid touches; the fleet of motor-cars at election time in the lurid Cowdray yellow, and the kilted piper on the lawn at Dunecht to wake the household; and they had a well-timed sense of proportion. Cowdray visited Greece and Italy in 1899, indulging his love of archaeology and ancient engineering. The King gave him an audience and after some polite formalities in which the contractor respectfully stood, asked him to build the Larissa

Railway. At this Cowdray sat down—'Now, Sir, we must consider this as business'. And in 1919 when enthusiastic Albanians offered him the throne of their uneasy kingdom he was kept by no grand delusions from refusing.

Rigidly they enforced their own rules. Lady Cowdray once walked on to the polo field and told off a well-known Liberal peer for using bad language during the game. Cowdray hated gambling and would never allow it in his house parties, preferring to give a prize at the end of the evening. Cocktails were never served: at Dunecht guests would creep into the butler's pantry, where Lockyer, who looked like his master, was a racing man and ruled the neighbourhood, gave them what was needed. Good wine appeared at dinner, but 'beer is no' served in the house of Dunecht!'

Behind this was a powerful sense of what was fitting. The strong and self-sufficient family was in some ways years in advance of its time, liberal, feminist, and enlightened about divorce. Cowdray had no objection whom his daughter might marry, except stockbrokers for whom he had a lifelong distaste. But 'You must have a standard'—'Those people have no standard' and in this they were quietly adamant.

It was Cowdray's pride as well as a family joke that his wife was a superb spender of money, taking infinite pains and time to buy whatever was best, whether Louis XV furniture or the rich materials produced for the 1925 Exhibition. In the last year of her life alone she spent £70,000. And when real need came there was no hesitation. Lord Denman, his son-in-law, was appointed Governor-General of Australia in 1910 and Cowdray wrote, offering to guarantee all expenses over and above his income, to £50,000 a year. 'You would of course have to do the thing as well as it could be done.'(g)

Harold, the eldest son, had no real inclination for the business and though he worked hard in Mexico, preferred to farm in Sussex. Cowdray was philosophic about it. Clive, his second son, after a gay career at Cambridge, worked successfully in the business, and his father relied on him, particularly in the oil negotiations. The youngest, Geoffrey, was killed in action in 1914. The family always remained closely knit; but the key to all his affections lay with his wife. From Mexico in 1909 he wrote:

'My Valentine . . . with all our years what children you and I are. Apart, we pine and long for one another; together we play hide and seek, are shy about giving freedom to our affection, are exacting and do not continuously enjoy to the full one another's presence.

'When I begin to realize that leisure I have been arranging for so long (and it must now be on its way) I shall regret that its realization has been so long delayed.'(h)

6

MEXICAN OIL

'Mexico is like a beggar sitting on a bag of gold.'—HUMBOLDT

BY 1903, Cowdray had been fourteen years in Mexico and held a position similar to the old East India Company 'nabobs'— trusted friend of the régime, powerful in his own sphere, but largely indifferent to the vagaries of local politics so long as they stayed peaceful and allowed him to carry on his business.

The long rule of Porfirio Diaz is a classic of dictatorship, as the revolt which ousted him is the prototype of modern revolution: rapid initial success, stability under a tough quasi-military rule, followed by the discontent of the intelligentsia and middle classes and final, total disaster. Diaz became President in 1876, as a caudillo with United States support. The work of his predecessor, Juarez, who had tried to build an educated, nationally conscious Mexico, and Lerdo who had refused Americans a concession to run the railway south of the Rio Grande, was swept away. Diaz stated the policy which for thirty years guided his personal dictatorship in the 'Plan of Tuxtepec': Mexico was a chaos, divided climatically, geographically, and socially, from tropical jungle to snowbound sierra, from Indian to pure blooded Spaniard; the old Empire had dissolved beyond repair; order must therefore be imposed, and economic recovery and development; democracy was no longer possible. So the famous phrase 'pan o palo' was coined— bread or the stick: 'a dog with a bone in its mouth does not bite or steal'. It was ruthlessly carried out; though Diaz did not kill wantonly he was not unlike another caudillo—'Do you forgive your enemies?' the priest asked. 'I have none: they are all dead.'

Before Pearson came to drain Mexico City, all the articulate classes had all come into line—clergy, landowners, generals, and local chiefs, and the middle strata, still an uncertain element in the traditional hierarchy. But the peasants and the Indians, 90 per cent of the population, lived dumbly outside renascent Mexico. Diaz gave concessions, first to Americans, then English and Germans to keep the balance: concessions to build and run railways, for mines, rubber plantations and oil, depleting the Federal reserves, abrogating State control of mineral rights and despoiling the Indians of millions of acres of hereditary land for which they held no documentary legal title.

The results were spectacular to the outside world. Capital investment poured in; the English debt was consolidated; foreign trade grew rapidly as the ruthless armed police, the *rurales*, 'pacified' the turbulent provinces. Peace was made even with Rome, after so much clerical blood had been shed, on Diaz's wife, Carmelita's initiative, and the Church identified itself, fatally in the end, with the dictatorship.

By 1900 there were 9,000 miles of railway, and the volume of trade was four times greater than when Diaz came to power. José Limantour, at the Treasury, floated the régime on a tide of financial success. For the first time in a century the Budget was balanced; surpluses followed. Under his direction between 1902 and 1909 the railways were steadily nationalized; and Mexico moved on to the Gold Standard, freed from the fluctuating price of silver.

Limantour, pale, elegant and Europeanized, a doctrinaire financier cast in the dreary philosophy of Comte and Herbert Spencer, but able, intelligent, and intensely patriotic, came to dominate Diaz after 1905. With him were a group of like minds, who called themselves 'Cientificos', full of theory and dogmatic reform. Under their influence Diaz lost the earthy touch of power and became slowly more remote—and it was said that his mestizo complexion grew whiter with the years.

The highmindedness of the Cientificos seemed, in this settled Augustan era, a surrender to foreign capitalists. Hearst, Guggenheim, Pearson, U.S. Steel, the Anaconda Corporation, Standard Oil, McCormick; their shadow lay heavily across Mexican nationality. Mexico, 'mother of foreigners and step-mother of Mexicans', held a United States investment alone of more than twice her national income. As Mexico City grew, its fine buildings founded on loans from the house of Scherer–Limantour, as the bureaucracy multiplied in what Latin Americans aptly call 'empleomania', a certain radical opposition grew, but in a different quarter from the vast anguish beneath, which like the troubled fire in a volcano waited for a fissure in the hard despotic earth. The sodden, brutish misery of the labourer, working for large landowners[1] for the same wages year after year, despite a threefold rise in prices, hardly troubled the calm Westernised surface. The break was to come from those who had done well and wanted more.

Pearson understood much of this and how much order and stability owed to the President. He respected Diaz greatly and counted him as a closest friend and Diaz returned the affection.

In April 1901 on the way to New York, Pearson missed his connexion at Laredo in Texas and had to wait nine hours. The town was wildly excited—the Lucas oil well at Spindletop had been struck a month before, and prospectors and 'wild-catters' thronged the streets while rumours of new gushers blazed through the crowds. In this short time Pearson was bitten by the mania which for more than twenty years became part of his life. He remembered the 'ochos chapopotes', the seeping pools of oil on his concession at Tehuantepec, and seized on all the information and prospectuses he could. First he thought only of oil for the railway but the idea ramified, like the wildfire enthusiasm round him, and he forced his way through the mill round the telegraph office to cable Body. 'Take all options you can, not only oil land but all land for miles around'. Then he wrote at greater length: 'You will see that oil deposits frequently extend over big areas, so the oil rights must extend over a large district to be really valuable: 10, 20, 40,000 acres appears to be no unusual size. Move sharply and be sure we are dealing with principals.'(a) For the rest of this whirlwind stop he talked incessantly, learning on the spot the fundamentals of this new enterprise.

Body worked quickly and two days later asked if he should buy more. Pearson told him to and meanwhile persuaded Captain Lucas himself to go out and inspect the San Cristobal area of Tehuantepec. When his report proved favourable, Pearson began to drill.

The main uses of oil were still lighting, heating and lubrication. Kerosene and heavy oils were used, the lighter spirits thrown away or burnt: the internal combustion engine was still in its infancy. But between 1901 and 1910 oil sprang to world importance as it became possible to use petrol and diesel oil in engines, motor-cars, trains and,

[1] Four men held 30 million acres in Lower California.

most important then, ships. This world revolution in transport, spreading faster than that of steam, is the background to the search for oil which revolved before 1914 round such personalities as Marcus Samuel of Shell, Henri Deterding of Royal Dutch, the Rothschilds in

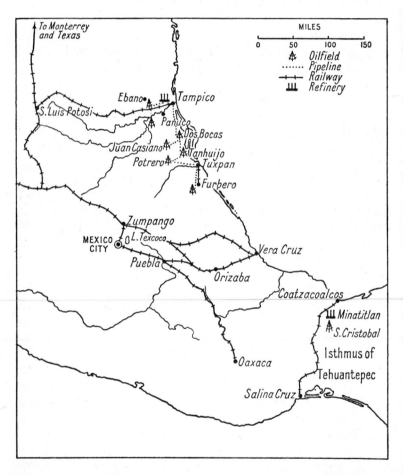

Baku, the Rockefellers in the U.S.A., Doheny, Clay Pierce and Pearson in Mexico. Some found it easily, others bought experience at bitter cost. Pearson entered it wholly without experience, trusting his ability to learn any business quickly and rapidly realized that the field was narrow and already occupied by forceful competitors.

Edward L. Doheny, an oil-driller from Texas, once down and out in Mexico City, began drilling at Ebano near Tampico before 1900, and was producing a steady quantity. His Mexican Petroleum Company had a profitable contract supplying part of the National Railways. Clay Pierce, of Waters Pierce & Co., a two-thirds-owned subsidiary of Standard Oil of New Jersey, had a complete monopoly of the retail trade in kerosene and lubricating oil in Mexico and refined Doheny's oil at Tampico. Pierce, with none of the old giant's suavity, modelled himself on the elder Rockefeller and had consolidated his hold ten years before Pearson began to drill. However as long as the Englishman was only a prospector, with a long way to go to find oil in any quantity, he was not afraid of competition.

The first wells sunk at San Cristobal were promising, but after two years Pearson realized that there would be hardly enough to run the railway, let alone his wider schemes. Though he had good American assistants he suffered inevitably, and wastefully, from inexperience, and from the fact that his concessions were simply not rich in oil. Many drillings produced few strikes because the early machinery could not drill deep level wells more than 2,500 feet.[1] When months had been spent, a well might blow wild, run dry, or worse, if the boiler fires were not put out fast enough, catch fire. 'A newcomer and an amateur, buying his experience as he went along' was how he described it. The lure, however, was if anything stronger. In 1902 he decided to put a million and a half into the venture and then cut his losses and clear out, yet six years later more than three times that had been swallowed up and he was more determined than ever to succeed.

He never accepted that he could fail. In the past, sheer hard work had always pulled him through, and though the risks ramified beyond anything a contractor had met since the days of 1866, this faith to some extent masked their potency. His business experience taught him what became his ultimate solution; that having spent more than he ever intended, he must still spend more, get wider concessions, drill more wells, plan bigger, until fortune repaid him.[2] Though by 1908, he had spent £5 million, and though his personal fortune was wholly pledged, Pearson scrupulously kept the contracting firm separate and

[1] Compared with 20-25,000 today.

[2] Deterding, the cool master of the oil world was the same—Marcus Samuel once told him to stop drilling in Egypt when he had spent a million, but he felt a hunch that it was there; overspent wildly and found it in the end.

its assets written down, so that he could have lost everything and the firm survived.

The promise was sometimes tantalizing. In September 1904, as he was writing: 'the amount of money we have spent is becoming serious', San Cristobal production rose. This made the refinery which he was planning to build at Minitatlan a possibility—not only to produce oil for Tehuantepec, but to export the surplus. The refinery was begun in 1905, and since it took two and a half years to build, another half million was laid out with no immediate return.

However Diaz, as the Tehuantepec Railway showed its worth to the régime, proved more than helpful. In 1906 he granted Pearson concessions of nearly 1¼ million acres to drill on all remaining State lands in the provinces of Vera Cruz, San Luis Potosi, Tabasco and Chiapas, for fifty years.

By this single stroke, the oil venture was put on a new scale, and Pearson at once decided to enlarge the Minitatlan Refinery to more than twice the original capacity. Deciding to double his expenditure before he found oil on the new lands was a gamble, but this was nothing to the scale of operations implied because, by aiming to produce so much refined oil, he committed himself to a large export trade in world markets and to competition in Mexico itself.

He planned the retailing programme in great detail, long before the refinery was expected to be ready in 1908, opening a separate office in London, to sell to the U.K. distributors, C. T. Bowring & Co. Perhaps his boldest stroke was to order, five years into the future, since he had to work far ahead, the first ships of the oil-tanker fleet which he hoped would cut his costs. In 1907 the first 3,000-ton capacity tanker was ready for service; two others followed shortly.

With so many hostages to fortune everything depended on finding the elusive oil. Being committed to supply Bowrings, Pearson was forced late in 1907 to seek help from a small English oilfield owned by Percy Furber; but, to get this extra, had to build a 54-mile-long pipeline and a narrow-gauge railway. No supply could be counted on for three years and during the rest of 1907 he was buying crude oil in Texas, refining at Minitatlan and re-exporting to Europe, losing slightly even on turnover with no return at all on his investment.

Some of the wide shadows of fear are shown in a letter to his wife from Tulsa, Oklahoma; written in February 1908, of his failure to get a supply from the Pennsylvania Oil Co.:

'I dined at San Antonio with "our friends". On Sunday we went by train to the oilfields, bitterly cold, and were shown round them—the grandest site imaginable. 2,000 rigs, 700 big tanks, a tract of country twice the size of Paddockhurst, & I marvelled and was both encouraged and frightened by the sight. Standard Oil are buying up the oil & storing it in tanks. It will not cost them delivered on the E. Coast above 30/- a ton & the quality is such that if they were prepared to work without profit they could sell cheaper than I could in the European market when delivering at cost price. This was the frightening aspect. But they do not work for nothing—nor is this low price likely to continue. I finally feel that they cannot undersell us without harming themselves as much as us. At first I felt they might be able to kill us without incurring any loss.'

But this glimpse of the Rockefeller distributive empire[1] and hint of a rate war could not discourage his optimism. 'If we find such a pool of oil in Mexico & I am sure we shall—it will be wholly ours instead of belonging to 10,000 people as it does here.'(b)

Months passed. Doheny, on the verge of bankruptcy, struck the rich well, Juan Casiano No. 7 in the 'Tierra Caliente', the narrow, inhospitable, marshy coastal strip of tropical forest, between Tampico and Tuxpam: the fever-ridden, humid 'Golden Lane'. Pearson had very large concessions here, but in March 1908, when the Minitatlan Refinery was finally ready, his only source of oil was still San Cristobal, and this field had been given just two years' life.

'Surely before then we shall have found further deposits' (writing to his son Clive). 'The oil business is not all beer and skittles. I entered lightly on this enterprise, not realizing its many problems, but only feeling that oil meant a fortune and that hard work and application would bring results. Now I know that it would have been wiser to surround myself with proved oil men ... and not relied upon commercial knowledge and hard work coupled with a superficial understanding of the trade.'(c)

Such honesty deserved better of the year which followed. In August not far from Doheny's well, the drillers struck oil at Dos Bocas. The well blew wild and caught fire and in spite of heroic attempts to block it off at the mouth, blazed for two months, losing a

---

[1] John D. Rockefeller's skill lay in ruthlessly cornering the distributive trade, keeping out of actual production, until all the oilowners were forced to sell through Standard Oil at his price.

million barrels of oil and giving Pearson a heavy bill in compensation to local landowners. Tired and depressed, he was struck again, by a fire which destroyed part of the refinery and immobilized it for months.

Yet if anything the Dos Bocas disaster reinforced his optimism, proving that oil was really there. It gave him the spur to plan a large-scale reorganization of the whole enterprise which had so outgrown its modest origins: the concessions, refinery, pipelines and rapidly growing tanker fleet. As early as February 1908, he wrote:

'After full consideration I have decided to form a Mexican Company to take over all our oil interests north of Vera Cruz. This Company will trade only in Mexico and I want Mexican capital to be interested. Then the Oil interests at San Cristobal and the Refinery would remain ours and be devoted to export business.'(d)

He had not committed himself to compete with the Pierce organization in Mexico itself yet; from June to July he talked with Clay Pierce in New York but the skirmishing came to nothing. The American wanted stiff terms to allow a competitor in and Pearson believed his prospects were good enough to refuse. The threat simmered; and Pearson left Mexico in the autumn, giving instructions to set up depots in the principal towns ready to sell his oil if necessary. War was declared; 'in a mild and quiet way', he wrote, 'I am going to be ruthless'. Early in 1909, he ordered seven more tankers, each of 9,000 tons.

He returned to Mexico in January 1909, passing through New York: 'Things look blacker when you are away from them than when you are getting nearer. I am having one more pow-wow with Clay Pierce before finally making arrangements (opening sales in Mexico) which will preclude, most probably, my doing so hereafter. But the chances of success are very remote.'(e) Nevertheless, behind Pierce lay the massive power of Standard Oil—able to crush him not merely in Mexican but European markets.

From Mexico a fortnight later, he wrote more confidently: 'We are rapping Waters Pierce hard. We are doing a third of the country's trade in illuminating oil & spirit. But the fight for supremacy is only benefitting the consumer. I am happier about the oil. . . . I feel, I know, that we shall come out of it all right if I only keep my ambition in regard to it within bounds & see that the money required for patient development is found without interfering with my other demands.'(f) The contracting business went on as before—and he had already completed the purchase of Cowdray on the profits he hoped to make. He succeeded in getting from the Government a contract to supply a third of the oil for the National Railways, thus hitting Doheny as well as Pierce; and though he was importing heavily and selling at a wildly unrealistic price, he felt his opponent was weakening and began to see success ahead. But, 'what fools we are: in the fight the goose that lays the golden eggs is being killed'.

Pearson fell seriously ill with 'flu in February and recovered slowly as he insisted on working at full speed through a developing crisis. Perhaps the showdown with the Americans came too soon—he would have been vastly more confident with a well like Dos Bocas in production.

'I have been reading', he told his wife, 'some of Sir Walter Scott's books & I cannot help but think what a craven adventurer I am compared to men of old. I am slothful and horribly afraid of two things—first that my pride in my judgement and administration should be scattered to the winds and secondly that I should have to begin life again. These fears make me a coward at times. I know that if my oil venture had to fizzle out entirely that there is enough left for me to live quietly at Cowdray. Yet until it is a proved success I continue nervous & sometimes despondent. I cannot excuse myself for having such fears. . . . I think the real *sense of responsibility would be* to be anxiously on the lookout but without fear. . . .'(g)

His rival attacked him bitterly; it was reported: 'Everyone knows of the Pearson–Waters Pierce war and how Clay Pierce newspapers dwell on the lack of oil in the Pearson camp, the white elephant of the Minitatlan Refinery, and the general foolishness of Pearson ideas, engineers, and ambitions.'(h) When oil prices were cut, and cut again, they talked of 'the brief time needed for amateur competitors to get tired of losing money in a vain attempt to secure some advantage'. In New York Pearson was shadowed by detectives, spied on in Mexico, his cables tampered with and attempts made to bribe his agents for information. In return, by January 1910, he had established 160 depots in the country, and won half the trade in retail oil. Prices, however, had been cut to a third of their 1905 figure. Both sides hung on, waiting for a break.

In May 1909, Pearson wrote to his wife, reassuringly: 'It is time Clay Pierce stopped the fight . . . I can no longer approach him, it is he that must come to see me. I doubt if he, with all his experience has ever been in such a bad fight before. We are not losing money, but a negative existence will not buy Cowdray. We are not here for our health but to make a profit and receive the reward of our labour and money.'(*i*)

In this hard year, his eldest son, Harold and his wife were a great help. They loved the country, roughing it in mining camps and revelling in the sense of pioneering. Pearson relaxed occasionally: 'each night the doctor and I walk to a restaurant at Chapultepec and have sandwiches and a bottle of German beer, a rest to smoke and talk for half an hour'. Watching the lights of the village in the warm dusk, he perfected his plans for the reorganization: 'I think a Mexican business ought to be partly owned by Mexicans. It would give us many a pull over Pierce and we would be assured of Government support much more than a foreign company.'(*j*)

He could be more high-handed when he heard that the great threat of Standard Oil had faded away. They were dissociating themselves from their subsidiary: 'Pierce's monopoly in Texas is being assailed as strongly as we are doing in Mexico. He is quarrelling with his old partners.' But this in no way alleviated the central problem; if he did not find oil soon, the immense reserves of capital which alone had propped up the Pearson enterprise would run out. Having spent £5 million, he felt the strain keenly and hated to return to England: 'There is no thinking here except what I do. There is an excellent machine for doing what it is detailed to do, but it will not do good work unless matters are cut and dried for it.'(*k*) His letters from London in the winter continued to be tense and curt.

He was back in Mexico City in January 1910, on the spot to hear of the first strike on his lands in the 'Golden Lane'. The well was small, in the area of Potrero de Llano, 40 miles from Tuxpam, but it was prophetic. In February came the big Potrero No. 1 and a continuous assured supply. Suddenly everything for which he had worked became possible; the refinery at full production, the tankers filled, the Mexican market flooded against Pierce. Most important the new company took shape with an issue of shares in May.

The Compañía Mexicana de Petroleo El Aguila—Mexican Eagle Oil—with an issued capital of $30 million (Mex.), took over all the Pearson oil interests except the refinery and the tankers. On the Board were Diaz's son, Porfrito, Body, Pearson and Guillermo Escandon, one of the largest landowners and Federal Governor, among others. Most of the shares were in fact taken by Pearson or sold on the European markets—Mexicans traditionally preferred to invest in land—but with so many of the Government involved in its interests Aguila could be called a Mexican enterprise, with all the advantages which this gave over his rivals. A howl was raised by Clay Pierce at giving an interloper Government protection; but, noticeably, Standard Oil's attitude changed, and in July Doheny came to terms on the common use of the new pipeline which Pearson was building to Tampico.

As if to cap this success came, in December, the biggest gusher ever struck—Potero No. 4. The well blew wild, spraying out 100,000 barrels of oil a day for two months. Pearson and his son Clive raced down from Mexico City to direct the capping operation. As the oil poured away, some 3 million barrels were caught in an old earth reservoir and saved; the rest ran into local streams, and farmers, furious at the pollution, set fire to it. Slowly, against the current, the blaze crept up the Buena Vista river towards the great well and, fearing another explosion like Dos Bocas, Pearson raised a local militia to stop the fires and frighten off the incendiaries. For perhaps the only time he betrayed his anxiety. Meanwhile his engineers invented the 'Bell nipple' and forced it over the terrific gush.

More oil was now assured than he could ever have dreamt of five years before. Aguila promised to grow so large that the Mexican trade became a sideline.

Standard Oil, who had again started a disastrous private war with Royal Dutch in world markets, and who were considerably shaken by the successful outcome of Mexican Eagle, were keen to write off Pierce and make terms with Pearson. They asked for a very large supply of crude oil, which Pearson agreed to deliver at Philadelphia in his own ships of the Eagle Fleet. The seven-year contract was easy to negotiate with men like Stillman, Rockefeller, and Archbold, for while Doheny and Pierce were roughnecks, pioneers of a hard school, these talked quietly and calmly. In addition to the supply they agreed on spheres of influence to which the seal was given at the dinner in New York, and in 1913, with some magnanimity, Pearson agreed to give Clay Pierce a fifty-fifty share in the Mexican trade.

Mexican Eagle bore the stamp of a colossal enterprise, with control from oil well to consumer. The Eagle Oil Transport Co. comprised twenty tankers, ten of 15,000 tons capacity which were then quite the largest and most efficient in the world; the Anglo-Mexican Petroleum Co. had absorbed the Bowring organization and marketed worldwide;

and this Company, under Clive Pearson, won a British Admiralty contract which took up a large part of the Mexican surplus. Aguila itself controlled concessions over 1½ million acres (about 2 per cent of the habitable area of Mexico), had 175 miles of pipeline, storage for 7 million barrels, and with a new plant at Tampico, two major refineries. Such an empire, before 1914, ranked as one of the great industrial combines of the world—small as yet beside the ramifications of Standard Oil, but, so geologists then promised, with as much potential as all the wells of Texas.

With all this, there were other activities on the fringe of the empire. Pearson could never resist widening his hobbies: an interest in mining with Robert Price, M.P., secured, among the myriad over-ambitious projects a solid holding in two of the best gold mines, Esperanza and the Mexican Mines of El Oro. The two controlled other mines, in Australia, Colorado, Montana, Maine, and Russia, but were most successful here; with large capital resources, as was done on the Rand, they could work on the vast scale which made the low grade ores profitable.

Rubber proved one of his rare failures. In the boom year of 1905, an Anglo-Mexican syndicate bought a 4-million-acre tract of forest land in Chiapas to develop the castilloas or wild rubber tree. Pearson took part, but the reports on which he worked were over-sanguine. Trees when planted took twenty years to come into production, and nothing came of it before Malaya proved a more profitable, easier ground. He continued to work in public utilities, carrying out gas and electrical works, until by 1914 he controlled some of the main works in Mexico; Vera Cruz Electric Light and Traction, Puebla Tramway, Light and Power, and Tampico Light, Power and Traction. In Orizaba he established a highly profitable jute factory, and built power stations there and at Puebla.

Life in Mexico City, the Paris of the Americas, in the elegant Spanish colonial house which had once been the British Legation, was pleasant. The family spent three months of every year at least here. Lady Cowdray gave large parties and her husband £100,000 to found the Cowdray Hospital in the city. Their prestige stood higher than that of any other foreigner in the country. 'Be more than meticulous', Cowdray once told his son 'in all your dealings with Mexicans; lean over backwards in their favour.'

Workmen as usual were busy altering the house, and furniture was shifted from room to room; there were picnics in friends' estates outside the city, weekends at his sister-in-law's lovely house at Orizaba, evenings at the Jockey Club, dinners, dances, riding, polo, excursions; a life of princes among the chiefs of the dictatorship, Diaz, Romero Rubio, Minister for War, Guillermo de Landa, Generals Mena and Dehesa, and Mariscal, lately ambassador to the Court of St. James.

Diaz however was growing old. As Limantour ruled more and more, it cost a bribe of 3,000 pesos for a Mexican to see the President. In 1910 Diaz made the fatal error, in an interview with an American journalist, of saying he was ready to retire without nominating a successor. Instead, he suggested Mexico was ready for democracy, and the pious sentiment intended for American ears resounded among the discontented at home. The unrest of years shifted the delicate political balance.

The Mexican Revolution began slowly, almost constitutionally, only in stages revealing its real content, as the skins of central authority were peeled roughly away. Nothing but the loyalty of inertia propped up the Cientificos; the dangers which had bound the articulate classes to Diaz thirty years earlier seemed remote. And an inchoate urge for change combined with envy of the corrupt élite round Limantour to create an opposition not rebellious enough to warrant death. Instead, Diaz temporized; and all who felt they had not shared in the golden rewards turned to the unlikely figurehead of the mild philosophic Francisco Madero, one of a powerful family with strong connexions in the United States. In the making of this opposition, American feeling against Diaz and his support of Cowdray, and the campaign waged by Clay Pierce, formed a considerable part.

Diaz imprisoned Madero but he escaped, issued a pronunciamiento, and launched a revolt which perished in oblivion. He might have remained supinely in exile in the States, but for the far more serious rebellion which Orozco and Pancho Villa began in 1911 in Chihuahua. Madero joined them, and in primitive Morelos, Emiliano Zapata began guerrilla warfare. Fire spread fast; Diaz was slow to act. Limantour returned from Europe, took charge and made peace in April. But the rift in the immovable façade could no longer be denied. Villa reopened war and won consistently. Limantour was forced to resign in May. Diaz hung on; he sat with raging toothache, in his palace, while his guards shot down the crowd outside in the rain. At midnight on May 18th, 1911 he gave in; fleeing to Vera Cruz. He stayed four days with Body before taking ship for Europe, where at the last, his friends stood by him; Cowdray offered Paddock-hurst for his exile but he preferred to retire to Paris.

Cowdray was hard hit. He had admired and loved the old dictator, and sometimes talked of him as his hero. Though Madero succeeded him, inoffensive and unlikely to cause trouble, Cowdray feared his inability to control the peace of the country and the effects of United States influence. In the spring of 1912 he wrote to his daughter, Lady Denman:

'These isolated risings [under Villa and Zapata] are doing the country harm. If the position of Aguila were doubtful, the present situation in Mexico would add greatly to the difficulty of finding money for development.'(l)

For, though Aguila seemed safe enough under Madero, the visit which Cowdray made in 1912 disturbed him deeply and proved, for many reasons, to be his last. At the dinner which was given him by Standard Oil in March they had made an offer for the whole enterprise. His confidence was still high enough to refuse it but he was shaken to find out that, for some months before, A. F. Corvin, their representa-tive, had been seeking concessions in Mexico,[1] and had reported that Aguila might shortly be in grave political danger.

Madero was a man of straw, dependent for his power on unstable brigand leaders. Constant intrigues threatened his presidency, helped by Henry Lane Wilson, the American Ambassador. There ensued the Ten Tragic Days, when in February 1913 Madero from the Ciudadela and General Victoriano Huerta from the Palacio Nacional bombarded each other regardless of civilian life. Huerta took the presidency and Madero was murdered, and politics were suddenly naked as they had not been since the early days of Diaz.

Huerta, half white, half Indian, was a man of strength and possibly a good Mexican,[2] but outside Mexico City chaos spread fast as the administration ran down. In Villa, a bloody butcher, devoid of human-

---

[1] Since Royal Dutch, their chief rivals, had obtained considerable concessions from Madero in 1911–12, Standard Oil felt impelled to carry competition into the enemy's ground.

[2] A diplomat's wife described him: 'A short, broadshouldered man, with ruth-less vigilant eyes, and tireless Indian perseverance . . . they say that the more he drinks the clearer his mind becomes.'

ity, and Zapata, wildly crusading with a peasant horde, lay the stark material of the first purely communist revolution, whose outward face bore such murderous xenophobia that no foreign concern could expect to survive unprotected by a Great Power.

Huerta then became, unpleasant as he was in outlook and habit, in Cowdray's eyes the only way to preserve his newly won oil empire. This explains much of what came later, because Cowdray and his interests were soon the shuttlecock in a far wider struggle which ultimately involved the good relations of Great Britain and the U.S.A.

The main trouble stemmed from Woodrow Wilson's succession to the American Presidency in 1912. Huerta was an abomination to him; despotic ruler, murderer of Madero, a drunken brutal licentiate, a half-caste and a master of political chicanery, he offended the narrow puritanism of the new President on every count. With a naive political fervour Wilson took Mexican affairs into his own hands and declared that he would destroy Huerta by overriding moral force[1].

He worked for the next two years largely outside the scope of the State Department, which had handled Mexican diplomacy for years, and disregarded its tradition of intelligent politics and its experience of the country. On the urbane state of diplomacy with Great Britain, this rectitude of the 'New Freedom' policy jarred bluntly, for Sir Edward Grey at the Foreign Office had recognized Huerta's Government for much the same reasons as moved Cowdray to support him, the last prop of order in a dissolving state. Wilson took this as a malicious affront to his declared crusade; in the sorry period of bad diplomacy, apart from the tangle of U.S.-Mexican relationships, however, what mattered from Cowdray's point of view was that a new and highly unpredictable hand was shaking the dice.

Wilson came to believe that Grey had recognized Huerta in order to safeguard the Cowdray oil interests, and that the Foreign Office had pledged him full support. The advice he took did nothing to dispel this illusion. It was one of Pierce's newspapers which had first coined the phrase: 'Cowdray has taken more out of Mexico than any man since Cortez', but this was no more extravagant than the letter addressed to the President by Julius Kruttschnitt, President of the Southern Pacific Railway Company (which had suffered severely from the competition of Tehuantepec):

[1] 'I am going to teach,' he said, 'the Latin American Republics to elect good men'!

(May 6, 1913). 'The British Government has already recognized Huerta in a most marked manner by an autographed letter from the King due to the efforts of Lord Cowdray who is using his efforts to obtain a large loan in England and has succeeded on condition that the Government recognise Huerta—which has been done.'(m)

Wilson's own representatives told him what he wanted to hear. W. H. Page, Ambassador in London, was convinced early in 1913 that Cowdray was moving the Foreign Office in Huerta's favour. By then Wilson was sure that he was fighting a moral battle not only against a usurper but a rampant defiance of the Monroe Doctrine.

The truth was far different. British recognition had been extended for reasons in accord with traditional diplomacy. It seemed to Sir Edward Grey that President Wilson simply did not understand what sort of men Villa and Carranza were, or the anarchic forces behind them; he himself saw no moral difference between one bandit and another. But he could not help Cowdray; he was naturally aware of his interest, but a century of careful demarcation in Latin American affairs had left the Foreign Office largely free from the taint of commercial preference. He might listen sympathetically to appeals but all that could be done was 'to appeal to the central authority, when there was one, to protect long-established and legitimate British commercial interests, or to leave it to those interested to make the best arrangements they would on the spot'.(n)

Grey was no Palmerston, to send gunboats, and there was also the irritant question of the Panama Tolls. The Panama Canal Act, 1912, had exempted U.S. shipping from Canal dues; a source of bitter British objection. One of Grey's main policies was to get this repealed.

Until late summer, 1913, Cowdray made no appeal, but he received then in quick succession the full blast of American pressure outside Mexico, the withdrawal of what assistance the Foreign Office had given, as Grey realized how much Anglo–American relations had been affected, and the threat of war in Mexico, when Wilson's covert support of Carranza and his Constitutionalists[1] turned to supplies of arms and money.

The immediate cause lay outside Mexico: the Pearson firm had built an important extension to the Dorado Railway in Colombia and Cowdray's influence ramified there in a new search for oil. Following

[1] Carranza's "Constitution" was set out in the Plan of Guadeloupe in February 1913.

the United States seizure of the Canal Zone out of Colombian territory, strong anti-American feeling raged. No attempt was made to settle the question of reparations. Cowdray foresaw in the underdeveloped country, shut in and split up by the ranges of the high Andes, possibilities of development as great as those in Mexico, and he determined to exploit them. He offered to undertake further railway development, and the remodelling of the harbours of Buenaventura on the Pacific and Cartagena on the Caribbean to provide modern outlets for the produce of the interior. In spite of some political difficulties, he was able by April 1913 to send out, as his agent, Lord Murray of Elibank[1] to negotiate an oil concession; and at the same time asked for other concessions in Costa Rica and Ecuador.

Cowdray undertook to spend £20,000 on exploring for oil, in return for complete protection for his concessions, and on May 27th agreement was reached; after two years' prospecting over an area of 10,000 square kilometres, Cowdray could choose what concessions he wanted on a forty-year lease. This was monopoly; and fearful of a repetition on a more protected scale, of the Aguila story, a number of American interests awoke. By the end of June, a Mr. Doyle was in Bogotá on behalf of the Asphalt Trust of Philadelphia, trying to upset the contract before it passed the Colombian Congress. The Caribbean Petroleum Company pushed in; and in the autumn, Washington exerted diplomatic force. The Colombian Minister was told bluntly that the Pearson concession would imperil any hope of a Canal Zone settlement. By November the thing was hopeless. Ecuador had already given way. Cowdray talked to Ambassador Page with no effect and Lord Murray broke off: 'I withdrew', he wrote on November 26th, 'as it was not in accordance with the dignity of our House that we should be used as a pawn in the Panama dispute.'(o)

Costa Rica, where the American dominated Colon Development Corporation and the Carib Syndicate held sway, followed suit. Cowdray had no illusions about the nature of the opposition. The New York Times put it from the American point of view: 'The Pearson syndicate would have exploited virgin oil fields in Colombia of great value and would have received the necessary rights for building railways, docks, quays, and canals. . . .' Yet, if Wilson saved Colombia from this fate, under American influence for nearly a decade afterwards none of these works, so necessary to the Colombian economy, was begun.

[1] A director of S. Pearson and Son, who as Liberal Chief whip, had been concerned in the Marconi Scandal.

Having thus fallen foul of the Monroe Doctrine, Cowdray was given little diplomatic help in Mexico against the protean figure of his opponents. As the Revolution spread it became unsafe for the Company for him to come out after 1912. Aguila depended entirely on its own staff and its head was reduced to making endless, and usually fruitless, representations in London.

Huerta, having raised his loan in Europe, was able to defy Wilson's demand for free elections. Fighting, however, continuously upset the northern provinces and although Wilson's embargo on the shipment of arms held good officially through 1913, Doheny brought in half a million dollars' worth of food and rifles and subsidies in cash. Cowdray was plainly concerned to keep Huerta's régime strong, and he, clearly, was still a powerful figure in Mexican politics: on August 20th he cabled Judge Gerard: 'I have suggested to Huerta absolute expediency of avoiding anything which could irritate your Government.'(p)

Meanwhile, Sir Lionel Carden was made British Ambassador to Mexico, and since he was also pro-Huerta, Wilson became increasingly irritated. In August he attempted to dissociate his country from, and break up, Aguila by advising all American residents to leave. Fortunately for the Company few obeyed, and Dr. Hayes, formerly in the U.S. Government service, in particular, stuck to his post in charge of the Potrero field.

Sir Edward Grey was becoming worried about the depths of mis-understanding which the autumn of 1913 revealed and decided to send Sir Walter Tyrrell to talk with Sir Cecil Spring-Rice (the Ambassador in Washington) and then personally to explain Britain's attitude to the President. Tyrrell told Wilson categorically on November 12th that Cowdray had no special privileges from Huerta and that if he obtained them in the future the British Government would not recognize them. The diplomatic breach was healed over at the price of ordering the British Ambassador in Mexico not to interfere with Wilson's policy even in defence of British oil interests.

Ambassador Page reported on November 24th: 'Lord Cowdray has been to see me for four successive days. I have a suspicion that instead of running the Government, the Government has now turned the tables and is running him. His Government contract is becoming a bad thing to sleep with. He told me this morning that he has withdrawn the request for any concession in Colombia. Lord, how he's changed! Several weeks ago he was humorous, almost cynical. Now he's very serious.'(*q*) The only consolation Cowdray had from these meetings was the suggestion that he go to New York and talk to the President himself, but he felt that this would prejudice his standing in Mexico too far.

He was worried deeply; enough to be prepared to talk terms with Royal Dutch; meeting Henri Deterding for the first time. He approached Lloyd George, Chancellor of the Exchequer (officially, because of the Admiralty contract). He pointed out that his concerns represented a total of £12 million in Mexico, endangered by revolution, and offered to dedicate Aguila entirely to supplying the Admiralty in return for a £5 million Government grant—which in effect would buy him out. But it came to nothing—the House of Commons would not have considered spending such a sum, and the Admiralty already had its assured Anglo-Persian supply. A merger with Anglo-Persian would have been best, but this Lloyd George discouraged, fearing to carry the American dislike of Cowdray into Middle East affairs.

In Mexico, after November 1913, a continuous crisis began for Aguila, as the rivals fought over the approaches to the key city of Torreon on whose defence rested the safety of Tampico. For six months, this remained the worst threat. Potrero was occupied by one of Carranza's bands under General Aguilar who demanded a ransom of $200,000 for the oil wells. Cowdray from London, Dr. Hayes and Body from Tampico, bluffed it out until Huerta's troops drove the rebels off. Then in December there was fighting in the suburbs of Tampico and the Aguila refinery was taken and recaptured. Admiral Cradock, British C.-in-C., West Indies, would guarantee only the safety of British lives, not property; but again the threat faded away. Aguila men stayed at their posts—some had been taken out to be shot at Potrero, and then spared, but their nerve held. However the taciturn Hayes was moved to write: 'The strain is beginning to tell on the efficiency of the organization. I trust you will not be expecting too much, at least until conditions become more normal.'(*r*)

In February 1914, President Wilson lifted the arms embargo and fresh supplies poured in for Carranza. Gradually a new Constitutionalist offensive began and by March his forces were again approaching Tampico. However, shortly before April 6th, when it seemed that Torreon and Tampico must fall, the repeal of the Panama Canal Tolls Act was forced through a reluctant Congress, thus freeing the British Foreign Office from its diplomatic commitment.

In one last semi-official effort, Cowdray persuaded Lord Morley, Lord President of the Council and a great friend of Grey, to see the Prime Minister on his behalf. He gave him a concise summary of the essentials of the position: of all his vast interests, only one really mattered, to him and to Britain: 'the Potrero field is our most serious danger spot. We did protect the big well there with concrete to such an extent as almost to make it bomb proof, but the oil leaked out and we had to reopen it. If the machinery and the capping is destroyed, it will flow to waste and most of the field—100 million barrels—will drain through it.'(s)

Asquith felt he must act and told Morley: 'Our best plan would be to write to Spring-Rice, requesting him to state the facts to the U.S. Government; the injury to oil producers, British and American, the irreparable waste of valuable products and so forth.'(s) And at last the Foreign Office was moved, and it had its effects.

Spring-Rice saw the President on April 8th and made the most of the chance he had waited for. He 'pointed out that H.M.G. *could not remain indifferent* to the immense loss which would be caused, and that it was impossible to say what action would be taken; public opinion in England would have taken a serious view of the menace to such immense British interests within eighteen miles of British ships'.(t)

This was 'quite beyond instructions', but it worked; and at last Cowdray had his help. Only the next day, a crisis came when a party of American sailors were inadvertently arrested by Federal police. The American Admiral issued an ultimatum, Huerta argued it out, and rebels fought in Tampico streets; but the U.S. Consul was told from Washington to warn both sides to respect the oilfields and to get Carranza's promise to this effect. Carranza agreed, though he later repudiated American intervention when the U.S. Marines seized the port. But though the whole imbroglio was removed in May to a mediation conference composed of Argentina, Chile and Brazil, one thing stood safe and certain—the oilfields under joint Anglo-American protection.

Early in May Potrero began to work again. The conference dragged on desultorily and finally accomplished for President Wilson what his threats had failed to do; Huerta's power wasted away and he was forced to resign.

The European War broke out, and fighting continued in Mexico, but the oil pact held good though American distrust of Cowdray still ran high. Other unpleasant facets of Mexican politics were far more important during the War; Villa and Zapata quarrelled with Carranza; Villa invaded American soil; General Pershing led a reprisal raid; Carranza hung on, surviving even the scare of the Zimmerman Telegram, when Berlin sought to use his pro-German feelings, and instead of acquiring an ally, helped to urge America in on the Allies' side.

Potrero was occupied but despite the constant fighting Aguila continued to fulfil the Admiralty contract throughout the war. Body and Hayes knew Cowdray's mind; he had so stamped his personality on the enterprise that his memory remained to guide them. He once said, 'I am as proud of my army as any general could be or ever has been', but it had become too big for a family concern; it was a constant burden to him, and after 1916 when he took on the Air Board he tried to curtail the responsibility. Standard Oil made him an offer in February 1917 and he asked Lloyd George, the Prime Minister, what the Government's attitude would be. Bluntly, he was threatened with D.O.R.A. if he tried to sell. And since he had neither help nor permission, with some doubts he held on.

At the end of the war he got his reward. Both Standard Oil and Royal Dutch were competing for new concessions from Carranza and a wild boom began in Mexican oil. Forecasts were made by competent surveyors that the oil potential was as great as that of the U.S.A. Production, which had been 18 million barrels in 1918, rose to 32 million in 1922.

Henri Deterding of Royal Dutch Shell, who had declined to buy Pierce's concern because he could not trust him, planned a vast merger in the spring of 1919. He approached Cowdray, now free to sell, and offered to buy a controlling block of shares in Aguila, leaving him with the control of his tanker fleet, a large share in profits, and 'perfect peace of mind'. It was the biggest deal he had yet attempted; and Cowdray at last agreed to sell. He was prospecting widely again, pursuing the lure of oil in a dozen countries and perhaps he had some prophetic sense of what was to come.

For, as Obregon succeeded Carranza, the great Potrero well, which had given 100 million barrels, turned to salt water. Doheny's Casiano followed; and by 1923 the sanguine estimates of Mexican production had been cut by half. Not least among Cowdray's talents must be reckoned a fair share of luck: by then his world-wide explorations were over, and the twenty-year obsession was finally quiet. One of the greatest contractors, he had become, through enormous difficulties, one of the greatest oil kings. Aguila was big—even Deterding called its acquisition 'one of the biggest deals ever handled'. And even Marxist writers were prepared to recognize the stature of such men:

'Their imperialism is a universal danger. But since it is neither cowardly, nor purely egotistic, it does not lack a certain greatness. And though their efforts may cause widespread harm, they do at least tend to develop to the utmost an economic equipment which may one day be turned to the profit of the masses of mankind.'(*u*)

Ambassador Page wrote to President Wilson just before the 1914 War: 'I believe that if Taft had had another four years, Cowdray would have owned Mexico, Ecuador, and Colombia ... with such a grip on their Governments as would have amounted to a mortgage. The more I learn, the surer I become that these countries owe their freedom from this dictatorship to you.'(*v*) Perhaps it was true—Cowdray's influence was one of the greatest in the long tradition of British 'economic imperialism' in Central America—and it was succeeded inexorably by that of the United States.[1]

---

[1] Aguila survived as an English company until its expropriation by President Cardenas in 1938; but it had none of the *political* power of Cowdray.

7

WAR

During the Mexican years the firm had carried on at the same high pitch as in the decade before, but Cowdray had taken less part in it. The machine ran smoothly; its reputation was beyond parallel; and his subordinates were capable, under his eye only as a last resort, of doing all that he could himself.

So between 1906 and the war, Pearsons built the new harbour at Belem de Pará, giving to the navigable entrance of the Amazon a modern port instead of the wooden wharves and shallow waters which had compelled the rubber trade to be carried on from lighters. The contract differed from others only in the fierce currents and poisonous water-snakes in the muddy tide of the estuary. Brazilian labour worked under English direction; and, as at Vera Cruz, the drainage and clearance of the foreshore left Pará almost free from yellow fever and malaria.

During these years the others in the firm had their best chances. Sir Frederick Hopkinson extended Aird's Hull Joint Dock to make it the biggest harbour on the east coast, north of London. The main basin was opened by King George V in 1914 and remained for years the best coal dock in the country.

From 1912 until 1914, when the Port of London Authority took it over, Hopkinson then worked on the Royal Albert Dock Extension and Edward Pearson came forward at last, having been somewhat shadowed by his elder brother. He negotiated in Chile and won the contract for Valparaiso Harbour; a work which lasted him from 1912 for twelve years until he died. The contract was worth £4½ millions in all and eventually gave Chile the largest harbour on the Pacific coast of

South America. Work had only just begun when war broke out; and he had to come home for his brother was more than ever busy.

Cowdray's first need after August 1914 was to secure the supply of oil. Aguila had to maintain the Admiralty contract as a patriotic duty; and this occupied Clive Pearson fully throughout the war years. Mexican affairs remained a constant headache, but he relied on the Anglo-American agreement, and in fact, though the Eagle Oil Transport Co. was requisitioned, and he lost three vessels by torpedoes and had five others damaged, Cowdray delivered over three million tons of oil in the four years of war. Perhaps even more than the courage of the men at Potrero, was that of the Eagle Company crews, sitting targets for submarines on a highly explosive cargo.

A great part of the firm's labour force was eventually called up; and the war works were more those of skilled direction than actual construction. Cowdray's own special skills were so much in use that he preferred it so. After the munitions scare of 1915, the Asquith Government decided to build a new, co-ordinated factory at Gretna to turn out 40,000 tons of cordite a year. This included, with all the plant, a township for 20,000 workers, spread over a 50-square-mile area near Carlisle, all to be built in eighteen months. Work began in August 1915 under the new Ministry of Munitions and the £9 million contract was divided between a large number of firms and subcontractors. The result was chaos, with which the Ministry was quite unable to deal. It needed as they found: 'a firm with long experience in the carrying out of the largest contracts'.(a) Cowdray was approached, as the best-known and most experienced industrial organizer in this complicated field. He took it exactly like a civilian contract; stipulating that Edward Pearson, who was to manage the work, should have a completely free hand, a thing unheard of by any Government Department. Since he was manifestly the best man available, the Ministry gave way, and Edward Pearson and the firm's staff succeeded in bringing the factory to production in thirteen months; reaching full blast by June 1917. 125 miles of railway, a huge central power house, chemical laboratories, the vast, intricate plant, and the new town were laid out: and the Ministry gratefully acknowledged the Pearson touch.[1] Like Brassey in the Crimea, the specialist civilian could still rescue a Government in

[1] 'The rapid progress realized was due in large measure to the success with which this firm co-ordinated and systematized the work of individual contractors.'(b)

trouble. In 1917 the King and Queen came to Gretna, and Edward Pearson received his knighthood.

Thereafter, there were, in 1917, the submarine defences of the Thames and of Dover Harbour, and when the Allied High Command decided to build a factory near the front line at Chateauroux to turn out the colossal sum of 1,000 tanks a month, to break the enemy with massive force, Cowdray took the work at cost price. Hopkinson was in charge of the site and the difficulties taxed even his inventive genius and stubborn, angular personality, for there were endless breakdowns of transport, labour, and materials and at least six nationalities at work. In the end the peace came before it was finished.

The firm, then, had 'done its bit'. Cowdray's own personal genius for organization was, however, used as that of few civilians in war. He had received a Viscountcy from Asquith before the split which drove him from power but, though all his allegiances were with the defeated Prime Minister, he responded to the offer which Lloyd George made him in December 1916 to take over the Presidency of the Air Board; for here clearly was a task of the greatest importance; something new, pioneering, and where his predecessors had manifestly failed.

The Air Board had had an unsatisfactory war history. The essential trouble was that flying was still in its infancy when war began. The R.F.C., formed in 1912, and the R.N.A.S., were regarded by their Army masters and the Admiralty as useful adjuncts to the main battle. There was, before 1916, no question of, no interest even, in a unified air service since none of the military or naval directors could conceive of any use for such a thing. But, as the design of machines, skill of pilots, and the course of the static war progressed, the two air corps became of greater importance and in the process began to achieve a separate identity, bitterly resented by the old Services as a possible encroachment on their powers.

The Zeppelin raids of 1915–16 had forced Asquith to appoint a Committee to devise some way of co-ordinating the supply and hand-over of aircraft to the Services. Lord Derby, who took charge for six weeks, gave this up in despair, and Lord Curzon replaced him. In May 1916 he reported in favour of the creation of an Air Board and became its first President. For the moment its powers were purely advisory and the presence of representatives of Army, Navy, and Ministry of Munitions (responsible for the manufacture of aircraft) on the Board seemed to ensure that it could take no independent action. To Curzon, chafing under Asquith's 'war weariness', this eventually became intolerable and was one of the chief irritants which drove him into the Lloyd George camp before the Coalition. His arguments, however were congenial to the new Prime Minister—and in December 1916 new legislation gave the status of Minister to the President and made his Board a Ministry.

However well this worked on paper, in practice it was cursed by sheer lack of aircraft. On the Western Front, Haig, and Trenchard, commanding the R.F.C., were being made powerless in face of German air superiority, the masses of machines of the era of Richthofen; while the Admiralty hung on to their R.N.A.S. planes idle at Dunkirk. The supply forecasts remained depressingly low and showed no possibility of rapid increase.

Lloyd George offered this *damnosa hereditas* to Cowdray because he was 'an organizing brain of the first order'. Irked by Haig's perpetual complaints, he called in a gifted outsider to break the deadlock. Though nothing but opposition to the new appointment can have been expected from the Service chiefs, on January 2nd, 1917, Sir Sefton Brancker wrote to Trenchard: 'I think he could be all right—he is certainly quick in the uptake.'(c)

Cowdray hated waste above everything; he was not a strategist but saw that to get the full use out of the existing capacity all inefficiency had to be stamped out, and all functions grasped under a tight central control. He never hesitated to lay down the law; and as a result he was shortly able to tell the Prime Minister; 'Today the Departments concerned ... have arrived at an agreement as to their varied functions in connexion with the Air Service. I am thankful to report that the draft Charter will be an agreed document.'(d) In the Hotel Cecil under his tireless, equable direction, the Board was solving the administrative problem.

The question of supply of planes was more difficult and Cowdray's industrial experience served him well, as, alternatively with threats and cajolery, he unblocked the channels of production, simplifying everywhere and ruthlessly sacking and bludgeoning as he needed. Early in 1917 he found Rolls-Royce production lagging and threatened to put in a Ministry of Munitions manager if it did not improve. During the Nivelle offensive the shortage reached such grave proportions that Haig and Trenchard were desperate. But the effect of the improvement was felt, and two months later Cowdray could write to Lloyd George:

'The Air Board is now turning out each week as many machines as were turned out in a month last year. By the end of 1917 it will be turning out fully ten times as many as it was in summer 1916.'(e)

So the second battle was being won. Nothing of comparable efficiency had ever happened on the Board. But in Cowdray's mind, greatly influenced by his technical expert, Sir William Weir, a new scheme was forming. Out of the new production figures he could see a number of planes which he called the 'Surplus Aircraft Fleet' and planned to use them as a long-range bomber group to strike far into Germany at industrial targets. To conduct operations of such complexity, however, he must have a full Air War Staff.

When hints of this scheme reached Haig and Trenchard, they were understandably furious. Haig had seen and was deeply upset by the demoralization of the French Army after Nivelle's catastrophic failure; at last he was receiving the machines he needed, but in face of heavy losses the demands rose constantly and he felt these 'surplus' aircraft should be used for the starved Western Front, not for madcap schemes of bombing; and he regarded as arrant presumption the mention of an Air Staff with executive power. The War Office and the C.I.G.S., Sir William Robertson, were equally put out by the proposed encroachment. Despite Cowdray's negotiating skill this opposition would no doubt have been too formidable; but on June 13th the whole picture changed with the first daylight bomber raid on London.

The damage was small, but the shock to morale great. The Cabinet wanted reprisals; Lloyd George suggested the immediate bombing of Mannheim. Then, in succession, drawing Trenchard's over-extended defences from one shore to the other, the Germans bombed St. Omer, the Allied Headquarters, and on July 7th London again. The capital was severely shaken, as was the Prime Minister. Though reprisal bombing was for the moment impossible, it had become a political necessity. And the whole basis of the Air Board began to shift.

At an Air Board meeting on July 11th Cowdray pointed out that the Board could hardly continue its affairs and the organization of defence against air raids by meeting once a week; it must have a permanent staff. While he was convincing and cajoling his colleagues, the Cabinet met in a more radical mood and called in the South African, General Smuts, to take charge of a Committee and report on, firstly, defence against air raids, secondly the general organization and direction of air operations. Smuts the same day told Cowdray 'The War Cabinet opinion was that the Board *should control air policy*'.

Smuts, vital in his enthusiasm, made him a convert to his view of the future of air fighting. At first Cowdray was uncertain: 'I felt that during the war to attempt to create an independent air service . . . was not wise nor practical, especially so, owing to the opposition of the Admiralty to any such scheme . . . but I am driven to request that the Air Board should now be turned into a permanent Ministry . . . so as to place it in a position to secure a war staff of recognized experts. This staff would recommend to the Board the policy which ought to be followed.'(*f*)

Smuts took a brief two months to prepare the Report which changed air history—an almost apocalyptic vision of air power, which as Trenchard sceptically observed was more suited to a war of the future than of 1917. As Cowdray himself admitted, it seemed unwise to upset the whole organization when it was at last beginning to work; but the Smuts Report was approved by the Cabinet and a Committee set up to prepare the necessary legislation.

Through September Lloyd George seemed listless and the War Cabinet made no further move until on September 4th/5th, night bombing began again, the German planes following the line of the Thames and dropping bombs with impunity on the East End and the docks.

Lloyd George, always sensitive to public opinion, was faced with another report from Smuts on shortages of aircraft, and similar protests from Haig. Out of these crossfires the Aerial Operations Committee (Sir Eric Geddes, Lord Derby, Lord Cowdray, and Churchill, Minister of Munitions) emerged, and became at the beginning of October the War Priorities Committee with full power to assign all priorities of munitions supply. At last something like central direction was being achieved. Even so, on October 10th, Cowdray told Admiral Mark Kerr that he felt certain the bombing force would never materialize. Kerr wrote a furious memorandum to Lloyd George, pointing out that this was just what the Germans wanted, and its effect on the War Cabinet at this stage seems to have been curiously decisive; for on October 15th Bonar Law, Leader of the House of Commons announced that the Government would bring in a Bill to create the new Air Ministry.

Cowdray had a reasonable expectation of this office, though he did not greatly relish it. 'When London is half levelled', he told Weir, 'someone will have to be lynched, presumably the Cabinet. Hence I do not particularly desire the job, but someone must face the music.'(g) And on 21st November Lord Crawford, introducing the Bill to the House of Lords, said, 'this progress was made possible only by the power of organization, by the experience in handling big things, by the knowledge of men possessed by Lord Cowdray'.

But such compliments came too late. Lloyd George, highly sensitive to the power of the Press, had been shaken by the outcry to which the air raids had given voice; his situation seemed unpleasantly close to that of Asquith a year before. The most vocal of the Press Lords, Northcliffe of the *Daily Mail* and *The Times*, having completed a successful tour with the British Mission in the U.S.A. was due home in November. 'Haig's kettledrum', as the Prime Minister called him, was a political force and could be a danger if he started to attack the Coalition with a new 'Munitions scare', so he wrote to Northcliffe offering him the Air Ministry.

On November 15th Cowdray opened his *Times* and read Northcliffe's reply.

'Dear Prime Minister,

I have given anxious consideration to your repeated invitation that I should take charge of the new Air Ministry.' [Then followed his reasons for refusal—a curious blend of self-righteous advertisement, unrealistic criticism and spite.] 'I have just returned from the virile atmosphere of the U.S.A. and Canada ... and I can do better work if I maintain my independence and am not gagged by a loyalty that I do not feel towards the whole of your Administration.'

It was a calculated insult to the man he despised.

Cowdray was furious. Weir found him drafting a flaming rejoinder and persuaded him to tone it down. There was no recourse with Lloyd George. So he wrote simply:

'It ought not to have been left for me to receive from Lord Northcliffe's letter in *The Times* the first intimation that you desire a change in the Air Ministry and I think ... you cannot be surprised to receive my resignation.' Lloyd George wrote a flattering reply, and cited Northcliffe's 'experience' with the American Air Force. Cowdray coldly shot it down. 'I have to admit, that my many years of intimate knowledge of America ... do not permit me to concur in your expressed reason for the desired change.' Though his family raised a hymn of hate, Cowdray never again said more than 'he should have written'.

But he had no further dealings with this Government. Lord Rother-mere, Northcliffe's brother, took his place.

Perhaps the fairest comment on his work was that of the official historian. Cowdray was not the sole influence in creating the Air Ministry, but his work made it possible; 'It is written clear in the minutes of the 150 meetings of his tenure of the Air Board. He had to guide men of conflicting interests, equipped with inadequate powers. The agenda . . . was usually a crowded one, made up of items of great diversity, but the discussions under his direction were business-like and the decisions . . . prompt and clear-cut.'(h) It was also no mean achievement to have dealt for nine months with Trenchard, Haig, Robertson, and the rest and never quarrelled once.

8

THE CHANGING WORLD

THE WAR seemed not to have disturbed him greatly. He was schooled by Mexican affairs to revolutionary changes and, more than most of the industrialists of the twenties, though far older, he was fitted to meet the postwar slumps, labour unrest and collapse of security. He had not lost any of his financial acumen. In 1918, in an intensely nationalist outburst of feeling, the bankers Lazard et Cie of Paris became worried about their wholly controlled subsidiary Lazards of London. It seemed necessary to bring in an English partner as well as the English directors already on the Board. Cowdray had had many dealings with their house and Sir Robert Kindersley advised the French directors to invite him in. Very large sums were involved but Pearson had no hesitation in accepting.

To all appearances the firm was untouched and ready to reconstruct. He was not yet tired of work; planning a prodigious oil exploration in a dozen countries, an electrical network for Chile, a new coal and iron industry for Kent. Though he was always threatening to resign, nothing was further from his mind. Asked for his comment on the prewar history of the firm, he replied; 'What a great many opportunities we missed!' He could say again: 'Never lose that last £100,000 —you can make the rest again.' But the bright future faded: the first plans were cut short as a world tide set inexorably against the contractor, and about 1920 he had a recurrent illness which, though not serious, at sixty-five betrayed his age.

What was not clear, not even much before the late twenties, was that the economy of 1914, interlocked and underpinned in a remarkable way, had been destroyed.

War had created, out of absolute necessities, a new extent of Government control. Government factories, public works, regulations of the economy—much of this had to be dismantled with peace but the experience and knowledge remained. Housing was an obvious example in most European countries: and many States began to take railway companies and further construction under public ownership. New works such as airports and harbours had more and more the aspect of national undertakings. 'After 1919 . . . the increased burden of overhead costs made the position of various types of large-scale enterprise precarious and discouraged new (private) investment in them.'(a) Moreover, when Governments paid for public works, they wanted better terms than the contractors' 5 per cent cost plus profit, and increasingly developed their own Public Works Departments—using the experience and ability of men such as Cowdray had trained. And many of the works were now so large that even contractors on Cowdray's scale could no longer undertake them alone.

These were the symptoms of a fundamental change. The balance of international finance of the years before 1914 had been upset. War had cut off many channels of trade and shifted others permanently. In most of the combatant countries vast budget deficits of war finance led to inflation and lack of confidence kept profits, also inflated, from being reinvested. Business relationships and the long groundwork which led to contracts were disrupted; bad currencies appeared, and contracting took on again the uneasy speculative tinge of Brassey's day. In the 1920s economies were adapting themselves to changes which the shrewdest brains could not fully appreciate—it was not a time for the private contractor, dependent on successive contracts to keep his firm continuously employed. Central Europe was collapsing into wild inflation; war reparations loaded the world capital market with huge sums unrelated to the normal channels of commerce; and the settlement achieved at Locarno, on whose promise of stability the return to the Gold Standard was made in Britain, proved a peculiarly false dawn.

So it was not perhaps surprising that Sir Clarendon Hyde noticed in 1923 that work was not coming in as it used to—and that this was no reflection on the capabilities of the firm.

At the end of the War, however, Cowdray was preparing for a new oil offensive. Mexico, though it promised to be even more profitable, could hardly be further developed as Standard Oil and Royal Dutch moved in. But the invincible temptation of oil moved him to prospect, even in England. The Government had decided to drill for oil at home and made, in September 1918, an agreement with him, as the most experienced Englishman, to develop British resources as Government representative.[1] Though a monopoly, it was scarcely profitable because Cowdray put the firm's knowledge and organization at the Government's disposal in return for a grant of £1 million—and worked for three years, without profit, till it was spent. The War Cabinet 'considered it a matter of greatest urgency', not only to get oil, but to prevent the indiscriminate drilling which had bedevilled many American fields. Oil was struck near Chesterfield but the small flow petered out after four years, and though some was found in the eleven other areas, British oil was not, at that time, a commercial proposition. In 1922 what had been essentially a wartime expedient was wound up.

But the Whitehall Petroleum Corporation, set up by Cowdray with Lord Murray as its chairman, pursued its master's dreams in Canada, China, Colombia again, Algeria, Argentina, France, Greece, Morocco, Tunisia, and Mesopotamia. The results were entirely negative; either the concession had no oil, or it was already the subject of national ambitions and consolidated opposition. The world of 1905 and the pioneers had disappeared for ever. China wanted a loan of £1 million in return for a concession. France objected to his control of the Oran Oil Co. and Cowdray lost £100,000 prospecting in the Sahara. The Argentine concession was vetoed on political grounds. The international forces centred in oil were now too powerful for any private freelance company. So in this, as in Mexico, Cowdray finally abandoned the great passion of his life.

His plan for Kent, however, was more promising and perhaps equally ambitious. From the days of Dover harbour he had taken an interest in developing the undoubted coal resources of the county and the large low-grade iron deposits which also existed, and he believed that good organization backed with sufficient capital could make a new industry pay. He created a partnership with Dorman Long, the steel company, and an enterprise with £3 million capital was founded.

In a memorandum of 1923 he set out what he hoped to achieve: the purchase or long lease of collieries producing $4\frac{1}{2}$ million tons a year, coke works, chalk quarries, brickworks, blast furnaces to produce half a million tons of pig iron a year, steel works and rolling mills, railway rolling-stock and workshops, foundries for the surplus

[1] Cowdray had already done some research on sources in England.

pig iron,[1] an interest in foreign ores to mix with Kentish, and an interest in, or ownership of a port and shipping lines. Betteshanger and Snowdown collieries were bought, and in 1926, when they were producing 1¼ million tons a year, the combine was given a £2 million Government guarantee loan to help it forward.

In other times it could have been a very great business and a remarkable example of co-ordinated production. To meet the objections that it would deface the 'Garden of England' elaborate precautions were taken against pollution and the best designs commissioned for industrial buildings, which should blend with their surroundings, like the model town of Saltaire which Cowdray had longed to emulate since he first admired it forty years before, and noted: 'The importance of such things. To beautify one's surroundings and introduce order & methods & cleanliness where such things are not, became to me an end in themselves.'

But the enterprise suffered as the Coal Strike followed the guarantee loan; iron and steel were seen to be in the throes of a vast depression, and, though he carried it through 1926, Cowdray never saw the scheme make a profit. The ore was very low-grade—at a time when development elsewhere was concentrated on higher; and the seams of coal were poorer than he had thought; but the worst difficulty was labour. In an agricultural county the craft of mining had to be created and he was compelled to bring in men from the depressed areas—who were unable to settle into the new surroundings. His enthusiasm for the final integration grew less, though he himself put £1½ million into it—the same sum which twenty years before he had been prepared to risk in Mexican oil.

He was disappointed; though he felt that if he had directed it personally the result would have been different; and the largest contract which the firm finished in the 1920s had to be his compensation. Since he had lost the Aswan tender to John Aird he had always wanted to work on the Nile, and never having built a dam in his life, tendered for the Sennar Dam in 1922.

Like most Nile projects, it had had a chequered history. Between the fast-flowing Blue Nile, and the slow White Nile emerging from the Sudd, lies the great plain of Gezira, running up to Khartoum where the rivers meet; a dusty windy plain, cultivated in patches where a slight rain falls. There had been plans to irrigate it after Kitchener's recon-

[1] He hoped to make the lining for the Channel Tunnel.

quest of the Sudan and, after Aswan was heightened, some 20,000 acres were actually reclaimed. But the problem remained that water taken here meant less for Egypt.

In 1914 Kitchener approved a double plan; a barrage at Gebel Aulia on the White Nile and a dam at Sennar on the Blue. Ultimately it was hoped to irrigate three million acres of the fertile 'black cotton' soil and put it under cotton. At least 300,000 acres were needed to make the project economically possible. War postponed any futher development. Afterwards, the Sudan Construction Company began work and in two-and-a-quarter years had completed only part of the work when the Sudan Government found it too costly to proceed and had to cancel the contracts. A rapid rise in prices of labour and materials had put all pre-war estimates out. The Governor-General pressed Whitehall hard for help and eventually, when Pearson, with his great prestige, offered to take over the dam the British Government gave way and guaranteed the interest on a Sudan loan of £3½ million for construction.

Having pulled the Administration out of its jam it remained to build with extraordinary speed to get the benefit of the first year's cotton crop as fast as possible. The design of the dam was not unlike Aswan; a two-mile wall with two rows of sluices, the top gates being fitted so that the overflow fell between the main gates. The wall was to be 128 feet high, rather less than Aswan. The river valley narrows at Sennar and a long outcrop of granite in the bed, with an island mid-steam, gave a solid foundation. But there remained vast excavation for the central 2,000 yards, and the 'unwatering' of the river either side of the island.

Very careful planning had to be made and a time schedule stricter even than at Dover, for the whole foundations of one side had to be finished before the flood, or it would be torn away; a work on a far larger scale than the five sections of Aswan. Cowdray never actually went out, sending Sir Frederick Hopkinson to take charge on the spot, but he planned it in the greatest detail, including the time schedule, filling his notebooks with sketches and calculations. It was, in a way, a living proof that he had not lost to old age his mastery in a race against unpredictable elements. Hopkinson was a difficult man to manage, and at this distance often got his own way. He was tactless and frequently rude; two failings which Cowdray disliked: 'That's not the way, but H. will do that sort of thing.' But Hopkinson had an intractable genius which reached its best on the Nile.

Work began in October 1922 as soon as the flood had gone down. In that season the western half was dammed, the foundations dug and 5,000 feet built to its full height, leaving a narrow, reinforced gap between the wall and the island. In the 1923–4 season the low river was diverted through this and the eastern, deeper channel unwatered, where excavation was far harder, often in rotten rock, and done partly by machinery and partly by fellaheen labour. A force larger than Aird's, of 20,000 men, was employed; the stone was cut from a granite quarry and brought in by rail, and the cement made locally to cut costs. 1,650 feet here were built to full height before the flood; this being the critical moment, for if any part of the wall was lost it would carry with it £2 million worth of the first year's crops. High flood submerged all the works, but they survived unharmed; and in the 1924–5 season both gaps were closed as early as April. The gates were fitted, 585 miles of canal in the Gezira finished, with regulators and sluices, and the whole enterprise delivered in June 1925, two months before contract date.

Lord Lloyd, High Commissioner in Egypt, opened it proudly a year later and by then the 300,000 acres were growing cotton. Such a feat in thirty-one months was unprecedented; made possible only by abundant supply of labour and Cowdray's ambition. Hopkinson earned the firm's £150,000 bonus and told Cowdray it had cost him quarter of a million to do it.

In spite of the war, the firm was still a model of organization, patience, good labour relations: Cowdray was still the architect of success although he said 'no man but Hopkinson could have done it'. And it was he, untiring, who, when Sir Edward Pearson had nearly finished the £4 million project at Valparaiso (before he died in 1925), perhaps the hardest harbour work[1] the firm undertook, launched into the electricity industry. With some of the Shell money from Mexican Eagle, Cowdray bought up the confiscated German enterprise of Weinher Beit in Chile: several small electric light and power companies, and extended them, with hydro-electric power plants, to make the Compañía Chilena de Electricidad, supplying the whole central region of Santiago and Valparaiso and electrifying the Transan-

---

[1] A massive breakwater had to be built in very deep water on a treacherous foundation, against the unfettered swell of the Pacific, its violent storms and earthquakes. It was done at last by creating monolithic blocks of concrete, 12,000 tons each, and by sinking caissons and filling them solid.

dean Railway. In 1929, after his death, it was sold to the United States.

At the same time, the firm built the Littleton Reservoir, then the largest in the world, for the Metropolitan Water Board; which was opened by King George V in 1925. Thereafter there were few contracts, and smaller, as Cowdray began to shut down the contracting side of his complicated industrial empire.

After 1925, after Sennar, he at last began to retire and take some of the leisure he had promised his wife so long. They lived more at Dunecht, and round themselves created family life again with their grandchildren. The hectic tempo of life slowed down. Queen Mary often used to stay; Annie Cowdray was one of her great friends and there was one hobby of which they never tired; to go to the cedarwood linen cupboards and pat the piles of linen sheets, the seal of perfect housekeeping. Lady Cowdray pursued her collecting; at Carlton House Terrace amassing the rich and, for the unappreciative age, remarkable, collection of French furniture. Cowdray watched the progress of his grandchildren in mathematics and gave them prizes for designing a maze in the gardens at Paddockhurst.

He had ten granddaughters to one grandson; and so offered one a place in the firm 'as if she were a man' if she went to Cambridge and read engineering. When he showed her the plans of Sennar, at his vast desk, bare of all other papers, she remarked, 'Oh, I see—the stress goes through the middle third', and Cowdray replied, 'I don't know anything about that, but it looks the right shape!' He loved to tease them—bursting in at breakfast with the news that floods at Sennar had swept away half the work; then, relenting, allowing himself a smile. At Christmas he would go round with a pocket full of sovereigns giving everyone in the house a golden handshake. He enjoyed young parties at Dunecht; and when he was ill in London and ordered for afternoon drives he would show them with pride the Blackwall Tunnel and the house in Camden Hill where the family had first lived in London.

Politics became a hobby to be enjoyed and a duty for his past neglect now that there was time; and he found himself deeply committed. In 1908 he had taken a part share in the Liberal *Westminster Gazette* and as others left it he eventually became proprietor. As part of his general support for Asquith it pursued a steady Liberal policy, but after the war, as costs rose, its deficit became alarming and he turned it into a morning paper, when for five years, till he died, it had its heyday.

He enjoyed the world of the Press, believing, as did most politicians of his day, that its powers were greater than they were; but the vagueness of its forecasting, the fluctuating costs of a national newspaper, offended his tidy mind. What mattered most, however, was that by this he was kept in the centre of Liberal affairs.

After the rupture between Lloyd George and Asquith which followed the Maurice Debate, he continued to attend Lord Oxford's Shadow Cabinet and to finance, almost alone, what he believed to be the true Liberal Party. He became in fact, after Lord Inchcape withdrew, almost their chief source of funds, as the *Westminster Gazette* was their only mouthpiece. His opposition to Lloyd George was deeply felt. Naturally the ex-Prime Minister thought the feud had its roots in his Air Board indiscretion, for he wrote in his memoirs, 'the ranks of the anti-Lloyd George Liberals received an influential recruit and in postwar years the Press which he controlled became a vehicle of his implacable resentment and hostility'.(*b*)

This was wholly untrue. Cowdray, not alone, had come to realize the essential instability of the 'marvellous little man' and Lloyd George's conduct in 1926 reinforced the judgement. He failed to attend the Liberal Shadow Cabinet of May 8th in the middle of the General Strike, and made the split final and irrevocable. Cowdray had at least a suspicion of what he was at: that his restless probings to get back to Downing Street had let him make an offer to the Labour Party; and he and eleven others, Lords Simon, Runciman and Grey among them, signed a letter to *The Times*:

'We cannot work with Lloyd George any longer. Confidential re-lations are impossible with one whose instability destroys confidence.'

Thereafter Cowdray made no political sallies. In March 1927, writing to his wife at Dunecht, he said sadly: 'Would that I were with you. But it is wiser for me to go quietly and slowly and avoid the giddy life.'

S. Pearson and Son was already parcelled out. Impartially and with-out regret[1] he decided that the contracting business should die with him, judging his sons to have neither the talent, nor in the late 1920's the chances, to carry it on as fitted. He left them still a wide empire: Whitehall Securities, the holding company; Whitehall Electrical

---

[1] He had no sentimental illusions. Lord Brassey, the contractor's son, once deplored the fact that he had been unable to follow his father. 'Just as well!' remarked Cowdray later.

Investments (Mexico and Chile); the issuing house, Whitehall Trust Ltd., and the interest in Lazards.

In 1919 he gave Cowdray Park to Harold, the eldest son: 'May you and yours enjoy it for many long years—its charm and all the advantages carried by its ownership. It is truly a princely estate, and notwithstanding my camouflage, it was a real test of our love, our passing it.' Every autumn and spring passed at Dunecht, in the broad grounds and woods he loved more even than Paddockhurst, and he amused himself with improvements of the estate and collecting masters of the eighteenth-century English school, Reynolds, Hoppner, Raeburn and Gainsborough.

Benefactions studded his last years; he began the restoration of St. George's Chapel, Windsor, endowed the Royal Air Force Club and the College of Nursing in Cavendish Square. In 1920 he had been made Rector of Aberdeen University and lectured, even then as an industrial Radical, on 'Labour and the Ideal Wage', suggesting how employees could participate in the profits of industry—a lesson lost on the mine-owners and industrialists of the day. And to receive, with his wife, the freedom of the City of Aberdeen he came up to Dunecht in 1927, feeling well after months of a long illness. On May 1st he died there quietly in his sleep. Among his family and tenants, with messages from the King and Queen, a horse drawn cart took his body to the little church-yard at Echt.

The Times' obituary was sonorous and fulsome. American papers came nearer when they spoke of 'his record for daring, originality and ingenuity—one of the greatest pioneers ever sent out by Britain'. To his family he was the greatest loss; to his grandchildren it seemed that a world had ended. Yet rarest of all, he had found what he most desired; the speech he would have given to the citizens of Aberdeen survives:

'I am ignorant of any secret knowledge. . . . There is not any positive or certain method . . . success demands many qualities, unfailing courage, consistency, perseverance, one's best efforts without inter-mission and without rest, and inexhaustible patience. Success is sweet: today truly I realize how profoundly sweet it is, but the joy is in the doing.'

FOUR

Sir John Norton-Griffiths

1

A PIONEER FROM AFRICA

THE INTENSITY of clear light on the high veld makes a man feel tall as the infinite horizon, sharply cut within his reach. In the afternoon heat, lying relaxed in the shade, or at night with the cold wind flicking the canvas of a tent under brilliant stars, anything seems possible.

Those who created South Africa and the Rhodesias, Kenya and Uganda, who imposed themselves not on virgin lands but an old broken continent: Rhodes and Lugard were never quite lifesize. In their element they were giants and outside it, restless, cut short, inexpressive. Rhodes himself, the living legend, at Groote Schuur was a king in his demesne, but in England, brought before the Commission of Inquiry into the Jameson Raid, he made an enigmatic figure, not merely because of his deep implication in that fiasco, but with something quite intangible about him, like the fabulous elephant sent from the Sultan Haroun el Rashid to the astonished medieval court of Pope Innocent III.

Narrowing frontiers and their own insatiable daemon drive the pioneers on into intractable thorny country. There is a type of man for whom the late nineteenth-century drive for Empire gave a forcing ground, for whom wild lands and savage races excited their impulse for dominion, and who, having conquered provinces, moved on, obeying a wanderlust which proved addictive and incurable. Certain nomadic tribes hack land from the forest, cultivate it and move on, leaving the bush to close in behind; and there are gold prospectors who having struck a rich vein will sell the mine to ride out and dig for more.

John Griffiths, son of John Griffiths, small building contractor in Breconshire, ran away from home like a thousand others, but, out of character, did not take ship for the Indies. Born in 1871, a year after Brassey died, he was educated for a while at St. Paul's School and articled at fifteen to a firm of architects. His home background was cramped and overawed by his domineering father's narrow and Nonconformist mind; and he threw up his articles to enlist as a trooper in the Horse Guards, giving his age as eighteen. The disciplined soulless life appealed to him no more than his home and, perhaps fortunately before he broke restraint, he was bought out by Sir Henry Kimber who sent him with his younger son to South Africa.

With little in their pockets the two failed on Kimber's sheep farm in the face of drought and tsetse fly and drifted to the Transvaal in the wake of the great Gold Rush. The wildest days of the Rand were over, as a major industry developed. A town called Johannesburg had grown up in five years on the bare veld, and, where the Widow Oosthuizen's farm, Langlaagte, had been, was the largest five-stamp battery working the conglomerate ore.

But it was still close enough to the pioneer days to carry the authentic flavour of the prospector. Only four years before, Edwin Bray had struck the Golden Quarry of Barberton, and Struben, Confidence Reef, the main Rand, which changed the whole aspect of the Transvaal. A colossal bubble of gold speculation had been punctured only months before Griffiths arrived in 1891 and, though the crash washed away the confidence of foreign investors for a time, it did nothing to stem the influx of foreigners seeking fortunes, the Uitlanders, anathema to the Boers.

But the Rand was not the place for amateur prospectors, if it had ever been. Those in control were experienced men, drawing their fortunes from the earlier diamond strikes at Kimberley; Barney Barnato, Werner Beit, Joseph Robinson. They forced in the smaller men or bought them out, because only money and large-scale operations could make the low-grade ore pay. Griffiths was too late. He beachcombed along, selling buttons, tending bars and graduating at last, like the rest, to small-time prospecting. On his father's building experience he got a good job drilling shafts for the Crown Reef Mine, but he could never resist even the rumour of war and was caught up in the Jameson Raid. Afterwards, restlessness took him and he trekked up into Mashonaland to become a Captain in the British South Africa Police and take part in Rhodes's brief and bloody war against Lobengula.

He collected a few things on the way, mining claims across what was to become Rhodesia, among the barren Matopo Hills, and certain useful friendships, among others that of Barney Barnato and his two adopted sons Solly and Jack Joel; little enough to show for eleven years of drifting, easy come easy go. He might have wandered on to vanish unknown in the interior if his father had not died in 1899 leaving his affairs in confusion. With no more than the mining claims in his pocket, Griffiths sailed back to England. At Zanzibar he met Gwladys Wood, fell in love with her, promised to change his way of life, and asked her to marry him. He would make money, his mining claims were good, he was carried away with expectation; only to find England very different from South Africa. Morosely he longed for freedom, away from the restrictions of English life and the milk-and-water sun, and with the frustration of raging energy flung himself in search of a job on which to marry.

After many letters he persuaded the directors of Rhodes's Chartered Company to help him turn his mining claims into the high-sounding 'Rhodesian Mining and Development Company' and returned to Africa, resigning himself to the separation from his fiancée. Resolution, latent in his character, was beginning to show, but the Boer War intervened and he threw it all up in the cause of Empire and volunteered. As a former freelance veteran he took command of a company of Brabant's Horse and later became Captain and Adjutant of Lord Roberts's Bodyguard, picked scouts with keen knowledge of the country.

This campaign with its small engagements and weeks in the saddle under the hot sky was the year he loved best; a war of scouts, sharpshooters and almost personal encounters under a General he respected more than any other military leader. He fought at Paardeberg and Modder River and was mentioned three times in despatches. All went well up to the relief of Kimberley, but as the war changed character in 1900 an end was made of the amateurs and the Bodyguard disbanded. Disconsolately he came home, to fit in, if possible, less than before; his temperament quite unsuited to conventional behaviour; restrained only by the influence of his fiancée, who at all stages of his life could control the unruly temper—even to sidetracking his determination to break up a pacifist demonstration in Queen's Hall.

Griffiths the rolling stone, with no engineering qualifications or experience but what he had picked up on the Rand, with no capital since the loss of his claims by default, badgered and blustered his way into the offices of contractors, developers, and mining companies; full of ideas, humour, and rich enthusiasm and a personal magnetism which swept aside objection, and could convince the most dubious that he possessed a dynamic business brain.

For eighteen months there was nothing but houses of cards destroyed by the cold suggestions of cash; then a connexion with Herbert Stoneham, a company promoter interested in mining, gave him a chance, in August 1901, to survey a project for alluvial mining in French West Africa.

Stoneham offered him £1,000 to go to America and examine gold dredging plant for the Ivory Coast fields. Griffiths rushed his fiancée and her family home from Germany, married her and began work at once. Back from the States after a whirlwind tour they both wrote his report; and Stoneham, after he had worked up the market in the shares, offered him £5,000 a year as Managing Director on the site.

Though Griffiths was still an employee he had made the first step, for in a year in the grossly primitive life of Grand Bassan, in steaming tropical heat working on 'placer' gold, he learnt most of the mining business and more of machinery. But the best of the field was over, prolonged only by the expensive new machinery and after their first daughter's birth in 1903 they came back. This time there was money in the bank and enough experience to set Griffiths up as a consultant mining engineer in London. Already he had many other important connexions. Through Sir Laming Worthington-Evans he met Frank Hilder, Atholl Thorne, and Temple Paterson, who sent him to Egypt to report on a Nile Valley mining scheme, and when his report was unfavourable, talked to him of their plans to build the Benguella Railway in Angola whose concession they controlled. Highly though they estimated his African knowledge, however, they were surprised when he suddenly offered to build it.

The plan of the Benguella Railway led from the Atlantic coast of Angola up the steep escarpment to the central plain, across 1,000 miles of almost unexplored country to the Belgian Congo border, Katanga and the great mining areas; then on to connect with the Rhodesian copperbelt and the projected Cape to Cairo Line. It was to cut 1,400 miles off the journey from England to Johannesburg, to attract the exports of the mines of all Katanga and Rhodesia; a mining dream, the imperial vision of the surveyor and engineer Robert Williams.

Great difficulties had so far prevented it. By the secret agreement reached in 1898 between Britain and Germany over a loan to relieve the bankrupt Portuguese Government, spheres of influence had been marked out which should be annexed by the two Great Powers if the ramshackle empire dissolved. North Angola was to be British, South, German; and the proposed railway ran between. Also, although Portugal had, by 1904, considerably recovered, and reaffirmed publicly her ancient alliance with Great Britain, the pitch of German colonial ambitions made such a railway, dependent entirely on through traffic, a doubtful investment. The immense length of line and its engineering difficulties added delays, and the first concession ran out for lack of time.

In 1903 it was renewed and Williams found more powerful assistance. He now controlled Tanganyika Concessions, a mining company small compared to the giant of today, but with a 20 per cent holding in, and four directors on the board of, the Union Minière du Haute Katanga itself. He approached George Pauling, then the most experienced railway contractor in Africa, who tried to impose stringent conditions for his assistance and then backed out. Williams turned to his friends in the City of London and found Paterson and the others willing to help. However, although the finances of the Benguella Railway Company were rescued, Pauling held a near monopoly in southern Africa, and it was hard to find another contractor.

Griffiths had watched Pauling build the Beira Railway up to Salisbury in Rhodesia and been fascinated by the sight: the gangs of African labourers on the line, stretching endlessly into the mirage of hot dusty plain; he was convinced he could do the same. He could learn technique quickly, as the gold fields had proved, and handle the most recalcitrant workmen; he could persuade, manage and command, and his relations with the promoters had shown that he could understand some of the complexities of finance.

His wife pleaded that he was an engineer not a contractor, but he would not listen. Impetuously and brilliantly he sketched out his plans to the group and, under the spell of his enthusiasm, they agreed to finance Williams and send Norton-Griffiths to Angola to inspect the work which had already been done. He was still a salaried manager but in complete control on the spot, and he was to find that at the range of 4,000 miles he was not only his own master, but that so long as the finances remained stable, no one but Williams cared for details of construction.

The Benguella terminus proved a port worse and more open than Vera Cruz to Cowdray—but it cost Griffiths only a hundred-pound bribe to get the captain to put into the almost uninhabited Lobito Bay, where an ocean liner could lie in safety four fathoms from the shore, and which became one of the finest natural harbours in the world. Making this the new terminus, Griffiths returned with a highly sanguine report, and in May 1905, with only eighteen months of the concession still to run before the railhead had to reach Katengue 160 kilometres inland, he and his wife sailed out to begin work.

Lobito was still no more than a few tents in the sand; a wooden jetty had been run out to take supplies and rails since his first visit, while across the narrow coastal plain ran the few miles of light track erected by Pauling. In the distance, stark against the morning sun, rose the escarpment, barren, utterly dry, tangled, broken rocks, rising 3,000 feet in 20 miles. This shattered landscape is the 'divide' between two areas of rain—where water never falls, totally uninhabited. Everything, food, water, labour, animals, had to be brought in. And in the face of strong German opposition he was told that unless he could complete the contract in time there could be no extension.

Griffiths set up house in the sandy waste which surrounded Benguella, a squalid colonial outpost riddled with malaria and inertia, where beri-beri and sleeping sickness were endemic. His wife arrived with a few domestic animals from Cape Town to try and make life civilized while he got down to collect the essentials of the railway. There was plenty of engineering advice from Williams and Sir Charles Fox the company's engineer; but little thought had been given to the labour question. The first shipment of 2,000 Malays and Hindu coolies from Natal turned out a motley crowd whose morale was low and who suffered heavily from sickness, disease and drink. Senegalese, shipped down from the Equator, proved better workers and more resistant, but before the work was done in 1907 Griffiths had reached as far as the Cape Verde islands and had at the peak 10,000, to 11,000 men under him. Managing them called for all his talent and variety of dialects from Zulu to Basuto learned in the Rhodesias. In particular he refused to employ Portuguese, using Greeks and other Europeans as his managers, and relying largely on his own driving power and capacity.

Simply to provision this army in the waste called for organizing

Sir John Norton-Griffiths

Benguella Railway. Rack section

Norton-Griffiths (*on right*) and Portuguese officials

genius. He brought in camels from North Africa to carry water in the early stages as the line was flung down across the plain. Workmen were rationed to two bottles a day. The Tropical School of Medicine gave what help it could. But the real race was against time. Three kilometres a day was sometimes laid before the line reached the beginning of the hills—making a racketing switchback track, but one which could be remade properly if the concession was saved.

Facing the jagged walls of rock there was no choice in time, money or distance but to go straight at it through the tangled boulders of the Lengue Gorge, and make a rack railway at the worst section. The alternative was 40 miles of detour, tunnelling and curves. Griffiths called home for engineers to build it on the Riggenbach system and they were shipped straight to Lobito. Meanwhile he made his first contact with Dudley Docker whose Metropolitan Carriage Works were building the rolling stock and who now had to deliver the special locomotives.

The Lengue Gorge had to be blasted smooth every foot of the way, widened and finally surmounted by two miles of the rack, at a gradient of 1 in 16. Even then the wall was not climbed, and for 40 kilometres more the line rose heavily. All the workers came up by engines; the food was out of tins; even in the hills the heat was terrible, beating off the rocks and heavy and humid at night.

Griffiths had malaria but refused to give way for more than a few hours and sweated it out on the track in the sun all day and by electricity at night, rushing the men on up the mountain. In the vivid blue light of arc lamps the Senegalese slaved to clear thousands of tons of rock to build vast embankments across the Gorge. With three days to spare before the term ran out he reached Katengue; and for a moment could rest. All the inhabitants of Benguella rode the first train up the rack and Griffiths left the line for a month to go inland and carry on the survey.

He had saved the promoters the contract and perhaps £200,000. But there remained 1,050 miles to Katanga. With his wife and a hundred natives he set off across the uncharted fertile plains checking the route of the line, prospecting, since Williams had concessions throughout Angola, and trekking as roughly as he had done in Mashonaland. They got back to Lengue in February 1907 and came home, his wife surviving a desperate illness in the boat; to find that his promoters were full of praise. The Portuguese Shipping Line, the Elder Dempster, and Union

Castle were already coming in to Lobito, while in the Congo the Katanga mines were proving their vast worth.

In 1908 Griffiths went out again, carried the survey up the Congo and the Rhodesian connexion and prospected for gold and diamonds without any success. The railway was complete for 250 kilometres beyond the summit to the plateau, and the way ahead was comparatively easy; but a slump in copper shares hit Tanganyika Concessions hard and Williams's syndicate was forced to stop work, for lack of money, soon after Crown Prince Louis of Portugal had opened the first section of the line. George Pauling now stepped in and offered to complete the line on his own terms; and backed by the finance house of Erlanger he carried it on intermittently up to the war. By the time it reached the Congo Frontier in 1929, it had partly been by-passed by the river and railway through the Congo itself and the settled route of the Rhodesian Copperbelt to the eastern coast, which for years deprived Angola of prosperity.

Nevertheless Griffiths had won a name with astonishing speed. His greatest quality, that of making friends, had brought him in touch with pioneers and men who were to be the supports of his future career; yet they were only stepping-stones. There were few real friends he cared about; outside the family, apart from Worthington-Evans, his business associates meant nothing except insofar as they influenced his career.

At thirty-seven he could pass for thirty; tall, unusually handsome, tanned and sporting the moustache of the born imperialist; powerful as a prize-fighter, impetuous and passionate, rarely restrained yet, schooled by domestic satisfaction, no longer foreign to the drawing-rooms of London. Idolized by women, sought after by men; no brilliant talker, but so full of gaiety and fun, enthusiasm and absurdity, he drew everyone to him; while preserving cloaked, except in moments of rare emergency, a nature ruthless and in its crude force, entirely elemental; he was the expression of all that characterized the empire-builders of the Edwardian era.

To a man of his reputation there was to be no more salaried work; he must be his own manager, find his own contracts, win his own battles against the harsh nature which was the only thing to stimulate his ambition. One thing only lacked; Cowdray, Aird, and Brassey had had capital; he had nothing which in the twentieth century could begin to justify him in founding a contracting firm. So he found supporters;

whose only use was that they gave him money, expecting an easy return; light masters until he met trouble and then the more clamant and obtrusive. In an ideal world Norton-Griffiths should have been a *condottiere*, a guerilla general; it was his fate to blunt his energies in the service of a hard master, international finance, and to emerge disillusioned, and drained by the circumstances of his life, with customs and habits which the world had made archaic.

2

THE 'HOUSE OF LORDS'

URING his years at Benguella, Griffiths first met Lord Howard
de Walden, one of the richest men in England, owner of vast
estates in Scotland and substantial areas of property in
London. Howard de Walden put up the money which enabled him to
form, in September 1908, Griffiths and Company, with a capital of
£100,000. Griffiths held all the voting shares and sat with Edward
Powles, de Walden's uncle, on the new board at Griffiths House,
London Wall. Worthington-Evans's firm became the company's
solicitors.

His expert sense of showmanship and timing and the spectacular reputation acquired in Angola, his wild dreams and sure touch in con-
verting fantasy into hard logic, made Griffiths the focus of a number of
speculative forces, interested in quick returns. As a friend of Howard
de Walden he was irreproachable, while his appearance and high spirits
made him famous in the society of the day. Slowly there gathered
round what he called the 'House of Lords', a number of gilded young
men prepared to put money behind his genius without asking questions
how he employed it, so long as they had their profit. Utterly without
snobbery, uninterested in their personalities, Griffiths wanted nothing
more; and Lords Clinton, Leconfield, Fitzwilliam, Newton, and
Harrowby among others took up £310,000 of debentures. With only
four years' experience as a contractor, quite unqualified as an engineer,
Griffiths found himself in as substantial a position as Cowdray had been
only ten years earlier.

To the contractor Sir John Jackson, a bluff, tactless, successful
Yorkshireman, who was trying to obtain the Chilean railway contract
from Arica to La Paz, these resources were tempting, and he proposed

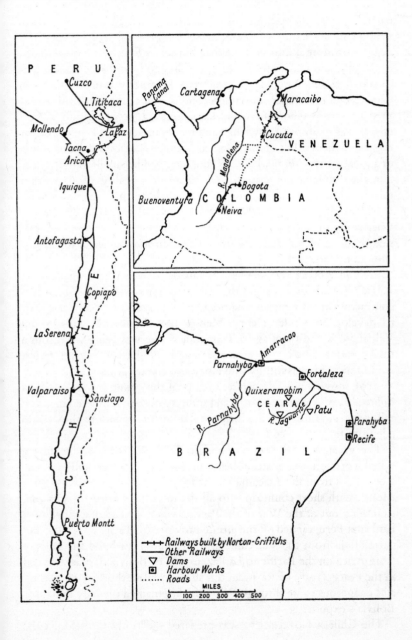

PERU
Cuzco
L.Titicaca
Mollendo
La Paz
Tacna
Arica
Iquique
Antofagasta
C H I L E
Copiapó
La Serena
Valparaiso
Santiago
Puerto Montt

Panama Canal
Cartagena
Maracaibo
Cucuta
VENEZUELA
R. Magdalena
Bogota
Buenoventura
COLOMBIA
Neiva

Amarracao
Parnahyba
Fortaleza
Quixeramobim
CEARA
R. Parnahyba
R. Jaguaribe
Patu
Parahyba
Recife
BRAZIL

Railways built by Norton-Griffiths
++++ Other Railways
▽ Dams
⊡ Harbour Works
...... Roads

MILES
0   100   200   300   400   500

partnership. He himself had been unable to get support for so large a venture in a country of poor financial reputation and he needed a negotiator more skilful and able than himself in South American affairs.

Griffiths saw it as a great chance, for though he disliked Jackson personally (a feeling cordially reciprocated) the other was undoubtedly an experienced contractor, ranking second or third among British entrepreneurs, from whom he could learn much. One of Griffiths's great talents was to absorb knowledge and techniques, not of engineering or economic theory, but of management, business tactics and the handling of a great enterprise; neither now, nor later had he any head for figures nor the fundamental critical and calculating ability of Cowdray; thrown almost by chance from being a manager into the harsh adult world of the international contractors he had to make up the deficiency by his superabundant energy and resource—to develop, outside the firm in public relations, and within it as leader, a touch fine enough to correct the balance.

Early in 1909 an arrangement was made between the finance house, Régie Générale de Paris and the 'Howard Syndicate' to assist the two contractors in the Chilean scheme. Until 1900 railways had been slow to develop in Chile. Henry Meiggs had connected Santiago and Valparaiso in the 1860s and a Transandean line was being cut through to Argentina, but in the immense length of the country the fastest communication was still by ship along the coastal ports. The civil war of 1891 showed how desperately regional the country was, and, as a political as well as an economic and military necessity, ushered in a vast railway programme—for which the state of the economy showed no adequate financial recourse.

The greatest need was the Longitudinal Railway—a line like a spinal cord on the plateau between the high Andes and the sea, 2,000 miles from the Atacama Desert to the rain forest south of Puerto Montt, with short connexions to all the towns and ports. In addition, stemming out of the War of the Pacific, when she had descended on a bankrupt Peru, carried off the nitrate provinces of Tacna and Arica, and cut Bolivia from the sea, Chile was committed to build the railway from Arica on the Pacific to La Paz, capital of Bolivia. It was specified in the Peace Treaty of 1904 that this should replace the slow, circuitous, and dangerous route through Peru which remained the only outlet for Bolivia's exports.

The Chilean Government was prepared and ready to construct the

Longitudinal south from Santiago; it looked to foreign capitalists to help with the northern section; and hoped to palm off the onerous obligations of the 'strategic' route to Bolivia. For five years they could find no help; a Chilean syndicate failed; the route was changed; Cowdray dabbled in the idea and withdrew; a German firm tendered but could not raise the money. Meanwhile Bolivia became worried, seeing put off indefinitely the export of her minerals. Only with the French support was the contract assigned to Griffiths and Jackson at a price of £4 million, half as much again as the original Chilean tender.

In May 1909 Griffiths sailed for Chile; workmen under Jackson were already on the spot renovating what had already been built of the line. The original route across the coastal plain from Arica was intended to climb the great Andean range by the Llute valley, but its curves and gradients had proved so difficult that the railway was forced to claw out of the valley by a rack section similar to Benguella. This decision was as far as the Chileans had got.

Skilled workmen as well as machinery and all the rails were shipped out from England; workshops set up in Arica, and material sent up by the Peruvian line to La Paz to begin work from the Bolivian end. No expense was spared to make the line a monument to engineering skill, as its undoubted difficulties warranted, and in view of the highly prosperous Bolivian trade which it was hoped to carry and the terms on which they were absolved from having to raise the money themselves, the two Governments had made few objections to a tender increased by so large an amount in three years.

Griffiths, on his first South American visit, set out to project his image as widely as he could, correctly judging that here was unlimited scope for British enterprise. Chile was not alone in its ambitious public works scheme; so he made contacts in Brazil, met Jackson in Buenos Aires and spent a fortnight in high Argentine society; stood at the National Day Military Parade in the President's party; and not till June, in midwinter, was ready to set out for Chile. Such interest and his lavish hospitality was as flattering to Latin Americans as Cowdray's solicitude for Mexican feelings.

But the best rewards were waiting on the west coast, and he and his wife set out, disdaining the Cape Horn passage, to cross the Andes. The Transandean tunnel was not completed, and in deep snow and bitter cold they crossed on mules the 12,000-foot pass above Las Cuevas past the sombre lonely Christ of the Andes with arms outstretched almost under the shadow of Aconcagua.

Such an entry struck popular imagination in Chile, where the local contractors had worked up a certain feeling against the foreign entrepreneur. The Press described Mrs. Griffiths as 'una señora muy intrepidosa y corragiosa' and Santiago did all it could to welcome them. Dinners with the leading families, race meetings, parties, repeated the pattern of the Cowdrays in Mexico City; only Griffiths made a far more ebullient and remarkable figure. (Jackson was less *simpatico*; typically, at a dinner in Panama, given to celebrate the cutting of the Canal, he was asked what his most striking impression was, and replied blandly that 'when it rained every workman put up his umbrella'.) Before the party left the capital, Griffiths had signed on his own behalf, in the face of stiff American opposition, a contract for the largest share of the Longitudinal.

They sailed up the barren coast, with its islands coated in a thousand years of guano, to Arica, where his wife left for home and he faced the drought, desert and the desperate winter cold of the mountains. Already the rack railway, thirty miles of the Abt system, was being built. Conditions were harsh. Before they trekked over the summit along the route to reach La Paz Griffiths and his foreman were reduced to sleeping in one fleabag with a bottle of brandy between them to stop it freezing. The workmen were an unruly crowd—even in the valley it was hard to keep them quiet and properly housed; a mixed lot of peons who worked well, drank heavily, fought wildly and averaged not less than two murders a week.

The 275-mile line rose 7,500 feet from the Llute valley through four tunnels and loops to Puquios. Winding on the ridges of the mountains, often supported only by immense dry stone walls, it passed through more tunnels and a deep gorge, finally climbing out of this tangle of spurs on to the cold dry slopes of the *altiplano*, till at General Lagos, bleak, flat and windswept on the back of the Andes, it reached 13,500 feet, the highest railway then to be built. Across the Bolivian plateau the going was easier and the line reached out to meet it from La Paz; the whole was inaugurated with the usual ceremony in 1913.

Both contractors did immensely well; and deserved their reward. Bolivian external trade in 1911 doubled its 1905 total; for not only was the route 250 miles shorter, safer and efficient throughout the year, but

Arica made a first-rate port. Minerals and oils flowed down; cereals, sugar and food up; the treaty was preserved and the conquered provinces finally voted their nitrate wealth by plebiscite into the Chilean nation.

Griffiths immediately took up the Longitudinal; in his name the Howard syndicate had accepted nearly 500 miles, far the largest individual section. However, so ambitious was the whole programme and set on such uneasy credit, that Griffiths exacted heavy terms; the syndicate undertook to find the capital and deliver the line in sections in return for 'creditos', Government bonds guaranteeing a rate of interest of 7 per cent—on condition that they should run the line as well and take the profits for seventy years until the entire debt was repaid.

His part of the Longitudinal was three sections connecting small existing works. In the north where the valley was comparatively flat from Toledo to Islon there were no difficulties; further south they were faced with ridges of mountains running out from the peaks round Aconcagua, and from Cabildo to Limahuida and Illapel to San Marcos had to lay 40 miles of rack railway and cut three large tunnels. The work was not finished until 1914 and Griffiths had to spend half of every year in the country.

Long before then the Government had overspent so heavily that they considered leasing all the State railways to foreign contractors; yet they had, by the agreement, to go on issuing the creditos. The Longitudinal cost £13 million, of which two-thirds was still an outstanding debt ten years later, when the working was taken back into Chilean hands. Nevertheless in linking the whole of Chile it helped to create an economic unit and a nation, and perhaps Griffiths's work may be counted as one of the strong influences which opposed German penetration at the start of the war. His prestige was great; he left the title 'Transcontinental Man' behind, despite grumbling at the enormous bill for his services. Certainly it could not have been built without such outside enterprise—as with Brassey in the Argentine fifty years earlier, the contractors had made the work possible to begin with, and carried it out, and like Brassey, they did it entirely on their own terms.

In 1910 Griffiths added his own second name to the firm which became Norton-Griffiths and Company. In four years he had reached a position which had taken Cowdray ten and Aird twenty. He was a

Member of Parliament, a rich man with schemes in Mexico, Canada and Australia. At home he was engaged on large-scale works for the drainage of London[1] while completing in Baku an aqueduct worthy of the Roman Empire, 105 miles, mainly underground, through the Caucasian mountains to supply the centre of the Russian oil industry.

There was a little insecurity over Chile, and a projected railway across Sicily as part of a programme to redeem the Mezzogiorno had come to nothing, but the image of the contractor was dazzling and unimpaired.

His passionate devotion to Empire and imperial dreams which had been born long before in the Rhodesias led him into buying large tracts of prairie land near Calgary in Canada, to set up a model colony. He knew well most of the prominent political figures, entertained them in England, and saw it as part of his duty to carry out the Dominion's public works. For the first time his rather cloudy ideals controlled his logic and led him and the Lords, already worried by the high stakes in Chile, to their first setbacks.

Griffiths and Company (Canada) was founded in 1911; and won contracts for the harbour of St. John's, New Brunswick, the first skyscraper in Vancouver, the enlargement of New Westminster, the main freshwater port of the Fraser River in British Columbia, and various public buildings in Calgary. He sailed out to Canada with his wife in 1911 and spent two months in the West, entertained by Prime Minister McBride who was as enthusiastic over the prospects of his State as he was carried away by the Englishman's infectious zeal and obvious desire to bring it wealth. 140,000 acres of virgin land were to be peopled with the slum surplus of his constituency, industrial Wednesbury, through his Imperial League.

Griffiths poured out money throughout his tour to accumulate goodwill and returned to England to organize the exodus. But there was already too much for his single-handed organization. Only a whirlwind visit to Baku saved the contract there; one of his great failings being a weakness in choosing his deputies, which worried his associates; and when the St. John's Harbour proved more difficult than he had expected, the cracks of the partnership began to show.

Some of the greatest tides in the world give the sheltered anchorage, the only ice-free Atlantic port, a 30-foot rise from low to high water,

---

[1] The Battersea–Deptford main sewer—a nine-mile tunnel nearly as big as the Underground.

and the requirements of this centre of the logging industry were considerable. Without the slowly won knowledge of harbour work which Cowdray had, progress was slow. Long before it was finished, when Griffiths visited it just before the war, getting more money out of the Lords was almost impossible, because, by becoming involved in an immense Australian contract he had finally passed the limit of what they were prepared to risk.

He could not be everywhere: these years were those of his busiest work as a Member, when he won the title of 'Empire Jack'; years of wide hospitality to colonial politicians, work for the Wednesbury League, world-wide travel, contracts at home and abroad. Yet though both he and his wife were worried by local difficulties in 1912 the Australian contract had seemed too great a chance to miss.

The Government of New South Wales, having projected a 1,000 mile railway system, from Sydney to the Queensland border, and linking Broken Hill in the interior with its minerals to the coast, contemplated spending a total of £10 million on public works, of which £3 million was required at once. So large a sum for a provincial legislature became a hotly fought political issue between the Government, who favoured an outside contractor, and the Opposition, who stuck out for local enterprise on a smaller scale.

The State's credit was not high enough to raise this easily, either on a State loan or by guarantee of interest on the railways, until T. C. Coghlan, Agent-General in London and a close friend of Norton-Griffiths began to cry the virtues of the British consortium. He cited Chile as an example of how the funds could be raised quite painlessly, for the syndicate could tap capital resources beyond the Government's reach.

Violently unpopular, and bitterly opposed in the New South Wales Parliament, this opinion was accepted. A contract with Norton-Griffiths was made in 1913, not at his original price of 7 per cent cost plus profit which had been altogether too much for the legislature, but 5 per cent. Even at this figure, and especially as the Chilean example proved expensive, Norton-Griffiths was lampooned in the Sydney Press as an imperial, Buddha-like figure, sitting cross-legged with 'Mr. 5 per cent' stamped across his vast, and fictitious, belly.

The Lords, however, refused to play; they were being asked to raise sums beyond anything they had anticipated on returns which projected further and further into the future. Finally, after a meeting in which all agreed to pull out, they wrote to *The Times* explaining that they had no connexion with the company which had won the Australian contract. Norton-Griffiths did not attend, for it came at a critical moment,[1] and, as his original company still retained the Howard de Walden interest, he was able to continue. As late as January 1915 he told Coghlan that the London County and Westminster Bank had guaranteed to find the £4 million which was, by then, the satisfaction needed for the contract to come into force.

But war had broken into all his arrangements with its over-riding necessities. In the first year he abandoned everything which interfered with his concept of military duty. His most ambitious scheme, a new subway system for Chicago, was left on paper; St. John's Harbour was assigned to another contractor and Griffiths and Company put in abeyance for the duration; all the other works were finished by July 1914, leaving only Australia. The course of that determined his last encounter with the Lords.

Signature of the contract had not overcome the local opposition to the terms, which were still regarded as outrageous, or the British identity of the contractor. As the war developed it became expedient, even at the delay of some years, for the work to be done by Australians, and the two agents whom Norton-Griffiths sent out only served to make him more unpopular. In 1916, when he was in the depths of Rumania, the New South Wales Government offered him compensation to rescind. His wife handled the negotiations and eventually settled for £120,000, but the Lords promptly served an injunction on the amount, claiming that the contractor was still their employee since he had never technically resigned. Norton-Griffiths, on his return from the special mission was too tired to argue and, embarrassed by his private relationship with Coghlan who had done very well out of the affair, he decided to settle for a third share. Thereafter there was no meeting of any sort with those who had paved his way and proved such demanding masters. What came after 1916 was born entirely of himself, his phoenix-like quality of resurgence, and the little which remained from six years of contracting on a scale which placed him among the half-dozen largest firms in the world.

[1] Manchester City Corporation had decided to employ him on a sewerage system, costing over £1 million, which was to be the most modern of its kind.

3

EMPIRE JACK

T HOUGH he had chosen the profession of contractor, Norton-Griffiths was not, like Brassey and Cowdray or even Aird, channelled into it either by training or business and engineering skill. To the end of his life he lacked the propensity for figures which gave Cowdray his mastery of detail, the vast practical knowledge which gave Aird his intuitive grasp of the viability of a project, or the wide, speculative mind of Brassey which marked him out from all his contemporaries. Norton-Griffiths possessed a fiery passionate nature, tempered only slightly by the logic of the possible. There was talk of gold, and he would prospect the deserts, there was a railway through the mountains—he would build it—there was crippling unemployment at home—he would solve it in the unpopulated prairies of Canada. Nothing he met in his life seemed impossible because he had again and again disproved it—by his genius for inspiring others and making them believe in him, by his insatiable optimism, his sweeping, humorous, and distinctive personality and his devastating drive.

The qualities of the pioneer, the prospector and the wild-catter overflowed; the calculating skills of the builder, backing the creative impulse with patient calculation, perseverance and cold courage were foreign to him, learned with difficulty and too often abandoned in impatience. Confident in himself, he would quarrel with caution, deliberately be reckless, lose his ungovernable temper; and because he nearly always won, or at least came through, he had no humility and little understanding of that quality in others. A contractor at first in the heyday of the individual master, he was the imperial and imperious man of affairs, and remained a soldier of fortune, campaigning as a contractor because it was his métier, but never absorbed as the others were, always ready to throw it up for the rumour of a fight.

His rise had been inordinately fast, almost as if he had seen prophetically that the old order was shifting before the crash, wiping away the opportunities he needed, and had rushed on taking them while he could. Yet when his backers found this irresponsible, he quarrelled, and in the end fatally carried those attitudes which had brought him his early success into the changed post-war world, having learnt nothing from what he had lost.

He was tall, very powerfully built, capable of great physical endurance, and endowed with enormous mental stamina. He was handsome, and attractive to women; perhaps one of the most dashing men of the Edwardian era. Yet he was completely faithful, centred on his wife and family; the infectious good nature, the amusing talk, the devilry and lightheartedness was spread carelessly among the horde of acquaintances, but his friendship given to very few. The rest he cared nothing for, they furthered his ambition, and gave him his career, success and money.

In the perpetual struggle to control his restless violence, his wife held the balance and maintained it through nearly all his life. She had given up a career as a fine singer for him without a thought; but she was the pivot on which he was able to rest, mature, and resolve his impatience.

A photograph of the Benguella days shows him in a typical position; sun-burnt, moustached, dressed in white drill and topee, relaxed, almost lying in his chair, his legs carelessly crossed; latent energy personified, tigerish, dangerous, and essentially defiant. With all the veneer of manners, his famous courtesy, wit and vigour, he remained basically uncivilized, an unruly force liable to break out in the most surprising ways. Yet for all this, he could be patient and gentle, particularly with animals, which he loved; and this quality was as disarming as it was natural.

He was so made that two deficiencies prevented him from being a great contractor. He could have overcome his lack of business ability if he had been able to choose able subordinates, but he admired in others chiefly the ability to stand up to himself. He could see, being a born commander, the military gifts, but had no depths of judgement in anything else. He could also be harsh, arbitrary, and unreasonable. During the war he once told his general that if a contract went wrong he sacked not only the man in charge but his assistant, on the principle that if there was trouble, one must have been jealous of the other. He never admitted himself in the wrong and was constantly let down.

Besides, he dissipated his energy. Cowdray had conserved his with the greatest care, knowing it could not always last, but Norton-Griffiths squandered it in a hundred enthusiasms, in war, empire, politics, and society. He could never sit down callously to think of making money and his stock-exchange speculations were all disastrous; what he gained came wholly from his work. As the over-generous are, he was immensely liked and loved, yet somehow apart; with a certain heroic capacity, imprisoned for twenty-five years in an occupation for which he was temperamentally unfitted.

About 1909 Dudley Docker, who had supplied all the Chilean railways with rolling-stock, suggested that Norton-Griffiths should stand for Parliament as a Conservative. The Metropolitan Carriage Works had a factory in the industrial town of Wednesbury, and Docker offered to help him with the campaign. His wife said he was wrong; he would have to delegate his work too much, and in the end she proved right, but as usual he would not listen. He fought a whirlwind campaign against the Liberal holder in the January 1910 election on the Tory slogan: 'We want eight and we won't wait!'; demanding the battleships in face of the German naval programme. But his chief banner was Empire, and Tariff Reform; he believed passionately in Imperial Preference and an Imperial Senate to bind together the Dominions and Colonies.

Throwing himself and his wife strenuously into the campaign, he used his undoubted talents as a showman to the best. On a platform he was a rousing and theatrical speaker, ready with a joke or a backhander for hecklers and his meetings were often rowdy. But his simple language and fervid enthusiasm woke a chord in the constituency in spite of the high unemployment figure. In the depressed streets amongst the tired and listless men, standing at corners or squatting on doorsteps of the sad squalid tenements and the filth and rubbish left over by the Industrial Revolution, his down-to-earth anger actually moved them. Devoid of all snobbery or class feeling he appealed to them with colour and sincerity and the full battery of the Press; ready to take off his coat and fight them if needed; and in the roughest areas he often did. He and his wife gave away a fortune in these years to relieve the apathy and misery which choked the narrow ill-built streets. He spoke with a vast map of the Empire on the wall behind, Primrose League badges in profusion; drove a four-in-hand through the constituency with his wife dressed in red on the box, and hired a balloon to make himself seen. 'Hell-fire Jack', 'The Monkey Man' (having once eaten monkey in Africa, he retold the story) were some of the names, but as 'Empire Jack' he was always remembered.

So, to considerable surprise, he entered Parliament with a majority of 600 over the Liberal. In the second General Election of 1910 he repeated this success; with torchlight processions every night while he drove the four-in-hand himself among the crowds with two amateur boxers inside to guard his wife. In the drab squalor his red colours and flamboyant life and generosity were famous; his meetings were one of the very few distractions. For eight years more he held the seat, and his popularity swelled until, when he retired, collected in pennies from the meanest houses, they gave his wife a jewelled Primrose League badge.

As a Member, however, his performance was very different from that on the election platform. Never a coherent speaker, he lacked a sense of what was needed for the House of Commons where vehemence rarely makes up for lack of logic. Empire Jack remained a well-known backbencher, though in 1911 he was able to raise a hundred signatures to a motion in favour of an Imperial Council. In the cause of Empire and Wednesbury he was more successful, sending out emigrants to his Canadian township from among the unemployed; but though the older men kept in touch, the younger ones soon disappeared. Until the stimulus given by war, the Imperial ideal as he understood it had not recovered from the Boer War.

For four years, in the intervals of Canada, Chile, and Baku the Norton-Griffiths lived the life of London society with a large entourage of servants and cars, spending well but not unwisely. They were well known politically and as a move against the new Liberal Ministry he decided to make a big Conservative bid for Empire support. If he took a large house and entertained colonial guests lavishly he could expect some help from the Party and by projecting the Conservative image overseas could do them a great service.

After Christmas he cabled invitations to the various Dominion Prime Ministers and looked round for a suitable mansion. Temple House, with its lovely gardens by the Thames, was available and they took it for six weeks. Each weekend brought a new houseparty, an ex-Minister and a crowd of Members to meet a Colonial Premier and his guests. There would be forty or more for the night and two hundred for lunch

Oil wells near Ploesti

Burning oil wells

Work in Colombia

Heightening the Aswan Dam

and tea; sixteen servants worked all week in preparation; boats plied on the river, bands played, tennis and croquet seduced the active, and the whole curious mixture was a success. Norton-Griffiths with his sense of timing and purpose was the perfect host for such an occasion and in the process made himself known in more countries than he had ever visited.

While the Liberal Government fought the House of Lords to the death, at Marlow he was useful to the Tories, achieving something which perhaps helped to bring about the striking and immediate response of the Dominions when war broke out. Westminster in 1911 knew all too little of the politics of the countries of its Empire.

With all this, Norton-Griffiths was restless as soon as the autumn came. A fine shot and sportsman, a director of Arsenal, a great clubman, lover of dancing and collector of people, he still found England too small. In the spring of 1914 he and his wife stayed with Lord Kitchener, then British Agent in Cairo, while he negotiated for works on the Nile. This beginning of a long interest in Egypt came to nothing with the war, but his friendship with the General had remarkable results. Kitchener abroad was a far different man from the gloomy colossus of the War Office two years later, and would rumble with elephantine laughter at Norton-Griffiths's jokes. Having built the Nile railway before his victory of Omdurman, he knew the value of contractors and their dreams and remembered this when Norton-Griffiths asked him to authorize his own private army.

The war was, in a way, a relief to the contractor. To have continued without his backers would have been difficult. He moved the family to Brighton and prudently put money aside in his wife's name in Canada.

In the *Pall Mall Gazette* of July 21st, 1914, appeared a notice entitled:
'If Duty calls: M.P's invitation to Old Fighters'
'With a view to working in unity if duty calls, all Africans, Australians, Canadians, and other Britishers who served in either Matabeleland, Mashonaland, the South African War ... should apply to Mr. John Norton-Griffiths, M.P.'

4

FORTUNATE SOLDIER

AFTER August 4th came the rush to enlist; and a surge of old soldiers to Norton-Griffiths's office in 3 Central Buildings; several thousand campaigners who had known or heard of him in the old days, saw him still as Empire Jack, or simply heard the legends which were already current. Three days later, 500 men paraded in a motley of uniforms on the Horse Guards, while Norton-Griffiths was conducting a difficult negotiation with Kitchener, now Secretary of State for War. This private army had no official existence and was financed so far entirely by Norton-Griffiths and his friends Lord Murray of Elibank, Lord Lonsdale, the honorary colonel, and the other officers. Kitchener's mistrustful attitude, even towards the Territorials, was already known.

However, the Under Secretary of State was a friend of Murray's, and Norton-Griffiths was well known to Kitchener; and before the end of August the regiment was formally authorized as the Second King Edward's Horse, the only band of irregulars to achieve official blessing.

But Norton-Griffiths himself, who had not taken command because of his worries over the Australian contract, could not get quickly enough to the war; and training, equipping, and waiting held the regiment back for months at Slough. As the war turned into the trenches a vast frustration made him restless and when he realized that the muddy soil of Flanders was to be the future battleground he took the chance of his special knowledge. Working in the heavy clay underneath Manchester on the sewers, his men had evolved a means of tunnelling known as 'clay kicking'; they lay on their backs on a wooden cross in the hole, and dug away the earth with a light long-handled spade in front of their feet. Working so, a man could move rapidly forward in a small space, and save much of the danger of falls and entombment. If this was to be a static campaign he saw, long before the Allied Command, tunnelling would be a vital part of it.

In December he put forward a scheme for 'moles' to the War Office where it was received sceptically. Then just before Christmas an Indian regiment was blown up by an underground mine at Festubert, and fled, their morale shattered. General French ordered his engineers to counter-attack, since the imponderable nature of the danger made it one of the worst to morale in the trenches, but they were already over-strained, and it was soon clear that the Germans' technique of mining was greatly superior.

Kitchener called Norton-Griffiths in and received a demonstration of clay kicking on the floor of his office. He was impressed and gave him *carte blanche* to raise the necessary men. On February 13th, 1915, Norton-Griffiths burst into H.Q. at St. Omer dressed in something be-tween uniform and hunting kit. Not for the first time his brash approach and disregard of rules in pursuit of speed and efficiency raised opposition, but his enthusiasm and the demonstration carried the Engineer staff with him and made him valuable allies. They inspected the front and found exactly the right soil and conditions in the water-logged battleground of Givenchy and Festubert. On the 15th he met General French and received War Office approval; returned to England, closed down the Manchester contract, enrolled the men and with sixty-six fully equipped miners reached France exactly a week later; on the day on which the 16th Lancers were badly blown up near Ypres.

Remarkable though the speed was and the urgency with which he began to form eight tunnelling companies, with himself as liaison officer, there were many of the disadvantages of improvisation. The miners were a wild body of men with no military sense and resistant to discipline; and his high-handed methods of extracting the best soldiers from infantry battalions infuriated commanders. But Norton-Griffiths was used to trouble-shooting; and as he moved at a furious pace through appalling Flanders roads in his two-ton Rolls he always carried a crate of champagne to console their irritation.

Working half on his own and half for the Engineers he soon had men at work from Ypres all along the front. Commanding the exposed British salient, a perpetual threat, lay the long line of Messines and Wytschaete Ridge; on which rose the unspectacular, but tactically deadly Hill 60; held by the Germans with secure emplacements, whose foreground was littered with the dead of defeated British frontal attacks. By March 1915 the tunnellers had gained some parity with their enemy and it was decided to concentrate them on this objective. On April 17th the deep mines were blown; and Hill 60 disappeared in a shambles which totally destroyed the German position, allowing an easy advance into the salient, which, however, proved untenable and was later lost after an attack with poison gas.

The 'moles' had proved their worth.

The effect on morale was remarkable, and it was freely said that the men would not remain above ground unless the miners were down below. Their courage was unspectacular and intense; they worked in the mud and freezing water, liable to be choked and buried by falls, listening for Germans tunnelling ahead until their nerves were stretched beyond bearing, and all the while labouring at work so hard, that it had to be done in shifts, with sheer exhaustion at the end.

Norton-Griffiths made his own position difficult; his bearing was too arrogant, his criticisms too pungent. He was recalled to France in May 1915 after complaints that he was skimming men from the factories in the Midlands. His chafing at authority paralleled the quarrels of the High Command, for in June, to meet Joffre's requirements, the British line was lengthened and the work of liaison officer increased to an impossible extent. He was in virtual control of 12,000 men, under R.E. command; and the usefulness of the whole scheme began to be questioned.

But for months, Norton-Griffiths, looking out on the three-mile Messines Ridge, its low hump pockmarked with a million shell holes, containing positions so highly defensible as to be untouchable, had become convinced it could be mined. He pushed the idea upwards and it eventually lodged with General Harvey, R.E. Inspector of Mines, who made him work out the first impressionist sketch in immense detail. By the end of 1915, at the time that Haig took over from French, the field plans were made. Some spectacular assault was needed and Norton-Griffiths and General Harvey were summoned to G.H.Q. to put their case for solving the Ypres impasse. Early in January they explained it—how the Ridge was a hill of sand resting on the blue clay, how immensely long and deep tunnels could lay a mine, not so much to blow the top off but shatter it with an explosion like an earthquake, destroying all human life.

For two months the scheme lay dormant until, with the preparation of a new offensive on the French front, it was set in motion on April 10th. What followed, dug over months with unparalleled skill and courage, belongs to the history of the Engineers, for Norton-Griffiths, having been promoted Lieutenant-Colonel, had long hinted that he should go. He had introduced new listening devices and brought over and tested a mechanical digger; he had inspired the great mining offensive and his work was now finished; had quarrelled with too many of his associates and needed something fresh. He was given two months' leave to sort out his contracting affairs and then attached to the Ministry of Munitions.

On June 17th, 1917, 933,300 pounds of ammonal from nineteen separate mines were detonated in the biggest man-made explosion ever created; a roar heard for hundreds of miles across the long battle-front. 'Out of the dark ridges of Messines and that ill-famed Hill 60 there flashed out and up enormous volumes of scarlet flame from the exploding mines, and earth and smoke, so that all the countryside was illuminated by the red light. Where some of us stood watching, aghast and spellbound—the ground trembled and surged violently to and fro.'(a)

Total silence fell; the Canadians advanced over perhaps 10,000 dead and took 7,354 prisoners and the smoking hills of sand which resembled nothing so much as a vast heap of porridge. The enemy suffered deep demoralization. It was never done again on such a scale, perhaps wisely. The miners received their glory; and Leo Amery, Secretary of State for War, wrote to Norton-Griffiths: 'Heartiest congratulations on success of great coup. . . . I hope they will give credit where credit is due.'(b)

Norton-Griffiths was too useful, too dangerous a man to leave with the Ministry of Munitions. He had been there barely a week when on November 23rd, 1916, he was again summoned to Whitehall, this time to the Office of the Director of Military Intelligence, General McDonough. Quickly the latter outlined the situation in Rumania.

For the first two years of war King Ferdinand had kept his country with its immense oil industry and corn-growing plains beside the Danube out of the conflict; selling impartially as he could, though very largely to the Allies. Under great diplomatic pressure, having judged the Germans the weaker and been promised the province of Transylvania in return, he declared war. Rapid gains were followed by a

German counter-attack; the supporting Russian armies gave way and after the battle of Hermanstadt (September 13th–15th, 1916) the Rumanian armies began to retreat. On October 8th they were defending the passes of the Carpathian Mountains, the last natural barrier before the oilfields of Ploesti. Falkenhayn and Mackensen, two of the ablest German commanders, threatened to break through at any moment, and British Intelligence was aware of the store set in Berlin and by public opinion in Germany on the stocks of petrol, oil, and corn which awaited them in Bucharest and Ploesti. The prize of an annual crop of $7\frac{1}{2}$ million tons of grain, and $1\frac{1}{2}$ million tons of oil was vital to blockaded Germany.

Secretly, as the armies retreated, the Allied Governments had bought up the 1916 harvest. The Rumanian Government agreed to destroy it and make the oil wells useless to the invaders. For this purpose a Commission had been set up; but by late autumn it was proving remarkably intractable. It was too late to send out even a brigade; Major Thompson, the Military Attaché, reported he was powerless; as a last hope Norton-Griffiths was sent to superintend the destruction.

'You are a skilled engineer, you will have men there, working for the oil companies, who will do the work, but you must direct it. If Mackensen breaks through with his motorized battalions the disaster will be far worse than the loss of the oil in Galicia.'

Norton-Griffiths asked only—'What regiments do I take?' McDonough replied: 'You go alone, but you may take your batman!' However, before he left the next day, with hastily packed bags and Finch, his servant, he saw McKenna, Chancellor of the Exchequer, and was authorized to tell the Commission that the British Government would pay compensation for the loss of machinery as well as the oil; and thus armed he left on a destroyer by a long circuitous route to Bergen. For two months he vanished; his only messages scraps of letters in the diplomatic bags which got through to England.

Driving winds and heavy snow held them up in the bitter cold off Norway; at the Russian front he forced his way through the frontier posts and, after neutral Sweden, resumed his colonel's uniform. Through the chaos of Russia, nearing the Revolution, his imperious manner and blunt tongue overcame the appalling delays of travel. On November 13th he climbed into a train at Moscow which took him 1,500 miles across the steppes to within reach of the frontier. The trains crawled, if they moved at all; all the ghastly unpreparedness of Rumania's defences was shown as the retreat became a rout. Information was unobtainable. Winter had begun, snow covering the bare black soil, and the clouds hanging heavily over the short depressing days. Finally he requisitioned a car and drove into Bucharest on the 17th.

The position seemed wholly desperate. Falkenhayn was ready to cross the River Olt only 100 miles from the capital. Mackensen was pushing north across the Danube. The only hope seemed that General Avarescu, the most reliable Rumanian commander, still held the Carpathian passes and staved off the advance on Ploesti and the oil wells. But when Norton-Griffiths met the Commissioners he was faced with a blank refusal. Under the guise of a long-term procrastination they had changed their minds and preferred to save their industry for posterity and let the Germans have the oil. Bratianu, the Prime Minister, was adamant and refused to hear of compensation.

Bucharest seemed already a doomed city; trains of wounded filled the stations but had no hope of ever moving out. Rumours sprung up creating panic; deserters and families fleeing from the threatened areas, dragging their belongings in carts, clogged the roads and streets. Norton-Griffiths wrote bitterly: 'A third of Rumania is occupied—the army walked out and the Bosche walked in before I could do anything. I am off tomorrow (to Ploesti) but they say it is doubtful if I can get there . . . the Rumanians don't give a damn for our wheat, the Bosche planes are all over the place and not a plane worth a damn here—they have *nothing*.'

There was hardly time for cool negotiations. The Commission met at Targovista in the centre of the oilfields on the 26th and settled down to a day's polite deliberation. Their only conclusion lay in what Rumanians were to shout later. 'Better for the Germans to have it and we have work and food, than destroy it.' Significantly also in Bucharest representatives of the Standard Oil and Royal Dutch had tried unsuccessfully to buy him off. It was understandable—to Norton-Griffiths's engineer's eye the country was marvellously developed; mile after mile the derricks marked thousands of bore-holes tapping the liquid wealth seeping through the soil of narrow valleys, close up against the great wall of the Carpathians. Years had gone into the creation of this industry, and the refineries, storage tanks, and installation in Ploesti itself held comparison with the largest Texas concentrations.

He heard the Commission out, then slammed the door on further discussion and made his own plans. William Guthrie, Director of Consolidated Oilfields at Targovista, the largest British-owned concern, and his managers, Masterson and Mejor would help to destroy their own plant and provide men to help with the rest. In return Norton-Griffiths, in his capacity as Government emissary, signed an assessment of the value of their refinery and works; a paper which was later to be the source of a celebrated lawsuit.

From now on he was quite against what semblance of authority remained to Bratianu's Government, yet he was privately assured of the support of the Royal Family, particularly of Queen Marie, and though he ran into constant opposition, the Commission stopped short of the ultimate sanction of arresting him. He had to use what he called: 'the cunning required to overcome everybody, to ignore definite government orders as if they were dirt—to say:

'My Chief is the War Office; if you want me to stop, cable them' . . . I moved so quickly that direct representation to the Minister or Military Attaché would not reach me or if they did to kick the deliverer to blazes or pull my revolver and say, "I don't speak your blasted language".' And while Avarescu held a brilliant rearguard action with the remnants of his army, and the French Military Mission gave him arms, Norton-Griffiths set out to fulfil his mission in a way far different from what the War Office in London had imagined.

He intended to destroy not only the Consolidated Fields but everything in a 20-mile circle, boreholes, derricks, pipes, refineries, storage tanks, machinery, and transport lorries; and he trusted no one but himself to do it. On the grey foggy morning of November 27th he and a French officer left in two cars for Targovista. As they drove towards the noise of artillery in the hills ahead he could see that his orders were being obeyed; lines of the companies' workmen were packing up with their families to go east to Braila and Galata behind the Russian lines, and they cursed him as he passed. Guthrie was ready to start work; benzine was let loose through newly dug channels from the reservoir to the refinery, until it lay a foot deep; vitriol was poured into the boilers to rot them and Norton-Griffiths walked to the edge of the sea of oil and calmly lit it. Within minutes the whole area was a flaming mass which burnt for ten days, thick black smoke pouring towards the Germans who entered Targovista only two days later.

At the works east of the town they began to plug the wells by cutting down the derricks and dropping the 'spoon' over 1,000 feet to the bottom of the shaft, then throwing in short iron bars and smashed machinery until it was so blocked that it could not be drilled out. At one works, while his men were laying charges in the engines, Norton-Griffiths seized a sledgehammer and reduced the main dynamo to wreckage, and thereafter carried it night and day.

Inevitably the work was slow, but at night the burning tanks gave a deep sombre light and, tired, black with fumes, they worked on. On the 29th the Moreni field was thoroughly destroyed. Slowly they fell back towards Ploesti. Sometimes it took minutes to light the oil, forcing him to kindle bundles of straw and throw them in; and the great tanks might smoulder under dense and choking smoke or blow up entirely, scorching his clothes and flinging out great lumps of iron and brick. At Baicoi he was nearly killed. 'After lighting some highly inflammable gas I had flooded the chamber with, I burnt my nose and was blown clean out of the big engine house, through the door, hair ablaze.'

In the valleys of Danbovitzna, Prahova, and Campina, Masterson and his men were ready with gelignite to complete the destruction of major refineries. Here he met the first severe opposition and had to ward off local officials with his revolver before he could set a timber yard on fire. At Bana he was arrested by a member of the Commission but fought his way out without having to shoot. And in the nightmare rush, with German cavalry patrols all round him his humour took on a grim tinge at obstruction.

'One obstacle of a blighter, a Rumanian official, I tried to trap in benzine, 20,000 tons of which I lit to put him out of the way, but the swine escaped only just in time.'

A dull tiredness set in; he had not slept for days, except a few hours hunched in the seat of the car; yet his stature seemed to grow, making him an apocalyptic figure with his huge hammer outlined against the blazing sky.

No certain news came through and Bucharest was evacuated on the 25th. Only the fact that Falkenhayn thrust for the capital rather than the oilfields to the north saved Norton-Griffiths's mission, giving him the few essential hours. When Bucharest fell the Germans turned north, but Norton-Griffiths was already at work in Ploesti itself. Scouting columns of cavalry had cut behind him twice and only the speed of his motor car enabled him to get away. Sweeping through the valleys of Doftana, Comarnic, and Tzintea he had completed the havoc begun only six days before.

What had begun in him with an engineer's unwillingness to destroy a brilliant industry had reached a peak of complete abandonment—fatigue, the danger of flaming petrol, explosions, the overwhelming sight and noise of inferno brought out his ultimate strength; as the layers of civilization fell away he remained an invulnerable force; and this alone explains how it was done. With all he had ever used to drive the Benguella railway up the mountains he now drove himself.

The scene over 200 square miles was like the pits of hell in a medieval picture—by night a red glow flamed in a thousand places and by day the sky was hidden in the dense clouds of slowly drifting smoke. Ploesti was a chaos of wounded, guns, equipment and all the desolate scenes of a rout. Since 50,000 tons of oil were stored as well as the two great refineries of the German Steaua and American Astrea companies, he had to wait until this town was clear before destroying it. At the greatest risk, for he would let no one else do it, he set charges under the main machinery, flooded the rooms with petrol, and then fired the explosive. The force of the flames drawing up the air nearly dragged him into the holocaust; the tall steel towers buckled and collapsed, and a huge incandescent cloud swept over the town, choking to death an encampment of Tziganes, the Rumanian gypsies.

At last the cars turned eastwards along roads crowded with refugees. Those who could were paying fantastic prices to get out, as all the railways were hopelessly blocked. But Norton-Griffiths's work was not finished; hundreds of thousands of tons of grain remained to be flooded with oil or burnt, all the way back, as the Rumanian and Russian lines formed and reformed. He reached Braila on the Danube. 'Here I got dynamite in play which made me feel quite happy. The New Year has brought in burning and wrecking. The next two or three days I am going to light barges full of corn on the Danube at night-time—our bank is covered by their guns in daylight.'

As winter set in, the hardest for years, freezing the river and the thick snow, the front settled down. The Mission was over. Though he had destroyed the life blood of the country Norton-Griffiths's repute stood high. While Queen Marie heroically tried to raise the troops' morale, he was invited at the end of January to meet the King and General Ilesco, Commander-in-Chief.

'Evidently the Queen was put up to get me there unofficially to ask if I would organize their railways, which I have here and there unblocked. A terrible lot of work and I am not keen as I want to get back.

Both King and Queen are desperately keen to keep me here and the whole interview resembled a patient taking advice from a specialist. The café talk is "our government is no good, we want a dictator—get that Englishman, he'd show them how to do things!'" But he was sickened of it. It had been a military necessity repugnant to him, as an engineer and creator, and for the rest of his life he loathed to talk of it.

'Time alone', he wrote 'can balance the gain against the loss and devastation into which it was the Mission's painful duty to lay waste the land.' He came back the way he went, by St. Petersburg, where the Czar invested him with the Order of St. Vladimir only two days before the February Revolution. An estimate could be no more than a guess, but it was said that he had done over £50 million worth of damage. Months passed before the wells came into production again. Falkenhayn admitted that the loss of expected supplies was worse than a major defeat in the field for the Central Powers. Norton-Griffiths was thanked officially by Lord Balfour and the War Cabinet and awarded a K.C.B., having already won a D.S.O. for the tunnelling work.

But it was not all glory, because at that moment the bitterness with the Lords broke out for the last time over the Australian compensation; and Norton-Griffiths himself needed months to recover fully from the strain and obsessive drama of the Rumanian War. Still he could not rest. As Cowdray had been called to Gretna, he was asked to help build large dock-works during the heavy submarine sinkings of 1916-17, and as a relief threw himself into it.

Lord Furness had been authorized by Lloyd George to build one of the biggest and most modern slipways in the world at Middlesbrough and a dry dock at Dublin, which Norton-Griffiths completed in record time. He enlarged the shipyards at Howden-on-Tyne, built a concrete jetty at Hartlepool, built Catterick Aerodrome, Hickling Broad seaplane station and the Knotty Ash Hospital camp for U.S. troops. By the end of the war he was again a contractor, his firm rebuilt.

Then General Childs, Director of Personnel Services, approached him, asking him to help with the problem of an army out of work. By the end of 1918 it was clear that there would not be jobs for thousands of demobbed soldiers and fearing boredom, disaffection, and a threat to the morale of those still under arms, the War Office wanted something to counteract it. Norton-Griffiths believed such an association should be non-political and enthusiastically founded the 'Comrades of the Great War', with the hope of a club for ex-servicemen in every village and town in England. But some of those he brought in, notably Lord Mount Temple, began to use it as a Conservative stunt and having seen it established, Norton-Griffiths, disillusioned, retired. In 1920 his Comrades were amalgamated with the other associations into the British Legion where they soon outlived the political associations.

Rumania, however, provided a sequel. Rumanian Consolidated Oilfields submitted a claim for £1,255,513 in respect of property destroyed, and, getting no satisfaction from the British Government, submitted a Petition of Right which was heard before Mr. Justice Darling in March 1920. An eminent group of counsel contested the case, Carson, Watts, and Caradoc Rees for the Company, the Attorney-General, Sir Gordon Hewart, and others for the Crown.

The case hinged on the paper signed by Norton-Griffiths—whether that was sufficient to bind the British Government. The Attorney-General contested that the Rumanian Government had ordered the destruction and was wholly responsible, and tried, unsuccessfully, to attack the validity of the oral evidence given by Mejor and Masterson. Norton-Griffiths's own evidence was vivid and conclusive. In the witness box he was incorrigible and the judge finally let him have his head. Pungently he scarified the government, though restrained by D.O.R.A. from revealing his secret instructions. 'I am absolutely sure the Company ought to have compensation. I gave them the assurance that I had the power to bargain.'

Darling's judgement was instructive: 'It is not a very easy task to determine what the agreement was because the British envoy was a person of flamboyant disposition who does not appear to have quite realized the difference between an executive and an executed contract. He went about like the great god Thor with a hammer.'(c) But he gave judgement against the Crown, though, unable to form an estimate of damages, he referred the sum to the Official Referee. There was, of course, an appeal, to the House of Lords, and the case languished till the Company dissolved in bankruptcy.

As the British Government divested itself of responsibility, so did the Rumanian. The Shell, Royal Dutch, and Standard Oil holdings were resumed, the German Steaua taken over; and the industry revived, though its relative importance had declined. Damage was impossible to assess—the retreating Germans again put many wells out of commission —but it is a fair comment on Norton-Griffiths's work that twenty-seven years later, when an aerial armada of 171 Liberators and Flying

Fortresses was launched against the Ploesti fields, again in German hands, only five out of seven refineries were hit and full production was regained within three months.

5

ILLUSIONS

THE WAR made no noticeable inroads on his physical strength. It purged him almost for good of his longing to fight and by freeing himself from his associates left him able to return to contracting on an even wider scale. Out of it stemmed his only scheme for oil. While the Rumanian Consolidated drifted into bankruptcy even before the case reached the House of Lords, where judgement at last went against the Company, Masterson proposed the foundation of a British Company to take it over. The Rumanian economy seemed to be reviving rapidly under the post-war administration, and before the oil industry moved under complete American control, Norton-Griffiths and his associates set up the Phoenix Oil Company and in 1920 bought up Rumanian Consolidated and eight smaller companies. Masterson was the organizer, but Norton-Griffiths remained active until about 1926, when it ceased to return large dividends, and he prudently backed out some years before it was nationalized.

At forty-eight Norton-Griffiths seemed in the prime of life. He had his great pre-war reputation, the firm which had been largely revived for the Middlesborough dock work, the men who had worked for him before and were only too glad to have a job again, the contacts he had made in the war, and the friendship and partnership of Lord Howard de Walden. There were many Spanish friends, influential in Latin America, and the enigmatic, powerful, arms king, Sir Basil Zaharoff. On his own at last he began to recapture the type of business which had flooded in before 1914. He bombarded Heads of State and Ministers of Public Works with offers to build the projects which had lain dormant for lack of capital. In 1922, for example, he wrote to Dr. Harrison Vegas, Argentinian Minister of Finance:

'My company, being aware that there exist works of great import-ance whose realization depends only on finding the necessary financial support, having great faith in the future of the country, and confidence in its government, offer to execute those of the works which the Government thinks are most necessary and urgent, and to find the funds up to a sum total of £10 million.'(a) Later, with more concrete pro-posals, to Evaristo Uriburu, Ambassador in London:

'Norton-Griffiths and Company are disposed, in association with the Atlantic Finance and Public Works Company of Canada [an offshoot of his earlier Canadian company] to conclude a contract with your Government for the work of constructing railways for £5 million . . . on a basis of cost plus percentage . . . the contractor's fee to be 10 per cent of the cost. . . . Our syndicate will sign the contract on condition that the bonds are Government obligations.'(b)

These terms were exceptionally high. The contract came to nothing, but that he could ask 10 per cent is a measure of the extent to which in South America a new sort of mania was spilling out into grandiose transport and utility schemes. Out of this, and his special knowledge and understanding of the region came his success.

The first post-war work was at Leixoes Harbour, port for the Douro and Oporto trade; leading on, in association with the Portuguese Government, to a major plan for Loanda, the chief port of Angola, some 200 miles north of Benguella. The old harbour, a wide bay between two rivers, protected by a long island of sand, had silted up heavily and become almost unuseable so that trade had fallen to nothing. As part of an eight-year scheme of public works, schools and agricultural reform, this was aimed to give new life to the moribund colony, the contract specified a 500-yard concrete quay and railway, warehouses, break-waters, a mile-long harbour wall and road in front of the town, jetties, a dry dock, and the dredging of the whole enclosure to 40 feet. Norton-Griffiths completed it between 1921 and 1923. But the harbour which could take five ocean liners never fulfilled its promise and, though profitable, continued to silt up.

Contracts were flowing in so fast that Norton-Griffiths needed only to choose the most attractive to be completely committed. Money was not yet easily come by in world markets; the massive American loans to Latin American states which filled the years after 1923 had not yet begun, and Norton-Griffiths's services as broker as well as builder were as vital as they had been in Chile in 1910, and were as highly paid for;

there was no hesitation to pledge the future for the politically and economically attractive present.

Three years before Cowdray was able to extract a British Government guarantee for the Sudan to build the Sennar Dam, Norton-Griffiths was invited on similar terms to Kenya to finish the historic Uganda Railway. Built from 1891 to 1903 as a strategic line of communication to safeguard, in Uganda, Britain's imperial needs on the Nile, this railway had made Nairobi a city and created, between the warring Masai and Kikuyu, a colony. Eventually it connected Lake Victoria with the sea at Mombasa, but though it passed beside the White Highlands it failed to serve the richest and most fertile area, the Uasin Gishu plateau, which was only colonized after its completion. The expense of building had burdened the Company and the colony with so large a debt that no further extension was thought of before the 1914 war, and indeed, until then, the plateau had attracted only a few Dutch settlers who found its open rolling country above 8,000 feet like the high veld of the Cape.

Transport was the key to its development. When the first survey was made to Eldoret and Trans-Nzoia in 1915, the report stated: 'The farmers can ride along the top of the plateau with their ox-teams, but to reach Londiani station means passing through a very difficult belt of country, through the Burnt Forest, over a summit of 9,000 feet and down a very difficult track to the Rift valley. No wagon dare travel alone, generally two or three together and when they get stuck it needs all their teams, 27 pairs of oxen harnessed to one wagon to pull it out of the ruts.'(c) Twice a year, in the rains, the escarpment was impassable.

During the war the existing railway was heavily used in the campaign against German East Africa, but repairs were neglected and a large bill met the Company at the end. Clearly the colony could not pay for a Uasin Gishu railway; whose route led, on paper, 205 miles from near Nakuru up the escarpment to Eldoret, past the lonely extinct volcano Mt. Elgon, to Lake Victoria and Uganda and the Congo border; though there was an increasing demand from a horde of new settlers, ex-soldiers among them. A Kenya Colony loan was raised in London in 1921 and £1¼ million assigned to it; Norton-Griffiths and Company, Nairobi, had signed the contract nine months before, at the same moment as his old rival, Pauling, signed one for the improvement of Kilindini Harbour, Mombasa.

The contract specified a route branching from the existing railway at the top of the Mau escarpment, but the old line included very heavy gradients and bends, and as the post-war cotton boom developed it seemed that it would be worth spending more to have a good freight line. The new plan was to branch off after Nakuru, and Norton-Griffiths's revised estimate rose to £2¼ million, cost plus 5 per cent profit, in three years. The settlers grumbled, much as the New South Wales Parliament, at the price, but the Administration was only too happy to have the contractor's services instead of their own rudimentary Public Works Department.

Across the broad valley of the great Rift the lines ran easily to the foot of the escarpment. Not so harsh a landscape as Benguella but higher, the mountain wall rose 1,200 feet in 10 miles through steep, heavily forested hills. Norton-Griffiths built the line extremely well, better perhaps than any other except in Chile, for he was now experienced in mountain stretches and enjoyed the struggle the difficulties gave him though he never, in fact, went out to visit it. In 1923 the first two sections were taken over by the the Administration and the next year plans were drawn up for the continuation into Uganda. Then suddenly there was a wave of complaints, labour troubles and delays. It was a year of labour shortage and Norton-Griffiths had to use forced labour and the death rate among the men rose to eighty-three a thousand. His agents may be blamed for the local conditions and after an inquiry which exposed them he ordered drastic improvements. The situation improved and with an easing in employment the line was finished.

But the contract, which paid Norton-Griffiths extremely well, was not extended. The Uganda section was built by the Uganda Government and their engineers were able to deal even with the vast M'pologama Swamp (as Brassey had dealt with the Fens). 'Departmental construction' proved to everyone's surprise, not least that of the great contractor, to be cheaper yet as fast. It was only a faint shadow on the sun of Norton-Griffiths's prosperity, but an indication of what was to come.

The Brazilian Government had already delivered the province of Ceará into his hands, with the Department of Public Works, in a contract whose visionary benefits matched its hazardous execution.

For centuries the north-eastern provinces had suffered from drought or irregular rainfall. Settled by the earliest Portuguese colonists, they were densely populated by a tough, independent people, penurious but

SIR JOHN NORTON-GRIFFITHS

proud, akin in their relationship with the other provinces to the Highland Scots. The land which had once been forest was reduced to the *caatinga*, or dry scrub; a long terrible drought in the late nineteenth century destroyed the sugar plantations which had been worked by negro slaves and halved the total population, driving more than a million people south into the states of Rio Grande and São Paulo. In the dry waste land, the *Sertão*, the only hope remained in the magic word irrigation.

Silva Pessoa became President in 1919 on a wave of prosperity induced by the post-war coffee boom. The United States promised loans for public works in large quantities, and a flood of spending was let loose, cascading into such extravagances as the Centenary Exhibition. The Inspectoria Federal of Ceará Province decided to restore the vanished agriculture by water conservation on a scale not attempted since the Roman cultivation of North Africa. For good measure they wished also to improve the ports not only in Ceará but on either side of the coast.

Norton-Griffiths captured the contract with measured ease and showmanship. He visited Brazil in 1919 and 1920, entertaining Ministers and officials in Rio and Ceará on a scale which put the ambassadors out of court, and in 1922 led a delegation of M.P.s to the Centenary Exhibition. He was, perhaps, carried away with the idea of making the desert green; enough certainly to call this expensive folly a monument to Brazilian greatness. It was clear even then, to an impartial eye, that the whole economy was being submerged in a tide of public debt.

However, Norton-Griffiths was wise enough not to offer to finance his project on the same terms he had offered Chile. The Provincial Government was to pay him for his works as soon as they were completed, with advances where necessary. His contract, signed in October 1920, provided for three major dams, at Patu, Quixeramobim and Acarape, none of which was less than 700 yards long and 120 feet high; conduits and canals throughout the basin of the Jaguaribe and Riacho de Sangue Rivers and their tributaries; a breakwater, two half-mile jetties and complete port facilities at the provincial capital, Fortaleza; a harbour at Amarracao farther north; the removal of a reef and dredging of Paraiba Harbour; and the complete modernization of Recife (Pernambuco) with a mile-long breakwater, a mole nearly as long, railways, granaries, elevators, and warehouses; a monopoly contract for nearly 600 miles of coast.[See map on page 261].

It is impossible now to calculate how much this would have cost—perhaps £17 million. The dams were finished by 1924 and Fortaleza soon after. Meanwhile Brazil, under successive Presidents, staggered into financial chaos, the result largely of the failure of the coffee boom. American loans were piled on European loans until the foreign debt amounted to £277 million on an annual budget of one-twentieth that sum. A period of *coups d'état*, of petty *caudillos*, began, culminating in the Vargas Revolution of 1930 when American money was cut short by the Slump. Well before then, Norton-Griffiths slackened off; by no means certain that he would continue to receive cash payment for his work. Slowly the vast programme halted and petered out in interminable lawsuits beyond even the solution of experts, for with the Revolution many of the relevant documents were lost, and litigation continued long after Norton-Griffiths's death over sums for which there was, and probably had been, no accounting. After the manner of such great projects only partly completed, his work was never interwoven into a coherent scheme, and Brazilians continued to plan haphazardly, and build, when finances allowed, without materially altering the desert.

In London Norton-Griffiths worked on the Underground for the first time, enlarging Clapham Common station for the City and South London Railway; and built the massive N.E. Storm Relief Sewer for the L.C.C. from Highbury to Shadwell, for which he created the Metropolitan Tunnel and Public Works Company.

He continued to dissipate his energy. From 1919 when he bought Wonham, the brick Gothic house built by Wyatt in 1810, the family led an intensely active and social life. He had wanted to retire from Parliament, and refused to stand again for Wednesbury, but, incensed by Lloyd George's attitude during the 'Coupon Election', and asked by the local committee of Wandsworth to stand against the Liberal 'Coupon' candidate, Captain Frederick Guest, he turned again to politics. His election was as rowdy as the others had been in the Midlands; heckled by a gang known as the 'Blizzard Bunch', he stopped his speech, strode off the platform, knocked one of the offenders out and returned to carry on. At the subsequent proceedings, where he was fined 10/- with 5 guineas costs, he extracted the maximum publicity. He held the seat through 1922, when he returned from Brazil only just in time for nomination, but eventually retired two years later, having been created a baronet for his war-time and other services.

He had loved the campaigning; the House of Commons itself meant very little. There were always weekend parties at Wonham, a house in London for the season, and wide travel on the Continent. In Scotland he and his wife stayed and shot with friends; bred golden retrievers (his wife carried the prizes at Crufts the year after the war); spent a fortune on maintaining and keeping up the house; days recalling the flavour of Temple House before the war. Norton-Griffiths seemed even more unexpected, wild, reckless, and amusing, and round him in concentric circles, revolved the family, his friends and the dance of almost heedless, slightly feverish, gaiety.

6

REALITIES

URING 1924 Norton-Griffiths fell ill with what was called ambulatory typhoid. It was not serious, but difficult to diagnose and harder to cure. Weeks of illness left a debilitating effect from which he never entirely recovered, taking away something of his carefree zest, making the lightheartedness a little harsh. Chiefly for this he gave up politics, and sold Wonham in 1926, but it was only the symptom of a wider malaise.

His ambitions, without lessening, began to turn sour within themselves. Apart from his disillusionment with the Lords, there had never been a setback which he himself could not defeat, nothing which was not tangible, malleable in his powerful hands. Now he became aware, much as Cowdray at the same time, of a vague uneasiness in contracting affairs, a lack of confidence which he could neither understand nor pin down. The post-war boom had given him more work than any other British contractor yet quite suddenly it seemed to run out, leaving him looking anxiously to keep his firm in being. This insecurity did not afterwards leave him; and explains many of his later decisions.

The situation was no sudden turn of the wheel. The things he stood for and in which he believed were dated in a way which the easy life of the early twenties had disguised. Norton-Griffiths's ideas of Empire and politics had not changed since he first met Rhodes—they were now out of date and soon to be incomprehensible. It may have made sense to the voters at the Khaki Election to demand that no candidate should receive a 'coupon' who had not served his country in the War, but as late as 1929 he had not accepted that a labour Government was fit to rule; nor that his brand of Imperial Free Trade could not be maintained in the slump. This attitude was only an example of a wider illusion, shared by many who saw in the Treaty of Locarno, and the return to the Gold Standard, the recreation of the Edwardian era.

Simply, he never altered his opinions as a result of the war; never made the effort of mind which could accept trade unionism, equal rights, socialism of any sort (which he equated with weakness), as anything but an evil to be fought as he had fought the Huns. The vitriolic and tempestuous side of his temper was unsuited to the age, and weaknesses previously hidden began to appear, as a tired man becomes irritable with his decline. He grew more demanding and his judgement of subordinates increasingly erratic; always a difficult man to oppose, he continued to choose older and less able men, who held the same views as himself, and the firm became out of date with alarming speed. He quarrelled with, rather than listened to, suggestions, and inefficiency and mistakes crept in; the inevitable result of too much done too fast for too long, unplanned in the long-term way which sustained Cowdray. Brilliance had covered the mistakes in the past, but it was no longer enough to state his old syllogism: 'it is possible and desirable, therefore I can do it.' He had never analysed problems, relying on his intuition and understanding of the world, and this, as the world changed out of all measure, vitiated nearly all his later work.

The results of war, in the world of public works, only became clear about five years after the Armistice. Governments preferred to do work themselves as contracting became more predictable; credit was not so cheaply obtainable as before 1914; there were fewer opportunities as areas of non-development shrank; and Norton-Griffiths learnt the more bitterly because he lived longer into the post-war years, what Brassey had meant when he called the contractor's life hard.

Uasin Gishu was a pointer—the contractor at 5 per cent profit, however great his prestige, cost too much; he must tender like his inferiors or lose work, and what had been felt in India about Brassey fifty years before at last became a commonplace—that only firms organized on a different pattern, with a different structure of management, working on far narrower margins of profit, highly economical and mechanized and with an industrial labour force, could hope to contract in the world at large. Other British firms were beginning to work towards this, but it was twenty years before they again reached the world market on the scale which Norton-Griffiths had occupied.

The facility which had inspired his best works, the true promoter's gift of handling millions, creating credit and matching it with enterprise, was no longer needed. As the United States swamped Latin America with loans, even provincial governments had only to ask to receive. The high-interest loans, carrying high-priced contracts, which Norton-Griffiths had to offer, lost their appeal.

For six years after 1923 he looked restlessly for work. Aggressive national policies militated slowly but impressively against private free-lance enterprise as Cowdray found in his oil exploration. There had been a time when Pearson's influence balanced American, in Colombia and Mexico; it was unthinkable that a British contractor could be so powerful after 1920. The whole world economy was profoundly unstable, the worst state for a contractor, surrounded by high interest rates, large short-term loans, and the possibility of large-scale default. Governments were soon to prove that for the first time in a century they could go bankrupt with impunity because their political value as allies outweighed their commercial prospects. Then came the crash.

Debtor countries like Brazil after 1929 could not pay even the interest on their loans. Prices fell, the volume of international trade declined absolutely by a third. Governments with less revenue had none for public works. German banking collapsed with the Credit Anstalt. Britain came off the Gold Standard, tariffs rose and the pretence of the old structure disappeared in a welter of purely national measures of ex-pediency. In this climate, even if he had lived, Norton-Griffiths could not have gone on. At best he could have retired handsomely, but it was his tragedy that he carried on, after six years of frustration, straight into the heart of the crisis, a disaster as much the world's making as his own.

His introduction to tunnelling work in London helped Norton-Griffiths win a £1 million contract for the extension of the Hamp-stead Underground. What was in many ways a feat of engineering speed and skill, however, lost him a great deal of money. His section lay south from Charing Cross, under the Thames to Waterloo and on to join the City and South London at Kennington—which is now part of the Northern line. Work began in the summer of 1924 and involved many difficulties. Shields were driven in both directions, from Water-loo and from the two ends, and the river crossing, being mainly in London clay, was at first straightforward. But the Charing Cross loop, where trains turned, lay on the course of the new line and had to be cut through twice, an interesting piece of tube surgery. The station was cut off and the ends sealed with concrete while compressed air work continued, and the time-schedule was spurred by the need to restore main services within a few days.

Seven thousand men were employed for two years. Isolated and unexpected patches of sand or gravel made progress under the river slow. Norton-Griffiths became worried by his completion date and costs rising well above his tender; he thrashed about furiously to find an answer. Conceiving that the men on night shift were slacking, instead of sending down an engineer, and bringing in an accountant to help with the finances, he sent his nineteen-year-old son on the shift to see what could be done. It was the curious obverse of his genius for initiating work—to say 'they must be cheating me' rather than reappraise—and it explains something of his business attitude.

As a cure for his typhoid, Norton-Griffiths toured in France and, late in 1924, set out with his wife for Iraq. His interest in irrigation had been thoroughly stirred by the Brazilian dream which he hoped to repeat in the valley of the Euphrates by building a dam comparable to Sennar and a massive canal system to grow cotton in Diala, as the Sudan Government did in Gezira. Travelling fast but pleasantly through the Middle East, they took one of the first desert buses from Damascus to Baghdad. The owner of the Diala plantations entertained them; Gertrude Bell became a friend, and they were introduced to King Feisal and Nuri es-Said who were both enthusiastic. The scheme, like the sun, gave him life; and the concession for development went through, in spite of popular objections that it would take the small farmer's water and give it to the great estates.

After a leisurely return through Palestine and Egypt Norton-Griffiths worked hard to get the concession under-written in London, but the public would take up only 5 per cent of the issue and although he slaved to keep up the market the scheme never matured, leaving him with a large and worthless holding. Some of the trouble came from Iraqi politicians; part from the history of the Middle East, for the rough hewing of new countries out of the old Turkish Empire was too recent to give the investing public confidence. Norton-Griffiths was deeply disappointed.

In 1925 the whole family sailed to Brazil where Norton-Griffiths's younger son was working. In the course of a hilarious voyage Norton-Griffiths learned enough about Colombia to tempt him into his last essay into Latin American affairs. A small railway contract in Venezuela for an oil company associated with his own Rumanian concern led him north first, and left him with some days before he was due to return to Rio.

Bogotá, the Colombian capital was then perhaps the most isolated city in South America. There was no road up from the Pacific shore and the long slow journey up the Magdalena River ended in a mule track before the short Dorado Railway, finished by Cowdray twenty years before. Cowdray had been forced out by U.S. pressure before his plan to reorganize Colombia could begin, and in the years since, nothing had been done. As transport was the key to development, stagnation might have continued, but for the fact that oil production rose from half a million barrels in 1924 to 15 million in 1927. Giants of the U.S. oil industry then moved in and Norton-Griffiths had the vision to see that communications had to be built at once.

From the start he had powerful competitors, mainly American, firms such as R. W. Hebbard and the Ulan Construction Company but he had the advantages of previous experience and undoubted panache. His talent for self-advertisement never had greater play; 'Quien es Sir Juan?' was the cry and he was at pains to provide an answer. Travelling the state like a Maharajah, he came at exactly the right moment; American loans were ushering in, to the sum of $171 million, what came to be known as 'the dance of the millions'. Among sectional interests, individual Congressmen fighting for the self-interests of their constituents and Ministers seeking reputations, Norton-Griffiths signed contracts; and within hours of his arrival in Bogotá was cabling to his friends in New York to arrange the loans for his particular works.

Colombia did not follow the reckless spiral of Brazil, for which only the United States, too closely linked to the oil interests to permit it, and the better contractors, Norton-Griffiths at their head, may be given credit. For although the Government did have a programme of roads, railways, ports and air services, everything was dissipated in trying to do too much. Money was grossly wasted, embezzled by officials, misapplied by local departments. Such companies flourished as the German Julius Konsortium which spent $4½ million on five different railways which were below specification and quite disconnected when taken over by the reforming Liberal Government of Uribe Hoyas in 1930.

But the ports which Cowdray would have built were completed; air transport linked the remotest cities; in one generation the mule was relegated from being the only means of movement to a beast of burden in the remoter areas. A transport revolution was created even if it was lame in the execution.

Norton-Griffiths, stimulated rather than discouraged by the perversity of Colombia's geography and the factiousness of its politicians, built two of the most important works; the 100 mile railway south from Bogotá to the head of navigation at Neiva in the Magdalena valley, opening up a wide agricultural belt and bringing in to the system the mining areas of Huila and Caqueta. Even larger was his road, the Carretera Central del Norte, one of the three trunk roads of the country, from the Venezuelan border near Lake Maracaibo, to Cuqueta on the eastern Andes, to joint the road north from Bogotá, and connect with the Magdalena steamboats.

The four hundred mile road was the only one completed on time, in 1929, and the only one in full working order until the Pan-American Highway became a political necessity. It was built 30 feet wide and elaborately ditched against the tropical floods which had destroyed earlier attempts, with a base of stone, gravel and clay, capped with decayed limestone which hardened like tarmac. Labour was cheap, plentiful and the climate of the plateau good; there were no difficulties except those of mountain engineering and the danger of sudden floods.

Norton-Griffiths was free enough of work in 1927 and 1928 to give Colombia his full attention. Characteristic of his judgement was the discovery, when visiting the railway with his agent, Major Gonzales, who had worked at Luanda, that all the earth-works was finished, and the rails laid, but that the girders for the bridges were held up in the barges on the Magdalena. Gonzalez asked what he should do; Norton-Griffiths looked round at the great forest trees and told him to build wooden bridges the whole way to the river and replace them when the steel arrived, so that all could then be built at once. Both the Colombian contracts proved extremely profitable.

But this promise of better times was spoilt when Norton-Griffiths lost a contract he particularly coveted. When rumours of a major reconstruction of Singapore Harbour became current in 1928 he set off at once for the Far East. He had met and hoped to take into partnership Gibson, an engineer who had done fine work for Cowdray on the Sennar Dam, and who was attracted by the size and complexity of the Singapore plans. A large family party left England for Ceylon and Penang, and Norton-Griffiths met Gibson on the spot. As usual they were fêted and entertained; but though Norton-Griffiths went long and carefully into the dock work with Gibson, he realized before he left that he could not put out a tender low enough to win the contract. He felt frustrated by the wasted effort, and liking Gibson, and with a certain respect for his ability, cast around for something else. And it was Gibson who fired him with the last plan, to heighten, for the second time, the Aswan Dam.

7

THE NILE

NO SINGLE work of any British contractor stood as famous and magnificent as John Aird's barrier across the Nile. For nearly thirty years it had given life to Egypt, and had been raised to hold more than double its original capacity. The reputation of British contractors and engineers was higher in no country in the world. The long reign of Sir Murdoch MacDonald ended with his retirement in 1921, but in the staff of the Public Works Department the tradition of engineering skill and integrity which had shaped the whole use of the Nile continued.

But the laws of population are inexorable. By 1929 a nation which had been seven million in 1888 when Lord Cromer first discussed the Dam had increased to twelve. There had been no redistribution of land except the sale of the old Ismaili estates by Sir Ernest Cassel; only the prosperity and fertility given by irrigation maintained the mass of the fellaheen; and, since Cowdray's dam had been built in the Sudan, the nightmare of Egyptians was that more and more of the Nile water might be cut off before it ever reached them. Agreements on sharing were made in 1921, but they were soon to be threatened.

There is no need to go into the details of Anglo-Egyptian relations after 1922 when Egypt became a 'sovereign state' with all its sovereignty still virtually under British control. A decade of bickering set in which reduced the power of the King, built up rich landlords and pashas, and saw the rise of the left-wing Wafdist Party, and Saad Zaghlul. Zaghlul in 1924 failed to get independence from the first British Labour Government by asking too much and, as a counter to his demagogic power, when the Sirdar, Sir Lee Stack, was assassinated, General Allenby issued an ultimatum which seemed to threaten to take more water for the Sudan as a reprisal.

The threat ought never to have been made and it remained a source of trouble in the conflicts which followed. But it was the population figures which were potentially fatal to the whole unstable economy. In 1920 the Nile Commission, headed by Sir Murdoch Macdonald, had reported in favour of continuing the scheme balanced round Aswan with a further barrage at Nag Hammadi, but six years later Egyptian nationalist dreams and the stark possibility of famine put life into the scheme Macdonald had rejected,[1] for heightening the dam a second time.

Political events had broken into the imperial vision of 3,000 miles of river worked as a single unit. Approached again in retirement, however, Macdonald agreed that this was an engineering possibility which would again double the volume of water, making five cubic kilometres. Following the usual practice, his plans and design were put before an International Commission which began to investigate in autumn 1928 and reported favourably in January 1929.

The engineering techniques were quite different from those used to heighten the dam before. The joint then planned by Baker had been so perfect that it could hardly be seen; rather than risk the problem of expansion and contraction again, the Commission advised that the new masonry should not touch the old at all, but that the 25-feet-high mass should rest on sheets of bitumen, and the new reinforced buttresses on plates of stainless steel; tie-rods all over would link it to the existing dam. They also recommended that, instead of assigning the work to a specified contractor as before, the Egyptian Government should advertise for tenders.

In this slack time of Norton-Griffiths's life his association with Gibson had a certain fatalistic touch. He had always been prone to work up great enthusiasm about people who, then, in his eyes, could do nothing wrong. He might conceivably have retired if he had not been upset by the failure over Singapore, but once the idea of Aswan was suggested to him its temptation over-rode everything else. His choice was not greatly different from that of Brassey in 1851, because, with the run-down of Brazilian affairs and completion of Colombian, there seemed to be no work for him in any part of the world. With his sense of the dramatic, it was intolerable not to end on a fine note; he

[1] 'It is quite certain that the project is not worth considering in the near future as an auxiliary work.'

would, he decided, make a quarter of a million out of the Nile contract and retire.

In November 1928 he and his wife went to Egypt and while sailing up the Nile met James Baxter, in the Egyptian Ministry of Finance, whom Norton-Griffiths persuaded to join the enterprise and handle its financial relationship with the Government. Gibson joined them, and they travelled as far as the Sennar Dam in the Sudan to see the living proof that Gibson knew his job. However, the brash Yorkshire engineer had an overweening pride; back in Cairo, as they discussed the dam in the long evenings at Shepheard's Hotel, small disputes grew, pointers to the future. Gibson wanted the firm to be called Gibson and Griffiths, but Norton-Griffiths was too experienced to give such precedence to a man only recently a subordinate of Cowdray and Hopkinson.

How much he depended on Gibson only became clear when they returned with Baxter to England. Gibson was to come home later, and Norton-Griffiths threw himself into the preparation of the massive tender, waiting anxiously for his arrival. Sir Murdoch Macdonald, having been appointed Consultant Engineer and arbiter of the scheme, hoped to ask for tenders in May 1929 and speed was vital. Gibson had the expertise in Egyptian affairs, the detailed knowledge which could help Norton-Griffiths to cut his margins fine enough, more accurately than at Singapore. And this now mattered enormously because Norton-Griffiths was again forced to return to the unsatisfactory borrowing of before the war.

Edward Powles had resigned, taking the Howard de Walden interest with him, just before Norton-Griffiths went to Egypt. Without any major contract on hand, with no accumulated plant, security or large capital assets (other than his own private fortune) Norton-Griffiths could not raise enough either through his bank or friends in the City, and so he had, during the spring of 1929, to bring to a head an operation of great diplomatic skill; to persuade his friends of South African days, Solly and Jack Joel (of de Beers, the Diamond Corporation, and nearly every gold-mine on the Rand) to put up the necessary £265,000.

All his charm, skill as a negotiator and publicist, and months devoted to satisfying the Joels' social ambitions, were needed but he won their agreement. Then Gibson came back, but did not come to the London office. Norton-Griffiths hesitated, giving him time to settle down; until in July, Gibson wrote coolly that he had promised his wife not to work in the tropics again and would take no more part in The Aswan Scheme.

Norton-Griffiths was shattered. He had relied utterly on his knowledge to prepare the final estimates. Since time was desperately short he called in everyone who could possibly help and slaved night and day over the pages of specifications. He never considered breaking off, even though he was committed to it only in name, and though his whole family tried to dissuade him. They were frightened, with justification, because he was without experience in dam work, and the international competition promised would mean a very different atmosphere from the cost-plus percentage basis of all his recent contracts.[1] He had never been good at settling down to work out figures, and now with only eight weeks to go he tried to repair the deficiencies of a lifetime.

The tenders were opened on October 2nd, 1929, three weeks before the Wall Street crash. Ten firms' prices were the same within £100,000; the lowest being Topham, Jones & Railton at £2,432,000. Norton-Griffiths's tender was £1,960,000, nearly half a million less. The engineering world reeled—surely there was a mistake? *The Times* reported that it was 'much lower than the Ministry had expected'. Macdonald who, if sometimes harsh and unbending, was fair and a friend, thought it absurd and impossible, and asked him to revise the offer or withdraw it. Norton-Griffiths refused; and in view of his international reputation, Macdonald had no choice but to accept.

Norton-Griffiths was admittedly shaken by the discrepancy, but remained confident of success. Yet his whole calculation seems to have been based on two highly dangerous premises—that he could bring barges up to all the south face of the dam during the whole period after the flood, saving time and double handling, and that, as was common practice at the time among contractors, there would be 'extras': necessary works and materials not included in the original specification on which he could make a larger profit.[2] But 1930 was one of the lowest floods of the century, not leaving enough water in the reservoir for the barges to get up after April, and there was to be no time for extras.

Norton-Griffiths left England in November 1929 and work began under John Burns, the Chief Engineer. By January, 10,000 men were

[1] They went so far as to calculate that with his assets he could live comfortably on £20,000 a year if he retired immediately and dissolved the Company.

[2] A habit which had led contractors in Africa to tendering at cost price, counting on extras to make up.

trimming smooth the rough granite wall of the dam to receive the steel plates, and dismantling the superstructure. Most of the subcontractors had been taken on by Norton-Griffiths from his old partner Sir John Jackson who had just finished the Nag Hammadi Barrage 150 miles to the north.

Aswan was now a pleasant town set among palm trees, well watered and civilized. Lady Norton-Griffiths came out, and Queen Marie of Rumania visited Cairo to see her old friends. The spectacular scenery south of the dam was less harsh than when Aird first looked at the cataract; the precipitous headlands of the great sandstone hills, with drifts of tawny-coloured sand, and the high, dark hills of Kasr Ibrahim beyond the eastern bank, no longer Arabian, but Nubian, desert and wild, seemed to be set in proportion by the vast calm man-made lake between.

But anxiety grew. The men who had done so well in Latin America were no longer with him. There were too many subcontractors, John Aird, son of the contractor, noticed when he visited Aswan; and as Norton-Griffiths realized the inaccuracy of his schedules, he began to drive his men and engineers with a ferocity he had not felt since Benguella.

Trouble began; the Government supervisors, in particular, trained in the tradition of the Nile Irrigation Department, not unnaturally resented being scarified to pay for his mistakes. There were difficulties over cement also. To save money he quarried the material locally and the consistency was poor.

In March Lady Norton-Griffiths took her husband by river-boat up to Wadi Halfa, which rested him a little; but a month later Burns resigned, and rumours of difficulties began to spread. Norton-Griffiths maintained a brave face, invincibly optimistic, and refused to ask for any sort of help. Outwardly the work seemed prosperous enough.

Much stronger forces were moving against him that summer. In June a Cabinet crisis in Egypt followed a second failure to win independence from the Labour Government in London. Nahas Pasha, Prime Minister with an almost absolute majority, to avoid the resultant unpopularity, resigned. Rioting and political disturbance culminated in abrogation of the Constitution.

Running parallel was a far more serious economic crisis. The world slump, sparked off by Wall Street six months earlier, dragged down the price of cotton, the staple Egyptian export. From £20 a kantar in 1929 it crashed to £12 in 1930, and in a hopeless attempt to maintain the price the Egyptian Treasury spent almost its entire reserve in buying up the crop. Committed to an enormous programme of irrigation they were hard put to pay Jackson for Nag Hammadi and unwilling to aid Norton-Griffiths in trouble largely of his own making. They decided to call for Macdonald's advice. Although Norton-Griffiths still professed confidence in July, soon afterwards he returned to England to ask the Joels for more credit. He was refused. The diamond kings had drawn their own deductions from the Wall Street crash and preferred to cut their losses.

Norton-Griffiths went back to Egypt, deeply worried and disturbed. His wife, recovering from a severe illness, had to stay behind. He went only to see what could be saved, if necessary by delaying tactics, but once on the spot saw quite clearly that there was no recourse and no salvation. A great deal had been done, even in his absence; the dam face trimmed, some of the new buttresses built, the steel plates laid and part of the top made ready for the wall; but the subcontractors themselves were restive, and the largest, the Italian company Sacco and Brancale, whose agent was Signor Pizzigalli, suspecting that he was about to go bankrupt, were correspondingly uneasy.

On September 21st Norton-Griffiths cabled his agent at Aswan to stop work. He was staying at the Casino Hotel, San Stefano, outside Alexandria and his overstrained condition was obvious to the other guests. He demanded that the Egyptian Government should hold an inquiry into affairs at the dam, since, he claimed: 'The work of inspection for the Government is carried on by inexperienced staff and the manner in which it uses its authority makes it impossible to carry out the agreement properly.' There may have been some truth in this; some of those who had worked at Nag Hammadi said that the supervising engineers were far more difficult here, but then so was the Aswan work; and it was unwise, so publicly, to attack the Government on the one Department which for forty years had been beyond praise.

Norton-Griffiths had reached the end; having spent nearly half a million he had no more and must stop. But under the penalty terms of the contract, if he gave up, the Government had power to assign the contract to anyone they chose, and he would have to pay the difference between his original tender and the final cost. Since all the Joels' money was gone, and his own, this meant bankruptcy.

Baxter did his best with the Government and might have extracted concessions from Sidki Pasha, Minister of Finance, but for Norton-Griffiths's charges against the engineers. The Public Works Department were extremely worried, and against any extension of time since the top of the dam had been cut down to receive the new work and had to be strengthened before the next year's flood. But even Baxter did not know how near bankruptcy the contractor was, and Norton-Griffiths himself would not ask for help. Although he saw Sidki Pasha on September 23rd, it was only to be told that Sir Murdoch Macdonald had been summoned from London in his position as consultant, and that no compromise or decision could be made without him. He was due to arrive on the 29th.

Early that morning in the cool pellucid light of Alexandria, Norton-Griffiths left the San Stefano Hotel in a small surfboat and paddled out to sea. Later, Pizzigalli, watching from a window, saw the boat floating upside down. Norton-Griffiths's body was found; he had shot himself in the head.

Baxter tried to carry on before the contract was annulled. Sir John Jackson offered to do it at cost price, to save something from the wreck. Other interests, old friends in the City, tried also, but at the end the Egyptian Government, perhaps wisely, refused, took over the subcontractors and gave the work to the firm of Topham, Jones and Railton who finished it early in 1934.

Nothing was left of the colossus; only an interminable, and since the relevant papers were lost, endless lawsuit with Brazil. Empire Jack was forgotten with the imperial programmes he had advocated. He had relied entirely on himself, believing himself to be invincible; and for such a man to face the reality of being broken was perhaps too difficult, even if he had not been worn out with months of overwork. Life being exhausted, he chose to end it, not without a certain dignity.

CONCLUSION

A HANDFUL of bankers and contractors controlled nearly all railway building in the world, outside the U.S.A., between 1840 and 1870, and a large share of transport developments in the half-century after. The scale of their work as individuals is undeniable. Brassey and Peto altered the economic history of Europe and the Argentine, Aird and Cassel changed the life of Egypt, and Cowdray made Mexico rich before the Revolution. Like the others, Hirsch, de Lesseps, von Siemens, Wheelwright, they are at least as important, and often more significant, in history than politicians and presidents. In their own countries, as Brassey did in England, the contractors laid the rails and built the ports, without which Britain, Germany, France, and the U.S.A. could never have become industrial powers.

The transport revolution was the fundamental premise of modern society. Without railways, harbours, and roads, change from the pre-industrial age would have been unthinkable. Because the late nineteenth century was a time peculiar in modern history, of widespread free trade beliefs and Liberal ideas, an international money market based on London, and a sensitive, international economy, and because the great crises which had periodically upset the balance, ended, in European financial centres, in 1866, and were succeeded by milder, more controllable recessions, the individual contractor was able to flourish.

But they were among the founders of the old capitalistic society in other ways which have been, and still often are, condemned. Not only industrialization followed the rails they laid down. They rarely looked for or expected help from their own governments and they often pursued their ideas in the face of the opposition of foreign powers. But, after the earliest days, governments followed them, supporting new trade with consuls and the paraphernalia of diplomacy, seeking concessions to mine or drill for oil. Whether it was the U.S.A. penetrating Mexico and Latin America, Britain dominating India on railways designed for military use, or Germany seeking colonial power along the Berlin–Baghdad route, the original freedom of action of the contractor was rapidly circumscribed. Very shortly it ceased to be a matter of indifference who built a railway or won a concession of land beside it. Brassey leased or was given nearly 30,000 square miles of the Argentine in payment for one of the easiest railways he ever built; but fifty years later the whole diplomatic resources of Washington were used to prevent Cowdray extending his oil empire to control of the sources in Colombia.

As the contracts became the ground of diplomatic in-fighting, the footholds of new markets or strategic ambitions, tensions were set up which could in the end only be resolved by force. The classic example is the Berlin–Baghdad Railway, begun by Baron Hirsch and the Credit Anstalt in the 1880s as the route to Istanbul, and continued across Turkey by Georg von Siemens and the Deutsche Bank. This was a constant source of political trouble in the decade before 1914 and contributed materially to the atmosphere of tension leading up to the War. And force destroyed almost completely the freedom of action of the free-lance individual contractors.

They should not therefore receive the odium of 'economic imperialists' because they did not often attempt it. Certainly Brassey in Canada, Cowdray in Mexico, and Norton-Griffiths in particular in Chile, exploited the country. But they did at least build or develop well, and in no case was it done with the shameless audacity of a Meiggs in Peru, a Strousberg in Rumania, or a Vanderbilt in the U.S.A. 'Exploitation' is also a very complex phenomenon, much more variable than Marxist theory will allow. As far as Government loans went, until 1930, Latin America certainly exploited the investors, British, American, and French who lent and lost enormous sums. India, it is probably true, paid very heavily for her communications, but the development of the Nile was done for Egyptian good and was the only foreign investment to give real prosperity. Canada was grossly overcharged for her first transcontinental but received benefits from it in other ways; and in cases like that of Chile or Brazil, ransomed to high terms by Norton-Griffiths, in default of anyone else who could do the work, it was possibly better that they should be built than not at all.

By their own standards the contractors fully deserved their price. Cowdray did not make his millions in Mexico without risking every penny he had; Brassey stood on the edge of bankruptcy for the Rumanian railway. Because they were prepared to stake everything when no one else would, they deserved success. Of all those with large capital resources in this period, they personally used them continuously, where banks frequently refused, and great landowners never considered financing new industrial development. Brassey's investments covered telegraphs, steamships, cables, gasworks—every facet of nineteenth-century progress; and Cowdray even in old age, because he hated it lying useless, used the money he received for his oil empire to finance the electrification of Chile.

They had very little control over the social changes in their labour force, however regrettable. Peasant labour was used by Brassey on all his foreign contracts after the first experiment of importing his own navvies. On his world-wide contracts the peasant was paid the higher wages of the navvy and was started off on the long change; first into navvy, dependent on the contractor, and finally into 'industrial labour', the proletariat. This is only part of a vast, slow, change; in which the contractors were important because the British, accustomed to quantities of men and cheap labour, used them wastefully, and because when men were attached to the retinue of a great contractor they were more protected and worked in better conditions than were usual. By contrast the small contractors of the nineteenth century were among the worst employers of all, unrestricted by law and independent, while their men were powerless.

Certainly in one respect the contractors showed the worst side of capitalistic enterprise. They wasted on the grand scale; not only in Britain were early railways grossly overcapitalized, ruinously competitive, subject to high costs of promotion and the buying off of competitors. Close supervision by impartial engineers, government control, restriction of abuses in government loans or financial panics like the crash of Overend and Gurney, or of contractors' own skimping and evasions, came very slowly. Bribery remained an integral part of overseas contracting during Cowdray's and Norton-Griffiths's time. In such ways, more than in direct financial exploitation, the world paid heavily for its necessities.

Nothing made the contractor but himself. Anyone could set up in business, given a little ambition, a head for figures and skill in managing men. But to be great; to raise and keep an army of men rivalling the largest modern industrial combines, to feed it, pay it, organize the work, and win new contracts to keep it in being, was the work of genius.

These four men would have been great in any age; they would have built roads and aqueducts for the Romans or cathedrals for medieval cities. Brassey, perhaps, appears the greatest because he built the most but this is relative—the others achieved less only because there were more competitors in later and less favourable conditions. Their stature may be measured by those who followed in the period after 1930—other types of firms, other contractors and ways of contracting, which only very slowly, in British enterprise, recaptured the lost position[1], and never in the same free unselfconscious way.

There is no common denominator in the qualities which brought success. Brassey and Cowdray seem temperamentally akin; Aird has certain similarities to Norton-Griffiths.

None of them was born really poor, and all found it easy to achieve in society the status they wanted, whether the simplicity of Brassey, the opulence of Aird, or the elder statesmanship of Cowdray. The century was not always one of social mobility but they were fortunate in the times at which they rose. They were lucky also in their associates, in being able to form loose, flexible and highly efficient groups. At all stages, whether as Peto, Brassey, and Betts, Aird and Lucas, Aird and Cassel, or Norton-Griffiths and the 'House of Lords' the contractors pooled money, skills and knowledge. These associations are one of the most important factors in the economic history of the period.

They were also part of a tradition, which helped, as is often the case, to prolong artificially the favourable climate within which they worked. Because British contracting abroad, begun in 1840 by Brassey, had by 1920 become legendary, Norton-Griffiths found it easier to capture his Brazilian market. After 1930 the legend was largely lost, but its parallel tradition was not—the Victorian tycoons left a legacy of hierarchical management in Britain which buoyed up inefficiency at the top far into the inter-war years, both in industry and banking.

But, with all these advantages, they succeeded because of what they were as individuals and what they believed in. None were qualified as engineers or accountants. They started simply, worked intensely, and

---

[1] American, German, French and Italian contractors took over in part, but the real loss, never recovered by private firms, was to Government Public Works Departments.

followed every chance of profit. Sometimes they paid lip-service to 'Progress'; but progress was not the same excuse which the annexationists used for Empire; it served to give a moral cover to work whose only real force was creative ambition. They had no set economic theories, but followed their lights, right or wrong. They had no political ambitions (three of them sat in Parliament, but only Norton-Griffiths had a serious political platform). They were not concerned with power, except as a means to create more. They did not build up fortunes to dominate, or simply to enjoy, because their energy was essentially creative. The rare attribute of millionaires, of giving money a mystique, was foreign to them.

They did not behave like the founders of dynasties. Although they kept their firms as family affairs, they made no attempt to pass them on. Brassey knew his son had no interest, Aird deliberately kept his children out, and Cowdray dismantled the organization before he died. A creative artist does not expect, or wish, his descendants to carry on 'the business'.

Nor were honours and fame much of a spur. Brassey particularly avoided publicity; and at a time when many peerages had the suspicion of a well-placed deposit, the contractors were not noticeably singled out. They gave great service to the State but it formed no regular part of their activities. Brassey and Peto helped to save the starving army in the Crimea; Aird partnered Cassel at Aswan in a service as great as the Rothschild's Suez Canal loan to Disraeli; Cowdray built the Gretna factory and helped create the Air Ministry; and Norton-Griffiths destroyed the Rumanian oil industry. All this was only part of their ambitions.

Every man has pride. But the pride of these was Promethean, in something stolen from perdition. Their epitaph could be *exegi monumentum aere perennius*—I have built a work to outlast bronze. The pride of creation explains their sense of magnificence—with Aird almost oriental, savage in Norton-Griffiths, and decorous in the Cowdray mansions. And they were driven, not simply by economic forces—to keep their firms in being—but by the spirit of enterprise, the one faculty they shared in common. Enterprise is restless, insatiable, and for this Brassey scoured the extent of Europe in the last year of his life; for this Aird refused to retire till completely paralysed; for this Cowdray gave up only when he could no longer deal with everything himself; and, driven by this, John Norton-Griffiths died.

NOTES

BRASSEY

Chapter 1

(a) W. Bagehot: *Lombard Street*. (1873) p. 158.
(b) Sir Edward Blount: *Memoirs*. (1902) p. 97.
(c) A. M. Andreades: *History of the Bank of England*. (1909) p. 360.
(d) Sir Henry Drummond-Wolff: *Rambling Recollections*. (1908) ii, p. 60.
(e) *Hansard:* May 11th, 1866.
(f) Drummond-Wolff: op. cit., ii, p. 54.

Chapter 2

(a) Cf. W. O. Henderson: *Britain and Industrial Europe*.
(b) Lord Brassey: *Work and Wages*. (1872) p. 9. (1916 ed.).
(c) Railway Register. III: 359.
(d) Sir Edward Blount: op. cit., p. 79.

Chapter 3

(a) Parlt. Papers: 1846, XIV, 52.
(b) Sir Arthur Helps: *Life and Labours of Thomas Brassey*. (1872) p. 111.
(c) Ibid., p. 113.
(d) Tooke and Newmarch: *History of Prices*. Vol. V, 355–7
(e) Lord Brassey: op. cit., pp. 28–9
(f) Ibid., p. 29

Chapter 4

(a) Helps: op. cit., p. 5.
(b) Parlt. Papers: 1846, XIII, 411.
(c) Chadwick: *Papers read before the Statistical Society of Manchester*. (1845).
(d) Lord Brassey: op. cit., p. 8
(e) Lord Brassey: *Lectures on the Labour Question*. (1878) p. 16.
(f) Helps: op. cit., p. 101.
(g) Helps: op. cit., p. 315.
(h) Ibid., p. 315

(i) Ibid., p. 114.
(j) L. Jenks: *The Migration of British Capital to 1875.* p. 127.
(k) Ibid., p. 134.

Chapter 5

(a) W. Lovett: *The Grand Trunk.*
(b) Helps: op. cit., p. 188.
(c) Glyn Mills and Co., papers.
(d) Ibid.
(e) T. E. Blackwell: *Report on the Grand Trunk.* (1858).
(f) Helps: op. cit., p. 212.
(g) Sir H. Peto: *Life of Sir Morton Peto.* (published privately, 1910).

Chapter 6

(a) Quoted in Helps: p. 173.
(b) Parlt. Papers: 1854–5, XXXII. Betts-Newcastle, November 30th, 1854.
(c) Ibid., Betts-Beattie, January 23rd, 1855.
(d) Quoted in Kinglake: *The Invasion of the Crimea.*
(e) Maj.-Gen. Sir Henry Clifford: *Letters from the Crimea.* (1958) p. 166 et seq.
(f) W. H. Russell: *The War.* (1855–56) i, p. 350.
(g) Parlt. Papers: 1855, XXXII.
(h) Jenks: op. cit., p. 173.
(i) Ibid., p. 169.
(j) Drummond Wolff: op. cit., ii, p. 54.

Chapter 7

(a) N. Sanyal: *The Development of Indian Railways.*
(b) W. J. Macpherson: *British Investment in Indian Railways*, E.H.R., 1955.
(c) Ibid.
(d) Glyn Mills papers. July 6th, 1850.
(e) Railways Home Correspondence, 1853 (Commonwealth Relations Office).
(f) Parlt. Papers: 1857–8, XIV, 161.
(g) Helps: op. cit., p. 352.
(h) Parlt. Papers: 1867–8, LI, Danvers Report.
(i) Sanyal: op. cit.
(j) Sir Anthony Cotton: *Papers, &c., on the Madras Famine.* (1877).
(k) Charles Dilke: *Greater Britain.* (1869) p. 332.

Chapter 8

(a) Brassey: *Work and Wages.* p. 29.

Chapter 9
(*a*) Helps: op. cit., p. 131.
(*b*) Ibid., p. 141.
(*c*) Jenks: op. cit., p. 252.
(*d*) Argentine Ministry of Information: *Origen de los Ferrocariles Argentinos.*
(*e*) H. S. Ferns: *Britain and Argentina in the 19th Century.* (1960) p. 343.
(*f*) *Origen de los Ferrocariles.*
(*g*) Helps: op. cit., pp. 367–9.

Chapter 10
(*a*) Glyn Mills papers.
(*b*) Bagehot: *Lombard Street.* p. 18

Chapter 11
(*a*) Helps: op. cit., p. 263.
(*b*) Ibid., pp. 265–7.
(*c*) Parlt. Papers: 1872, IX, 1.
(*d*) Jenks: op. cit., p. 262.

AIRD

Chapter 1
(*a*) Charles Aird: *Diaries* (unpublished).
(*b*) Ibid.

Chapter 2
(*a*) Ibid.

Chapter 3
(*a*) Manchester Ship Canal Bill: Minutes of Evidence, 1886.

Chapter 4
(*a*) *See,* R. Robinson and J. Gallaher: *The Victorians and Africa.*
(*b*) Herbert Addison: *Sun and Shadow at Aswan.* (1959) p. 35.
(*c*) Foreign Office Papers: Consul-General, Egypt (P.R.O.). December 5th, 1897.
(*d*) Ibid., December 5th, 1897.
(*e*) W. S. Churchill: *The River War.* (1899) ii, p. 13.
(*f*) Lord Cromer to Cassel: Cromer Papers (P.R.O.). February 26th, 1898.

(g) Churchill: op. cit., ii, p. 19.
(h) M. Fitzmaurice: 'The Nile Reservoir', *Procs. of Institution of Civil Engineers*, CLII, 1902.
(i) Sir W. Willcocks: *Aswan Dam and Lake Moeris*: Lecture (1904).

Chapter 5

(a) Parlt. Papers: 1909, LVIII, 435.
(b) Ibid., 1912–3, LVIII, 533.

COWDRAY

Chapter 1

(a) *Diary of European Tour, 1875.*
(b) J. H. Spender: *Weetman Pearson, first Lord Cowdray.* (1930) p. 23.

Chapter 2

(a) Spender: op. cit., p. 24.
(b) Ibid., p. 27.

Chapter 4

(a) Spender: op. cit., p. 31.
(b) Cowdray papers.
(c) J. W. Wallace: *Evidence to U.S. Senate Committee on Interoceanic Canals, 1896.*
(d) Cowdray papers.
(e) Quoted in E. B. Glick: 'Tehuantepec Railway', *Pacific Historical Review*, 1953.
(f) Spender: op. cit., p. 135.

Chapter 5

(a) *Truth.* XXXVIII, 1895, 137.
(b) Cowdray papers.
(c), (d), (e) Ibid.
(f) Judge Gerard: *My first 83 Years in America.* (1951) p. 166
(g) Letter in the possession of Lady Burrell.
(h) Cowdray papers.

Chapter 6

(a) Spender: op. cit., p. 149.
(b), (c), (d), (e), f), (g) Cowdray papers.
(h) H. S. Denny, in *Mining Journal*, June 4th, 1910.

(*i*), (*j*), (*k*), (*l*) Cowdray papers.
(*m*) R. S. Baker: *Woodrow Wilson: Life and Letters.* (1932) iv, p 247.
(*n*) Grey of Fallodon: *Twenty-five Years.* (1925) ii, p. 94
(*o*) F. O. Papers: *Mexico.*
(*p*) F. O. Papers: *Mexico.*
(*q*) R. S. Baker: *Woodrow Wilson.* iv, p. 290.
(*r*) Spender: op. cit., p. 198.
(*s*) F. O. Papers: *Mexico.*
(*t*) Ibid.
(*u*) E. Delaisi: *Oil: its influence in Politics.* (1922) p. 81.
(*v*) F. O. Papers: *Mexico.*

Chapter 7

(*a*) Spender: op. cit., p. 222.
(*b*) Ibid., p. 222.
(*c*) Quoted in A. Boyle: *Trenchard, Man of Vision.* (1962) p. 207.
(*d*), (*e*) Spender: op. cit., pp. 231–3.
(*f*) Raleigh and Jones: *Official History of the War in the Air.* (1937) vi, p. 8.
(*g*) Spender: op. cit., p. 234.
(*h*) *Official History.* vi, p. 22.

Chapter 8

(*a*) W. Ashworth: *History of the International Economy.* (1952) p. 196.
(*b*) Lloyd George: *War Memoirs.* (1933) p. 1875.

NORTON-GRIFFITHS
Chapter 4

(*a*) Sir Philip Gibbs; quoted in A. Barrie: *War Underground.* (1961) p. 259.
(*b*) Norton-Griffiths papers.
(*c*) Times Law Report. March 29th, 1920.

Chapter 5

(*a*) Norton-Griffiths papers.
(*b*) Ibid.
(*c*) E. F. Hill: *Permanent Way.* (1954) p. 221.

BIBLIOGRAPHY

General Works

American studies have begun to cover the contractor or the entrepreneur as a general economic factor. For this, see J. A. Schumpeter: *Capitalism, Socialism and Democracy*; and recently a collection of essays: *Change and the Entrepreneur*, published by Harvard University, who also produce a journal: *Explorations in Entrepreneurial History*. The best study of nineteenth-century financial trends in Britain remains L. H. Jenks: *The Migration of British Capital to 1875*. Sir John Clapham: *Economic History of Modern Britain*, and his *Economic History of France and Germany* cover much of the period in considerable detail; for a shorter account of the early industrial history, see T. S. Ashton: *The Industrial Revolution 1760 to 1830*, and for the later, W. Ashworth: *A Short History of the International Economy*. A view of the problems of imperialism is contained in J. A. Schumpeter: *Imperialism* and a recent diagnosis in R. Robinson and J. Gallacher: *Africa and the Victorians*. For good modern studies of individual engineers, see L. T. C. Rolt: *Isambard Kingdom Brunel*, and *Thomas Telford*.

Particular Sources

A great number have been consulted, of which this can only be a selection, and may be useful for further reading.

Brassey. Sir Arthur Helps: *The Life and Labours of Thomas Brassey* is a Victorian eulogy of the good employer, but contains the assessment of a contemporary. For the contracts abroad, W. O. Henderson: *Britain and Industrial Europe*, and R. E. Cameron: *France and the Economic Development of Europe*, are the most up-to-date studies; as is H. S. Ferns: *Britain and the Argentine in the 19th century*, for South America. Earlier works are C. de Biase: *Il Problema della ferrovie nel Risorgimento*, and N. Sanyal: *The Development of Indian Railways*. C. H. Ellis: *British Railways* deals with the history of most railways in the British Isles; A. M. Andréades: *History of the Bank of England* is useful and W. Bagehot: *Lombard Street* gives the opinion of a disillusioned contemporary. More personal memories or sketches are; Sir Edward Blount: *My Memoirs*; P. H. Emden: *Money Powers of Europe*; H. Drummond Wolff: *Notes of the Past*, and *Rambling Recollections*.

Aird. The London works are surveyed generally in Sir Joseph Broodbank: *History of the Port of London*, Sir William Besant: *London in the 19th century*, and T. S. Wickwar: *The Public Services*. S. Everard: *History of the Gas Light and Coke Company* is the story of the largest gas company in Britain. For the general history of Egypt, see J. Marlowe: *Anglo-Egyptian Relations*, and Lord Cromer: *Modern Egypt*; for the Nile irrigation, the many volumes by Sir William Willcocks; and for the Dam itself, Herbert Addison: *Sun and Shadow at Aswan*, and *Land, Water and Food*.

Cowdray. J. A. Spender: *Weetman Pearson, first Lord Cowdray*, is a most useful source for the whole period. Mexican history after 1900 has encouraged many books, often greatly biased and inaccurate polemics. J. B. Parkes: *History of Mexico*, and A. Tischendorf: *Great Britain and Mexico in the Era of Porfirio Diaz*, are reliable, and to a lesser extent H. Cline: *The United States and Mexico*, and L. B. Simpson: *Many Mexicos*. The story of the oil companies is given in detail in M. Gerretson: *History of the Royal Dutch*, R. D. Henriques: *Marcus Samuel*, R. W. and M. E. Hidy: *History of Standard Oil*, and, more wildly, by Percy Furber: *I Took Chances*. For Cowdray's tenure of the Air Board, see Andrew Boyle: *Trenchard, Man of Vision*, and the *Official History of the War in the Air*.

Norton-Griffiths. Alexander Barrie: *War Underground* gives a vivid picture of one of his war activities. George Pauling: *Chronicles of a Contractor*, P. H. Emden: *Randlords*, M. Vicuña: *Los Ferrocariles de Chile*, E. F. Hill: *Permanent Way, the Story of the Uganda Railway*, and J. F. Rippy: *The Capitalists and Columbia* provide some background for his work. See also Addison: *Sun and Shadow at Aswan* for his final failure.

Collected Sources

Foreign Office Papers (Public Record Office).
Company Records (Bush House).
Cromer Papers (Public Record Office).
Brassey, Aird, Norton-Griffiths, documents, &c.
Whitehall Securities Archives (Pearson Records).

Periodicals &c.

Economic History Review.
Engineering.
Geographic Journal.
Herapath's Railway Review.
Hispanic-American Historical Review.
Mexican Year Books.

Pacific Historical Review.
Proceedings of the Institution of Civil Engineers.
The Builder.
The Mining Journal.
The Times.

Finally, the inexhaustible resources of Parliamentary Papers, including Consular Reports, and Proceedings in Private Bill Committees.

320

INDEX

Aberdeen, Lord, 79
Admiralty, 200–2, 233–4
   oil contract, 220, 227, 229, 232
Agadir, 200
Agra, Masterman & Co., 31
Agricultural Bank of Egypt, 146
Aguila, el, 163, 216, 218–20, 222, 225–227, 229–30
Air Board, 229, 233–8
Air Ministry, 236–8
Aird, Alexander, 131
Aird, Charles, 125, 130–1
Aird, John, 91, 117, 121–7, 130
Aird, Sarah, 125, 132
Aird, Sir John, 23–4, 118, 122, 124–6, 171–2, 179, 188, 242, 244, 258, 265, 269, 300, 304, 307–311
   Beckton, 128–30
   partnership with Lucas, 130, 134–7
   character, etc., 130–3
   London Docks, 134–8
   West Highland Railway, 138–9
   Aswan Dam, 141–5
   Bristol Docks, 156–7
   Singapore dock failure, 157–9
   death, 159
   sons take over, 157–9
Allenby, General, 300
Andrew, W. P., 97
Angola, 254–8
Argentina, 100
Arrol, Sir William, 118
Asquith Herbert, 204, 206, 228, 233–4, 245–6
Assiut Barrage, 146–8, 151–2, 155
Aswan Dam, 118, 143–55, 183, 242–3
   engineering of, 150–1
   1st heightening, 153–5
   2nd heightening, 299–306
Austria, 71
Avarescu, General, 279–80

Baker, Sir Benjamin, 143, 147, 149, 151–5, 181, 193, 301
Baku Aqueduct, 266
Ballard, Stephen, 49–50, 56, 84, 94

Balzagette, Sir Joseph, 126
Bank of England, 144–5
   and 1866 panic, 29, 31
   Act of 1842, 31, 81
   Bank Rate, 30–1, 63, 81, 98, 107, 110
Banks, country, 21, 34, 37
Banks, Sir Edward, 20
Barentin Viaduct, 43, 56
Baring crisis, 118, 144, 171, 182
Baring, Thomas, 58, 63
Barings Bank, 62, 73, 76, 134, 140, 194
Barnato, Barney, 252–3
Barned & Co., 43, 106–7
Baxter, James, 302, 305–6
Beck, Simon Adams, 128–30
Becton Gasworks, 128–30
'Bends', 181–2
Benguella Railway, 254–7
Berlin Waterworks, 124–5
Betts, Edward Ladd, 57, 61, 64, 73, 77, 92
Birkenhead, 33
Bismarck, 111, 113
'Black Friday', 29–32, 107–9
Blackwall Tunnel, 188–91
Blount, Sir Edward, 30, 37, 39, 41–5, 53, 56, 58, 70, 73, 92, 96–7, 114
Board of Health, 123
Body, J. B., 186, 197, 211, 218, 222, 227, 229
Boer War, 253
Bolivia, 262–4
Bombay cotton boom, 82, 86–7, 106
Bombing, 1914 War, 233, 235–6
Boulé, M., 143, 149
Boulton, 19
Bradford, 165, 168
Braithwaite, 21
Brassey, Maria, 36–7, 39, 57–9
Brassey, Thomas, 17, 20, 24, 124, 126, 128, 135, 165, 167, 171, 173–4, 180, 196, 232, 240, 258, 265, 269, 294, 304–11
   youth, 33
   ambitions and character, 47–60

Brassey, Thomas—*contd.*
    economic philosophy, 55, 65, 91–2,
        99, 102
    first contracts, 34–6
    in France, 38–45
    1848 Revolution, 44
    Railway Mania, 46–51
    depression of 1851, 50–1
    Grand Trunk Railway, 61–9
    in U.S.A., 65
    Italian railways, 70–3
    other European works, 73–6
    Crimean Railway, 76–9
    1857 crisis, 79–81
    Indian railways, 82–9
    British in 1860s, 90–3
    Ireland, 91
    development of London, 92–3
    Australian railways, 94
    Danish, 96
    Austrian, 97–9
    Argentina, 99–104
    panic of 1866, 30–2, 105–10
    recovery, 111
    Danubian railways, 111–13
    Euphrates Valley, 113–14
    Relations with navvies, 53–5, 115
        with his agents, 40, 48, 55–6, 74,
            111
        with Peto and Betts, 61–9, 74, 92,
            94, 98
    fortune, 51, 108, 110, 115
    death, 115
Brassey, Thomas, Lord, 17, 41, 58
Bratianu, M., 279
Brazil, 286, 289–91, 295, 297, 306, 308
Bribery, 167, 184, 309
Bridgwater, Duke of, 26
Brunel, I. K., 21
Brunel, Sir M. I., 188
Buddicom, William, 40, 42–3, 45, 73,
    92
Bunsen burner, 128
Burgoyne, General, 79
Burns, John, 303–4

Caisse de la Dette, 142–6, 155
Canada, 61–9, 266, 269, 272, 308
Canada Works, 64, 66, 90
Capital and Counties Bank, 172
Carden, Sir Lionel, 226
Carranza, 199, 224, 227–9

Cassel, Sir Ernest, 134, 144–6, 149,
    151, 153, 158, 159, 205, 300
Cavour, 70–3
Ceará irrigation, 289–91
Central Argentine Land Co., 103
Central Argentine Railway, 100–4
Chadwick, Edwin, 53
Channel Tunnel, 57, 59, 114, 242
Chaplin, William, 35, 38, 51, 73
Chateauroux tank factory, 233
Chicago subway, 268
Chile, 262, 308–9
Cholera, 123
Churchill, Winston, 145, 149, 151
'Científicos', 210–221
'clay-kicking', 274–5
Clarke, Stephenson, 124, 129
Clifford, Capt. Henry, 78–9
Coatzacoalos, 194, 197
Coghlan, T. C., 267–8
Colombia, 224–5, 296–8
Colonial Office, 62, 69, 95
Congress of Paris, 72
Connaught, Duke of, 151
Copenhagen Waterworks, 124
Contractors, development of, 14–26,
    34, 60–1, 63, 69, 76, 79–81,
    98, 117–18, 130, 171, 173–4,
    239–40, 289, 293–5, 307–11
    Governments acting as, 240, 293–5
Cowdray, Lord (Weetman Pearson),
    23–5, 118, 132, 141, 146–7,
    156, 163–4, 258, 260, 262–5,
    269, 271, 288, 293, 295, 297,
    307–11
    youth, 165
    American tour, 166–7
    early contracts, 167–8
    marriage, 168
    methods and character, 178, 247
    major works, 179–80
    Hudson Tunnel, 180–2
    Mexican Grand Canal, 182–7
    Blackwall Tunnel, 188–91
    E. River Tunnel, 191–2
    Tehuantepec Railway, 194–9
    Dover Harbour, 199–202
    political life, 203–4
    family life, 205–8
    Mexican oil, 209–30
    war work, 232–3
    Air Board, 233–8

postwar plans, 239–42
Sennar Dam, 242–4
closes down firm, 245
estates, 177–205
relations with agents, 174, 186, 197
and navvies, 173–4, 186
strikes, 173
labour conditions, 174, 182, 186
Cowdray, Lady (Annie Cass), 168–9, 176–7, 182–3, 187, 189, 195, 204–8, 220, 245
Cowdray interests:
gold mines, 220
rubber, 220
electricity, 220
oil, 211–13, 220, 223, 227–30, 239–240, 244–5
concessions in:
Mexico, 214, 220
Colombia, 224–5
Costa Rica, 225
Ecuador, 225
Gt. Britain, 240–1
Whitehall Petroleum company, 241
rate war, 216–8
retailing, 214, 219
Eagle Oil Transport Company, 219, 232
Cowdray Park, 17, 205, 217, 247
Couza, Prince, 15, 112–13, 115
Cradock, Admiral, 227
Crampton, Thomas, 124
Credit Anstalt, 118, 308
Crédit Foncier, 98
Crédit Mobilier, 97–8
Crimean War, 63, 72, 76–9
Crofters Commission, 138–9
'Crofters War', 138
Cromer, Lord (Evelyn Baring), 118, 143–5, 147, 151, 153, 155, 300
Crompton, 19
Crystal Palace, 124
Cubitt, Thomas, 21
Currie's Bank, 124
Curzon, Lord, 233–4

Daimler, Gottlieb, 19
Daira Sanieh estates, 146, 153
Dalhousie, Lord, 82–5, 89
Danvers, Sir Juland, 88
Delta Barrage, 142–3, 154

Denison, Edmund, 49–51
Deterding, Henri, 172, 212–13, 227, 229–30
Devaux, Charles, 73–97
Diala cotton estates, 296
Diaz, Porfirio, 14, 182–7, 195–6, 198–9, 210–11, 214, 217–18, 221–2
Dilke, Sir Charles, 89
Disraeli, Benjamin, 31, 79, 142
Dixon's Bank, 33–4
Docker, Dudley, 257, 271
Doheny, Edward L., 212–3, 215, 217, 219, 226, 229
Dover Harbour, 156, 172, 174, 199–202, 233
Dufaure, 38
Dunecht, 205–6, 245, 247
Durham Report, 61

Eads, Captain, 194, 197
East River tunnels, 191–2
E. and W. India Docks, 135–7
East India Company, 82
Eastbrook, Sir John, 38, 51
Edward VII, 144, 153, 156, 205
Egypt, 141–4, 155, 300, 304
Egyptian Government, 145, 147, 149, 152, 301, 304–6
Electricity in industry, 129
Elgin, Lord, 65
Engineers, role of, as contractors, 20–1, 34
Entrepreneur, function of, 19–26
Erlanger & Co., 258
Esneh Barrage, 155

Falkenhayn, General, 278–81
Farquar Harries Bank, 130
Fashoda, 142, 147, 155
Fell Railway, 96, 114
Finance, loans, British, 263, 265, 267, 308
American, 287, 290–1, 295, 297, 308
Finance Companies, 60, 97–8, 106, 111
(see also individual titles)
Fitzmaurice, Maurice, 149–50
Foreign Office, 30, 97, 109–11, 197, 223–4, 227–8
Fowler, Sir John, 135
Fox, Sir Charles, 73, 124
France, 141, 144
French, Sir John, 275

Franz Joseph, Emperor, 59, 76
Furber, Percy N., 214

Galt, A. T., 61–3, 69
Garstin, Sir William, 143, 153
Gas industry, 122, 124, 128–30
Gas Light & Coke, Co., 128–9
General Credit & Finance Co., 97
George V, 231, 233, 245, 247
Gerard, Judge, 206, 226
Gibson, Arthur, 298–9, 301–3
Giles, Francis, 35
Giles, Netlam, 71, 112
Gladstone, 31, 58, 70, 79, 203
Glyn, George Carr, 30, 48–9, 51, 58, 63, 73, 84, 105, 108
Glyns Bank, 30, 37, 62, 65–6, 69
Grand Trunk Railway Co., 57, 61–70, 74, 84, 86, 92
Grant, President Ulysses, 106, 194
Greathead, Sir William, 181
Gretna munitions factory, 232–3
Grey, Sir Edward, 204, 233–4, 236, 238
Guizot, 38, 44
Gurney, Henry, 29, 107
Gurney, Samuel, 107, 115
Gzowski & Co., 62–4, 69

Haig, Field-Marshal Lord, 234–5, 238, 276
Halifax Dock, 179
Hamburg, 80, 124
Harcourt, Sir William, 199
Harvey, General, 276
Haskins, de Witt, 181
Hayes, Doctor, 226–7, 229
Helps, Sir Arthur, 24
Henderson & Co., 73
Henfrey, Charles, 71, 86–8
Hincks, Sir Francis, 62, 64, 69
Hirsch, Baron Maurice de, 23, 117, 141, 144, 307–8
Hopkinson, Sir Frederick, 175, 231, 233, 243–4
'House of Lords', 260, 267–8, 283
Howard de Walden, Lord, 260, 262, 268, 286, 302
Hoyas, Uribe, 297
Hudson, George, 32, 44, 46–7, 49–51, 57
Hudson River Tunnel, 172, 180–2
Huerta, Victoriano, 222–4, 236–8

Huish, Mark, 51, 90
Hull, 138, 175, 231
Hyde, Sir Clarendon, 175, 186, 240

Ibramieh Canal, 152
Imperial Gas Co., 125, 128–9
Imperialism, Economic, 81, 102–4, 307–8
   British, 17, 24–5, 143, 187, 230, 265, 267
   French, 144
   German, 145, 153, 255–6, 265
   United States, 183, 187, 195–6, 210, 222, 225–30, 297
Inchcape, Lord, 204, 246
India, 82–9, 308
Indian Mutiny, 81, 84–5
India Office, 88
International Finance Society, 97–8, 112
Irrigation, 142–3, 155
Italy, 70–3

Jackson, Sir John, 118, 140–1, 157, 200–4, 304–6
Jackson, Sir William, 61–2, 64, 66, 106
Jameson Raid, 251–2
Joel brothers, 253, 302, 305
Joliffe, Sir William, 20
Joubert, Count, 38
Juarez, President, 209

Katanga, 254, 257
   Union Minière, 255
Kennedy & Co., 106
Kent industry, 202, 239, 241–2
Kenya, 288
Kerr, Admiral Mark, 233
Khedive Abbas, 151
Khedive Ismail, 142, 146
King's Lynn Docks, 168
Kitchener, Field-Marshal Lord, 144–7, 149–50, 243, 273–5
Kirk and Randall, 137

Lafitte, Charles, 38, 41, 44, 70
Laing, Samuel, 97
La Marmora, 72
Law, A. Bonar, 175, 236
Lawrence, Thomas, 38
Lawrence, Lord, 88
Lawton, 33

Lazards Bank, 239, 247
Lehalleur, Pepin, 42
Lesseps, Ferdinand de, 23, 26, 117, 197, 308
Limantour, José Yves, 198, 210, 221
Litteton reservoir, 245
Lloyd George, David, 227, 229, 233–7, 246
Lloyd, Lord, 244
Loanda Harbour, 287
Lobito Bay, 250, 258
Lobnitz & Co., 175, 180, 185, 199
Locarno Treaty, 240, 294
Loch Katrine, 125
Locke, Joseph, 21, 34–5, 37–8, 42, 47, 181
London County Council, 189–90
London, County and Westminster Bank, 268
London Docks, 134–8
London Sewers, 93, 126, 266, 291
London Water Supply, 123–4
    Water Companies, 122–3
London Underground, 93, 126–7, 193–194, 291, 295–6
Lowestoft, 74
Lucas, Charles and Thomas, 126–7, 130, 134–9, 141
Lucas Oil Well (Texas), 211

MacAlpine, Robert, 130, 139
McCormick, John, 19
Macdonald, Sir Murdoch, 154–5, 300–303, 306
McDonough, General, 277–8
McHenry, James, 80, 105–7, 112, 144
McKenna, Reginald, 278
Mackensen, General, 278–9
Mackenzie, William, 38–40, 43
Macnab, Sir Allan, 62
Madero, Francisco, 221–3
Malta Harbour, 202
Manchester drainage, 268, 274–5
Manchester Ship Canal, 139–41, 179
Marie, Queen of Rumania, 280, 282, 304
Masterman, J. L., 35, 37, 43, 51, 73, 106
Masterson, Thomas, 280–1, 284, 286
Medical air lock, 182, 189
Mehemet Ali, 142
Meiggs, Henry, 23, 25, 57, 99, 113, 117, 262, 308

Menufieh Regulator, 154, 157
Mersey Docks and Harbour Board, 139
Messines Ridge, 275–7
Metropolitan Board of Works, 126, 169
Metropolitan Carriage Co., 257, 276
Mexican Eagle Oil Co. (see Aguila, el)
Mexican Grand Canal, 185–7
Mexican Revolution, 199, 211, 221–3, 226, 229
Mexico, 25, 106, 182–7, 195–6, 198, 204, 209–30
    U.S. relations with, 223–9
Mexico City, 183–5, 209–10, 220–2
Milford Haven Docks, 179
Millwall Dock, 128, 135–6
Mining in 1914 War, 275–7
Minitatlan Refinery, 214–7, 220
Mitre, Bartolemé 100–2
Moir, Sir Edward, 172, 175, 181–2, 189–91
Mond, Sir Alfred, 204, 206
Monroe Doctrine, 224–5
Mont Cenis Tunnel, 59, 96, 114
Morley, Lord, 228
Morrison, James, 46
Moss, William, 33, 35
Mowlem and Burt, 125
Munitions, Ministry of, 232–3
Murray, Lord, 225, 274

Nag Hammadi Barrage, 301, 304–5
Nahas Pasha, 304
Napoleon III, Emperor, 59, 71–3
National Bank of Egypt, 146
Naval race, 201
Navvies, British, 34–5, 39, 40–2, 47–8, 51, 64, 78, 94, 133, 150, 173–4, 197, 256, 264, 309
    conditions of living, 53–5, 66, 174, 182, 190, 197, 289
    French, 39–41
    Mexican, 186, 197
    strikes, 66, 125, 173
Naylor-Leyland, Captain, 203
Newcastle, Duke of, 76–7
Nile, 142, 155, 242–4, 273, 300, 308
    Commission, 301
    Irrigation Department, 304–6
Northcliffe, Lord, 237–8
Northcote, Sir Stafford, 30

N. European Steam Shipping Co., 74,
77
Norton-Griffiths, Sir John, 16, 24, 132,
307–11
in Africa, 251–4
Benguella Railway, 254–8
and 'House of Lords', 260
contracts in Chile, Canada, Australia, 260–8
character and political life, 269–73,
291–2, 294
in 1914 War, 273
mining on Western Front, 274–7
Rumanian oilfields, 277–83
postwar boom in contracts, 286–7
Kenya Railway, 288–9
Brazil irrigation, 289–91
lack of work in 1920s, 293–5
Colombian contract, 297–8
Aswan Dam, 300–5
death, 306
Norton-Griffiths, Lady, 255–6, 264,
268, 270, 304

Ofenheim, Victor, 109, 115
Overend and Gurney, failure of, 29–32,
66, 97, 106–8, 127, 130
Overstone, Lord, 115

Pacific Steam Navigation Co., 99
Paddington, 133
Paddockhurst, 177, 222, 245
Page, W. H., 224–6, 230
Panama Canal, 57, 109, 195–6, 199
Canal Act, 1914, 224, 227
Railway, 194–5
Panic, financial, 1847, 31
1857, 31, 80–1, 91, 97, 105, 124
1866, 29–32, 105–10, 127, 130, 307
Pará Harbour, 231
Pauling George, 255, 258, 288
Paxton, Sir James, 86
Pearson, Clive, 169, 178, 207, 215, 219,
232
Sir Edward, 172, 231–3, 244
Geoffrey, 169, 207
George, 165–9, 191
Harold, 169, 207, 218, 247
Sarah, 165–6
Pearson, S. & Son, Inc., 191
Pearson, Weetman (see Cowdray,
Lord)

Peru, 25, 113
Peto, Sir Morton, 51, 54, 57–9, 61, 63,
65–6, 69, 73–4, 76–7, 80–1,
84, 94, 98, 101, 103, 115, 117,
126–7, 135
partnership with Brassey, 43, 44, 61–
69, 74, 92, 94, 98
bankruptcy, 30, 105–10
Peto and Betts, 29, 61–9, 74, 92, 94, 98
Philae, Temple of, 143, 149, 151–2, 154
Phoenix Gas Co. 121
Phoenix Oil Co., 286
Piedmont, 70–1
Pierce, Clay, 212–13, 216–19, 221, 223,
229
Port of London Authority, 138
Potrero oilfield, 218–19, 226–9, 232
Powles, Edward, 260, 302
Press, American, attacks on Cowdray,
192, 198, 221
Price, Robert, 220

Raglan, Lord, 76, 78–9
Railway Mania, 21, 44, 46–51, 53, 82,
90, 123
Railways, British, 46, 192–3
Acts of Parliament, 46–7, 49–51
cost, 50, 71
early development, 33–4
mileage, 47
state control, 50
railways, Caledonian, 48
E. Anglian, 48, 51, 90
Great Northern, 49–51
Great Western, 48, 90, 193
Highland, 138–9
Lancs. Derby & E. Coast, 193
London, Chatham and Dover,
106–7
London and Southampton, 35, 37,
46
London and South-Eastern, 37, 43,
106
London and North-Western, 47–
49, 51
London, Tilbury and Southend,
74, 91–2, 108
North British, 138
Trent Valley, 48
West Highland, 131, 138–9, 141
Africa:
Algeria, 76

Railways, Africa—*contd.*
   Benguella (Angola), 254–7
   Kenya, 288–9, 294
   Mauritius, 94
  America:
   Argentine, 99–104
   Brazil, 99
   Canada (Grand Trunk), 57, 61–70, 74, 84, 86, 92
   Chile, 99, 262, 267
    Arica–La Paz, 260–4
    Longitudinal, 262–6
   Mexico, 194–9
   U.S.A., 99, 105–6, 191–2, 195, 223
  Asia:
   China, 199
   Euphrates Valley, 57, 113–14
   India, 57, 74, 81–9
    cost of, 86–8
    guarantee system, 83–4, 88
  Australia, 94, 108, 267–8, 274
  Europe:
   Austria, 76, 97–9, 107–13, 115
    Lemberg–Czernowitz, 98, 108–109, 112–13
   Belgium, 73
   Berlin–Bagdhad, 111, 114, 118, 141, 153, 308
   Crimea, 76–9, 92
   Denmark, 73–4, 92, 96–7, 108, 110
   France, 36–46, 73
    P.L.M., 73
    West of France Railway Co., 73
   Greece, 206
   Holland, 73
   Italy, 70–3, 95–6
   Norway, 74
   Rumania, 111–13, 115
   Spain, 45, 95, 180
   Russia, 76, 99
   Turkey, 76
Rand, Transvaal, 252–3
Ransomes and Rapier, 151, 154
Redesdale, Lord, 139
Rennie, 20
Revelstoke, Lord, 144
Revolution, 1848, 45, 47, 49, 70–3, 124
Rhodes, Cecil, 251–2
Robertson, Sir William, 235, 238
Rockefeller, House of, 163, 212, 215, 219

Rosebery Lord, 178, 203–4
Rothermere, Lord, 238
Rothschild, House of, 37–8, 71–3, 76, 79, 112, 134, 140, 145, 212
Royal Albert Dock, 136–7
Royal Dutch Shell, 172, 219, 222, 227, 229, 240, 279
Royal Edward Dock, Avonmouth, 156–7
Rumania, 97
  in 1914 War, 277–83
Rumanian oilfields, 277–85
Rumanian Consolidated Oilfields Co., 280, 284, 286

Sacco and Brancale, 305
Sadleir, John, 73
St. Johns Harbour, 266–8
Salamanca, José de, 96, 105, 112–3
Salina Cruz, 194, 197–8
Salisbury, Lord, 144–5, 147
Samuel, Marcus, 212
Sanchez, Delfin, 194
San Cristobal oilfield, 211, 213–6
Sapieha, Prince Leo, 112
Sarmiento, 101
Sarsfield, Velez, 101
Schiff, Jacob, 144
Schwartz and Klein, 111
Seaham Harbour, 199
2nd King Edward's Horse, 274
Séguin, Marc, 37
Sennar Dam, 242–4, 245, 302
Shell (see Royal Dutch Shell)
Shield, for tunnels, 181–2, 189–91
Shrimpton & Co., 30
Siemens, Georg von, 23, 141, 307–8
Singapore Harbour, 298, 301
Six Weeks' War, 105, 108–10
Slump of 1929, 295, 303–5
Smiles, Samuel, 14, 19, 22, 52, 58, 122
Smuts, General, 235–6
Spring-Rice, Sir Cecil, 226, 228
Société General, 73, 114
Southampton Docks, 179
Southend, 91–2
Southport drainage, 167–8
S.W. India Dock, 136
Standard Oil of New Jersey, 163–4, 213, 215–20, 222, 229, 240, 279, 297

Stephenson, George, 19, 21, 32, 34, 35, 50
Stephenson, Robert, 21, 42, 48, 68–9
Strousberg, Doctor, 57, 113, 308
Stoney, Richard, 147
Sudan, 142, 144–5, 147, 149, 155, 243, 300
Suez Canal, 79, 88, 137, 142–4, 180

Tampico, 213, 219–20, 227
    'Incident', 228
Tanganyika Concessions, 255, 258
Tanjong Pagar Docks, 157–9
    Lawsuit, 158–9
Tay Bridge, 125
Tehuantepec Railway, 175, 180, 194–9, 214, 223
    National Railway Co., 196
Telford, 20, 33, 37, 138
Temple House, Marlow, 272–3
Texcoco, Lake, 185
Thames Embankment, 126
    condition of, 123, 126, 134
Thomson, Bonar & Co., 43, 103
Tilbury Dock, 137–156
Topham, Jones and Railton, 157–8, 303, 306
Torricelli, 143
Transvaal, 252
Trenchard, General, 234–6, 238
Tyrrell, Sir Walter, 226

Uasin Gishu Railway, 288–9, 294
Uganda, 142, 155, 288–9
Urquiza, President, 100
Uzielli, Matthew, 35, 44, 73

Valparaiso Harbour, 231–2, 244
Vanderbilt, Cornelius, 32, 57, 105, 308
Vera Cruz, 194–5
Victor Emmanuel, 71, 73
Victoria Bridge, 63, 66, 68
Victoria Dock, 92, 108, 135–6
Victoria Gas Co., 93

Vignoles, Charles, 34
Villa, Pancho, 221–2, 224, 229

Wagstaff, Edward, 109
War, 1914—effect on contractors, 199, 239–40
War damage to contractors, 96, 110
War Office, 35, 77, 235
'War Priorities Committee', 236
War work of contractors, 283
Water supply, London, 123–4
    Europe, 124
Watkin, Edward, 51, 69
Watt, James, 19
Wednesbury, 266, 271–2, 291
Weir, Sir William, 235–6
West Highland Railway, 131, 138–9, 141
Westminster Gazette, 245–6
Wheelwright, William, 23, 80, 96, 99–104, 308
Whitehall Securities, 246
Whittle, Sir Frank, 19
Wilkinson, John, 19
Willcocks, Sir William, 143, 147–8, 151, 155
Williams Deacons Bank, 172
Williams, Sir Robert, 254–6, 258
Wilson, Henry Lane, 222
Wilson, President Woodrow, 223–8, 230
Wilton Park, 131–2, 159
Wimpey & Co., 130
Wolff, Sir Henry Drummond, 31, 81, 97
Wonham Park, 291–3
Worthington-Evans, Sir Laming, 254, 258, 260
Wythes, George, 73, 86, 126

Yorkshire Banking Co., 196

Zaghlul, Saad, 300
Zaharoff, Sir Basil, 286
Zapata, Emiliano, 186, 221–3, 229
Zimmerman Telegram, 229
Zollverein, 46